Getting to Know
ArcView®

the geographic information system (GIS) for everyone

Discover the world of desktop mapping and GIS

➤ Learn what GIS is and how it works

➤ See ArcView software in action

➤ Use ArcView software

GeoInformation International
a division of Pearson Professional Limited
307 Cambridge Science Park
Milton Road
Cambridge
CB4 4ZD
and associated companies throughout the world

Distributed in the Americas by
John Wiley & Sons, Inc., 605 Third Avenue, New York, NY 10158-0012.

Address enquiries relating to ArcView® software to Environmental Systems Research Institute, Inc., 380 New York Street, Redlands, California 92373-8100, or to your local distributor.

First published 1996.

British Library Cataloging-in-Publication Data
A CIP record for this book is available from the British Library.

ISBN 1 899761 62 4

Library of Congress Cataloging-in-Publication Data
A CIP record for this book is available from the Library of Congress.

ISBN 0 470 23609 4 (Americas only)

Printed in the United States of America.

B2.398

Contents

CONTENTS

ENVIRONMENTAL SYSTEMS RESEARCH INSTITUTE, INC.

Part 2   Using ArcView

Section 1   ArcView basics

Section 2   Querying data

Section 3   Working with spatial data

Section 4   Managing tabular data

ENVIRONMENTAL SYSTEMS RESEARCH INSTITUTE, INC.

Section 7   Creating your own data

Section 8   Customizing ArcView

ENVIRONMENTAL SYSTEMS RESEARCH INSTITUTE, INC.

Preface and acknowledgments

Getting to Know ArcView comes from the world leader in GIS software, Environmental Systems Research Institute, Inc. (ESRI). Founded in 1969 as a research organization to develop new methods for managing geographic information, ESRI provides software, data automation, and consulting services to thousands of GIS users around the world. ESRI's early research and development set the stage for the revolution in automated mapping that we see today.

We at ESRI know that better information makes for better decisions. Our reputation is built on contributing our technical knowledge, special people, and valuable experience to the collection, analysis, and communication of geographic information. Our product, ArcView, allows you to manage geographic information from your desktop. It's changing the way we all do business.

We would like to acknowledge the following data publishers for their respective contributions to this work:

City of Albuquerque data provided courtesy of the City of Albuquerque—Geographic Information System (GIS) Division and is used herein with permission.

City of Ontario data provided courtesy of the City of Ontario GIS Division and is used herein with permission.

GDT data, including counties, census tracts, streets, and highways data, provided courtesy of Geographic Data Technology, Inc., and is used herein with permission. Copyright © 1990–1995 Geographic Data Technology, Inc. All rights reserved.

GNP per capita, population density, and birth rate data provided courtesy of The World Bank, Washington, D.C., and is used herein with permission.

Marsabit District of Kenya data provided courtesy of the Range Management Handbook Project and the Kenya Government Ministry of Agriculture, Livestock Development and Marketing (MOLD)/Deutsche Gesellschaft für Technische Zusammenarbeit (GTZ) and is used herein with permission. Copyright © 1995 Kenya Government Ministry of Agriculture, Livestock Development and Marketing (MOLD)/Deutsche Gesellschaft für Technische Zusammenarbeit (GTZ). All rights reserved.

Mata Atlantica data provided courtesy of Conservation International, Conservation International–Brazil, Conservation International–Brazil/Universidade de Brasilia, Fundação Biodiversitas, and Sociedade Nordestina de Ecologia and is used herein with permission.

A Conservation Priority-Setting Workshop was held in December 1993 for the Atlantic coastal forests of northeastern Brazil. The workshop utilized GIS to help determine regional conservation priorities for this species-rich area that is under severe development pressures. The data was compiled prior to the workshop and GIS was used to integrate the data, generate base maps, and analyze the synthesized information for the participating biologists and socioeconomic experts. The workshop approach provided a scientifically sound forum for determining which areas are of greatest concern for a range of conservation issues. It also generated a detailed database of the best available information on the region that will be used to support future research and decision making.

MicroVision Lifestyle Segments data for Fulton and Dekalb County areas, including population, household segments, per capita income, banks, shopping centers, and hotels data, provided courtesy of National Decision Systems (NDS), a division of Equifax Marketing Decision Systems, Inc., and is used herein with permission. Copyright © 1995 Equifax, Inc. All rights reserved. For further information about NDS data, please contact NDS at 1-800-866-6520.

Maps of downtown Portland provided courtesy of Thomas Bros. Maps and are used herein with permission. Copyright © 1995 Thomas Bros. Maps. All rights reserved.

Redlands and San Francisco satellite imagery data provided courtesy of SPOT Image Corporation and is used herein with permission. Copyright © 1991, 1993 CNES. All rights reserved.

Schools data provided courtesy of the Atlanta Regional Commission and is used herein with permission.

The Atlanta Regional Commission (ARC) is the official planning agency for the 10-county Atlanta Region in a wide range of areas including transportation, environmental quality, land use, public facilities, job training, aging services, and other human services. It was established in 1971 to assist local governments in planning for common needs, cooperating for mutual benefit, and coordinating for sound regional development. Board membership on ARC is held by 23 local elected officials and 15 private citizens. The work of the Commission is supported by local, state, and federal funds.

Shopping Center Database data for the Atlanta area provided courtesy of National Research Bureau and is used herein with permission. Copyright © 1995 Blackburn Marketing Services (U.S.), Inc. All rights reserved.

ENVIRONMENTAL SYSTEMS RESEARCH INSTITUTE, INC.

Introduction

Move over text files, move over spreadsheets, and databases: geographic information systems have arrived on the desktop. Geographic information systems (GIS) let you visualize information in new ways that reveal relationships, patterns, and trends not visible with other popular systems.

Getting to Know ArcView presents the concepts upon which this technology is based, how it works, and what it does. In part 1 of the book, you'll see how people in a wide range of fields are using desktop GIS to find potential customers, locate the best place for a new business or facility, identify natural areas needing protection, find the best places to develop real estate, manage extensive road networks, inventory forest lands, do emergency planning in urban areas, manage resources after fire and flood—the list goes on and on. You'll find out how you can use desktop GIS to study and analyze situations and create high-quality maps and charts. You also get to see, in chapter 6, an entire application using a particular desktop GIS, *ArcView.* In part 2 of the book (chapters 7–25), you'll learn how to use ArcView by working through exercises that are based on real-life situations.

To supplement the material in this book, we also provide a multimedia CD–ROM. The CD–ROM has three parts. The Desktop GIS Primer mirrors the content of the book's first six chapters, presenting similar information in a dynamic way. The ArcView Showcase demonstrates how ArcView software works; you'll see ArcView in action, performing the tasks described in chapters 1–6. The ArcView Tutorial contains a version of ArcView that's locked to the data and exercises in the book, a help file that contains all of the exercise steps, and videos that let you see ArcView performing each of the exercise steps. We've designed the book, the Desktop GIS Primer, the ArcView Showcase, and the ArcView Tutorial so that you can use them independently or together. The choice is yours.

Before you install the CD–ROM, be sure to read the license agreement in appendix C and the installation instructions in appendix D.

Throughout part 2 of the book, you'll see teal-colored boxes like this one:

> **Zooming in and out in a view.** ArcView gives you a variety of ways to zoom in and out. You can zoom from the center of the view or from a position or area you define with the mouse. For more information, search for these Help Topics: *Zooming in and out on a view, Zoom In, Zoom Out, Zoom In tool, Zoom Out tool.*

These boxes offer more detailed explanations for topics covered in the exercises. To search for a Help Topic, select "Search For Help On" from the Help menu.

Finally, if you're looking for information on how to contact ESRI, the makers of ArcView, please refer to appendix A, where you'll find the telephone and fax numbers of our offices in the United States and throughout the world.

Getting to know desktop GIS

These first six chapters introduce you to desktop GIS and its concepts. You'll learn why desktop GIS maps are dynamic, how to get information from them, and how to use them to study relationships and analyze locations. You'll see how to use desktop GIS to create quality presentations, including maps, charts, images, and more. You'll find out where you can get data and how to evaluate it. You'll even learn how to create some data of your own. Finally, you'll see how related GIS tasks are performed, step-by-step, using a real desktop GIS.

Desktop GIS:
What it is
and what it does

The new source of power is not
money in the hands of a few
but information in the hands of many.

—John Naisbitt
Megatrends

Desktop GIS: What it is and what it does

Desktop GIS. If you've already heard of it, you may know it as an immensely powerful computer mapping system. It is that. But it is much more. It is a tool for managing information of any kind according to where it's located. With it you can keep track of where customers are, decide where to site businesses, manage sensitive wildlife habitats, optimize delivery routes, track the spread of infectious disease.

In this chapter, we'll show you some of the things that various kinds of organizations are already doing with desktop GIS. But before we do that, a few words about maps—those fundamental tools that help us communicate where we are, manage what's there, and figure out how to get someplace else.

Maps: who needs them?

You're flying home from a business trip. The woman sitting next to you has never been to your town, and you want to tell her how to get to the little café that serves the best omelettes in the world. How far do you get with "turn left on Main Street and go three blocks and turn right" before your acquaintance looks completely lost? So you grab a piece of paper and a pencil, and a few squiggles later you've identified a location, explained how to get there, and described the major landmarks she will pass along the way. And however crude or inaccurate your map, it does what every map does—it represents where objects are in the real world in relation to each other.

The urge to understand where we are is universal. The Babylonians recorded land ownership by drawing boundaries of parcels on clay tablets. The Mongolians painted the plans of their towns on their walls. The Chinese drew topographic maps on silk, using colored symbols to show locations of military installations in relation to streams, mountains, roads, and settlements.

Some people even mapped the winds and the seas. The Marshall Islanders made navigational charts with sticks for prevailing winds and wave patterns and shells for islands.

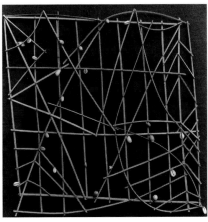

The Science Museum/
Science & Society
Picture Library

A nineteenth century version of a navigational chart. The South Sea islanders have probably been making these for thousands of years.

The Romans used paper maps to promote the growth of commerce in their rapidly expanding empire.

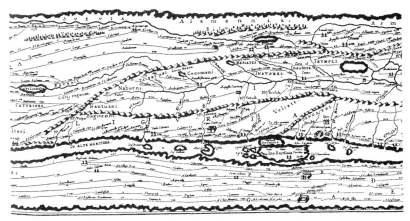

The Peutinger Table, an early medieval road map, may have been copied from a Roman map of the third century.

Whatever they were made from, wherever they were made, maps in the past shared two characteristics, they could only be made by skilled cartographers and they were static.

Mapping systems that run on desktop computers, however, give everyone the ability to make maps. And the maps they make can be changed in a flash, over and over again.

The diversity of mapping systems

The desktop mapping systems on the market today range from display-only systems like electronic atlases to full-featured geographic information systems (GIS). The dividing lines between one type of system and the next are not sharply defined. The systems do differ in a number of important ways: how they link geographic locations with information about those locations, the accuracy with which they specify geographic locations, the level of analysis they perform, and the way they present information as graphic drawings.

Electronic atlases, for instance, allow you to display pictures of geographic areas on your computer screen. They provide limited information about the geographic areas, and limited ability to alter the graphics. Without any tools for analyzing the information, these systems are most useful for providing graphics that can be used in presentations and reports.

Unlike electronic atlases, thematic mapping systems enable you to create graphic displays using information stored in a spreadsheet or database. These systems are especially useful for creating graphic presentations. Each map produced is based on a *theme,* such as population or income, and uses colors, patterns, shading, and symbols of various sizes to show the relative value of the information stored for that theme, at each geographic location.

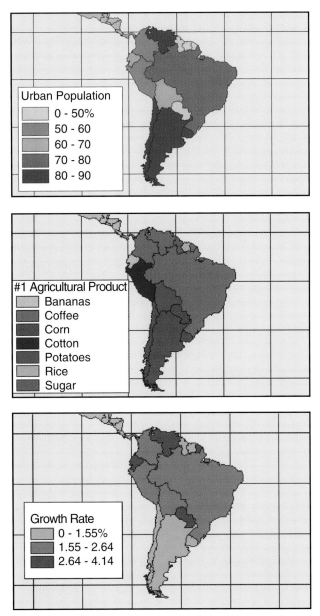

Population, agriculture, and income information are used to create these thematic maps.

Street-based mapping systems are more sophisticated than electronic atlases and thematic mappers. They link information to geographic locations. Street-based mapping systems can display address locations on street maps as points.

More sophisticated desktop mapping systems can import database or spreadsheet files or provide direct access to outside information sources. Some desktop mapping systems let you create and manage tabular information, use tabular information to create charts and graphs, and even analyze information statistically.

Desktop GIS puts it all together

Desktop GIS can do all these things and more. Desktop GIS combines all the capabilities of display-only, thematic, and street-based mapping systems along with the ability to analyze geographic locations and the information linked to those locations. Furthermore, you can either access information from the map or access the map from information.

And desktop GIS is dynamic. That means you can create maps that are not limited to a single moment in time. Simply update the information linked to a map and the map will automatically reflect those changes. You can do this quickly, without special training.

Desktop GIS lets you create map displays and maps for presentation simply by pointing and clicking. Desktop GIS lets you visualize and analyze information in new ways, revealing previously hidden relationships, patterns, and trends.

          ENVIRONMENTAL SYSTEMS RESEARCH INSTITUTE, INC.

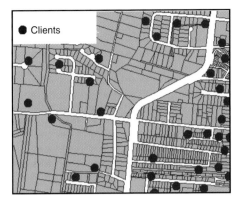

Visualizing customer locations is critical to businesses trying to make better marketing decisions.

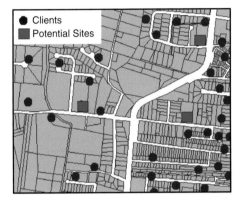

Analyzing location is key to making decisions about where to set up a business or service.

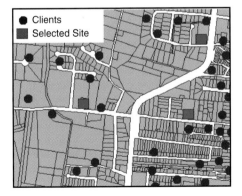

Presenting information as maps reveals relationships and patterns that may otherwise be hidden.

People in business, government, education, and natural resources are already using desktop GIS to analyze markets, manage parcels of land, conduct research, and protect natural resources. Desktop GIS can change the way you do business, whatever field you are in.

What people are doing with desktop GIS

Development that improves the land

Bob's development company has just purchased a beautiful hilly area covered with oak trees and fed by woodland streams. The draw for future residents is the area's "natural" feel, so he has to put in roads and houses without destroying the woods and streams. He also wants to avoid the steeper slopes of the hills. Local environmental regulations, which require him to avoid protected streams and sensitive bird habitats, complicate things even more. With desktop GIS, however, Bob can balance these conflicting needs.

He can quickly locate suitable areas by eliminating the unsuitable ones. And he can update, revise, and refine his information as often as he needs.

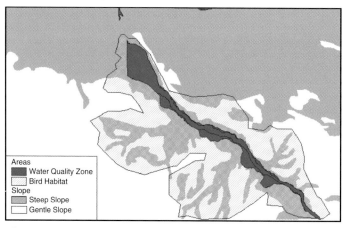

This map shows several areas (the white patches) that are suitable for development. They have gentle slopes and don't intrude on protected areas.

On the road again

Maintaining roads and highways and improving safety is a big job. John, a transportation planner, uses desktop GIS because it integrates information from a variety of sources.

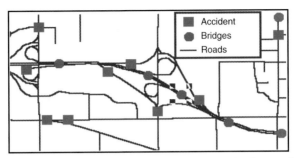

A transportation database might include roads, bridges, and locations of traffic accidents.

John's duties as a transportation planner include deciding which portions of which roads need to be repaired and when to repair them. Finding the road segments that require immediate action helps a planner decide where to allocate resources and when. It's not enough to know where roads are damaged. John must also know how badly they're damaged, how much traffic they carry, and when that traffic is heaviest. Only then does he know which crew to send out and where to send it.

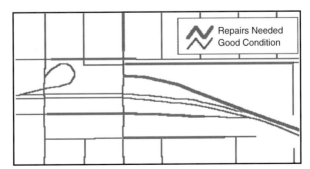

Road segments are displayed based on pavement condition and traffic volume. Segments in poor condition with heavy traffic become obvious on the map display.

John also analyzes traffic accidents to identify causes and plan corrective actions. This involves looking for places where accidents occur in clusters and then accessing information about those locations to try and determine possible causes.

John can retrieve information about accident sites, such as scanned images of accident reports, photos of accident sites, and tabular information about road conditions and traffic volumes.

The ability to link photos to these clusters can be particularly helpful in seeing contributing factors that might not otherwise be apparent, such as large trees or shrubs close to the road that block the view of a blind curve or intersection. Perhaps pruning the trees at these sites would improve conditions. Or maybe straightening a curve would help keep motorists on the road.

This old mall

Developers have been using GIS to choose sites for new shopping malls for some time. But what about when the mall is old and needs a facelift? Consider the case of Old Town Mall. Already in a good location, Old Town Mall is easy to get to. But it's almost 30 years old, and shows it. It has only two department stores, and they no longer pull in the customers. The smaller shops are also suffering.

Across the street from the mall is a 40-year-old open-air shopping center with one department store and a parking lot full of weeds and old newspapers. Joan, an energetic young developer, is thinking about buying both properties.

She has big plans: put all three department stores into the mall, make it two levels instead of one, and convert the open-air center across the street into a "power center" of large specialty discount stores selling electronics, appliances, clothing, toys, and the like. But she cannot act until she has a lot more information.

So Joan uses desktop GIS to find out who is likely to shop at the new mall, the demographics of the people who live in the area, and how the trade areas of competing malls compare with the new mall she is planning. First, she uses sales information linked to postal code areas to define the trade area for the new Old Town Mall.

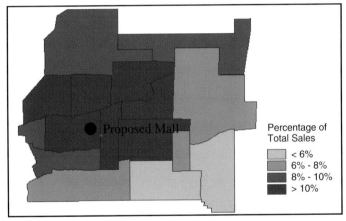

This map shows postal code areas ranked according to sales. Contiguous areas contributing 75% of total sales define the trade area for the mall.

Then she studies the demographic information to find out how many people live in the area and other things like how much money they make.

Trade Area ID	Population	Average Income
1	65504	35500

GIS calculates the population and average household income of the trade area and places these values in a table.

She then uses GIS to generate trade areas for each competing mall and compares them with the trade area for Old Town Mall.

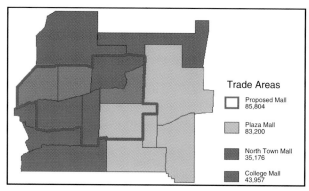

A map comparing the populations of trade areas shows a higher density in the proposed area.

Now Joan knows that more people live in the trade area for Old Town Mall than in any other trade area. But she needs to know how those numbers relate to income. Using the GIS software's ability to make charts, Joan can plot population and income categories for the trade areas of regional malls.

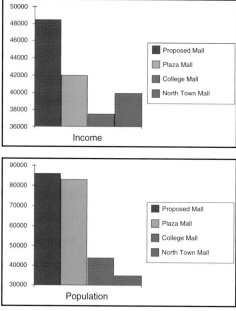

The bar charts demonstrate that the new mall's trade area demographics are as good as or better than the leading mall in every income category.

ENVIRONMENTAL SYSTEMS RESEARCH INSTITUTE, INC.

Since it looks to be a safe bet, Joan decides to buy the property and Old Town Mall is on its way to becoming a shopping center showcase.

The clearly compliant bank

Banks and financial institutions in the United States must comply with state and federal regulations and demonstrate that their lending practices do not discriminate. At the same time, they must show board members that they are profitable.

Midtown Bank is a perfect example. Henry, the branch manager, needs to show that Midtown Bank's loan distribution practices are not discriminatory. Until recently, that would have meant poring over stacks of spreadsheets and computer printouts, long after everyone else had gone home. But now, with the aid of desktop GIS, relationships, patterns, and trends become instantly apparent when the information is visualized on a color-coded map.

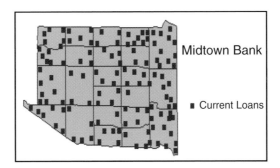

This map clearly shows a bank's lending patterns across neighborhoods.

With desktop GIS, Henry can see where Midtown's customers live and compare that information with demographics for the census tracts his bank serves.

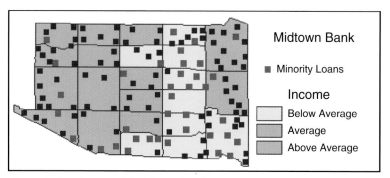

By overlaying demographic information, Henry can track and analyze income and minority loans.

This type of information can help Midtown Bank target prospective customers, compare its performance against that of the competition, and determine the best sites for expanding its services.

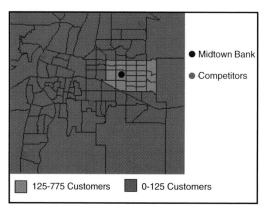

On this map, Midtown Bank can see that most of its customers live close to the bank. Seeing where its competitors are, on the same map, could help it decide where to target prospective customers.

Midtown Bank is discovering that desktop GIS brings new insights into many phases of operating and managing a financial institution.

The fire's aftermath

Fire fighting is hard work. But after the fire is out, even more work remains. Blackened structures need to be cleared away and new ones built. Polluted streams need to be cleaned up. Utility lines need to be repaired. Rachel, who works in the county planning department, uses desktop GIS to evaluate everything from which building codes may have contributed to the fire's spread to which routes will be best for emergency teams and cleanup crews.

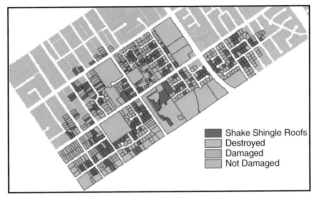

This map shows which houses were destroyed and which survived but were damaged. Homes with wood shake roofs were identified as major culprits in the fire's spread.

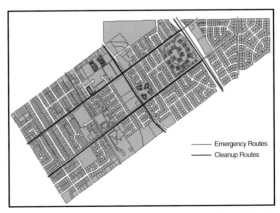

Rachel combines parcel and street maps to identify the best routes for getting emergency equipment into an area and debris out of it.

After the fire, other effects need to be considered. A fire in hilly country commonly results in landslides. The county soils department uses GIS to provide Rachel with information about landslide-prone areas so they can be reinforced before rebuilding, or avoided completely.

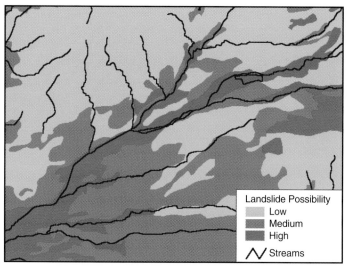

By comparing soils, slopes, drainage, and vegetation information, areas most prone to landslides can be identified.

GIS can supply this kind of information and may be the best tool for avoiding disasters in the future.

Chemicals where you need them

Ted has a hard job. He's a farmer. He not only has to battle the weather and various pests, but he has to do it without endangering the environment and without losing money.

One way Ted can save money and still protect the environment is by applying chemicals such as fertilizers and pesticides to fields only where they are needed instead of applying them uniformly. But this requires more detailed information about the health of each field, and the information comes from a variety of sources, such as field work, maps, and photographs.

GIS's ability to link descriptive information and photographs with maps makes it a natural solution. Ted combines infrared images with maps and information about soil types and nutrient status. This helps him identify problem areas, evaluate crop stress, and target specific areas for fertilizer applications.

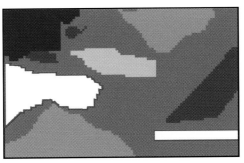

This crop stress map shows the lighter areas as low in nutrients; they should be targeted for fertilizer applications.

Since the process of identifying problem areas is visual, maps are perfect tools. Ted need only draw a perimeter around a problem area on a map to identify it. Then, if a ground sample shows an unusually low yield or the presence of a parasite, he knows where to target fertilizers or pesticides.

Providing the care where it's needed

Whenever Theresa has an asthma attack, she often ends up in the emergency room of the local hospital. But emergency room care is expensive, and many conditions such as asthma can be successfully treated in an outpatient setting, especially when care is administered early.

The problem comes when the type of outpatient care needed is not accessible to patients. Brookside Hospital decided to use desktop GIS to solve this problem. With GIS's mapping capabilities, and access to emergency room records, hospital staff were able to map the locations of thousands of patients who had visited their emergency room. They also mapped the locations of community clinics and primary care physicians.

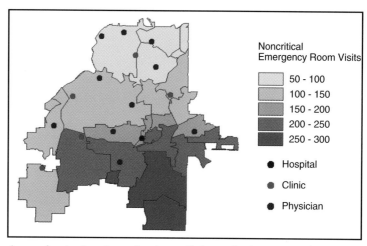

A map showing locations of patients, clinics, and primary care physicians shows the gaps in access to primary care.

Using these maps, the Brookside staff were able to better focus the available primary care resources, and determine where more family, primary care, and general practice physicians were needed.

ENVIRONMENTAL SYSTEMS RESEARCH INSTITUTE, INC.

Whose woods are these?

People need space to live in. Animals need space to live in. Sometimes it's the same space. Larry works for a wildlife organization that has begun to use desktop GIS to identify where wild species could live without using human space.

The first step is generating maps of wildlife habitats, one map per species.

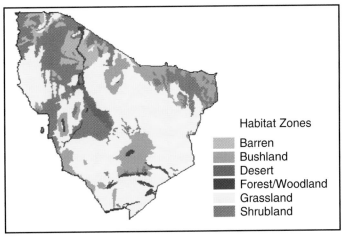

Larry generates a map of habitats used by each species.

Larry must consider each species separately, because each one ranges differently. Some nest in one place and forage in another. Some migrate and need corridors to get from winter to summer homes and back. Some range widely and the whole of their range must be preserved.

Larry then combines all of the species maps to determine which areas are used by the greatest number of species.

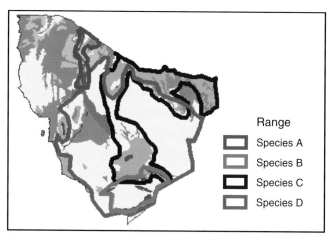

When habitat maps of all species are combined, those areas used by the largest number of sensitive species become obvious.

When Larry combines these maps with public land maps, he sees immediately what needs to be done.

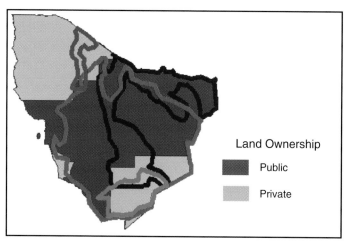

Combining maps of wildlife areas with those of public lands shows the extent to which species are already being protected on public lands. It also shows areas not currently in public ownership and in need of protection.

ENVIRONMENTAL SYSTEMS RESEARCH INSTITUTE, INC.

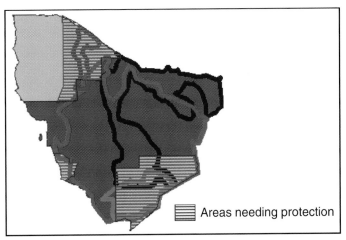

A final map shows lands that should be protected to meet long-term conservation needs of sensitive species.

These results give Larry's organization what it needs to work with governments, planning councils, and the private sector to make a place where all animals can have a future.

What you can do with desktop GIS

You don't have to be a farmer or a wildlife manager. You don't have to be a developer or a traffic engineer. If what you do involves managing information, and that information can be linked to geographic locations, then GIS can help you organize that information in new ways so that you can make new discoveries and get more out of the information you have. The possibilities are endless.

So read on. The next chapter gives you the basic concepts you need to understand the technology. And we continue to address the topic of what you can do with desktop GIS throughout the first part of this book.

This is how it works

The most incomprehensible thing about the world is that it is comprehensible.

—Albert Einstein

This is how it works

Desktop GIS represents the real world on a computer similar to the way maps represent the world on paper. But desktop GIS has power and flexibility that paper maps lack. This chapter will introduce you to the basic concepts of desktop GIS—what it has in common with maps and what's different.

To help you understand how desktop GIS works, we'll break it down into the conceptual pieces, and take them one piece at a time. We'll start with basic ideas, like how maps convey information about places and how scale influences the size of what appears on the map. Then we'll advance to the principles governing how a desktop GIS works, like how it stores and links information and where it gets its power and flexibility.

What you see on a map

Map features represent objects in the real world

Maps are graphic representations of the real world. Since the real world is infinitely more detailed than a map can be, we say that maps give us a generalized view of the real world. Natural objects, such as mountains, rivers, and valleys as well as man-made objects such as cities, roads, and buildings can all be represented on maps.

The objects represented on maps, whether natural or man-made, are called *map features,* or simply *features.* Looking at a map of downtown Portland (on the next page), we can identify some of its features.

ENVIRONMENTAL SYSTEMS RESEARCH INSTITUTE, INC.

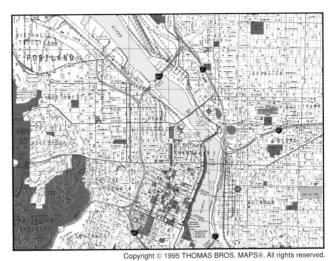

The features representing downtown Portland are shown on this map.

Each map feature has a location, a representative shape, and a symbol that represents one or more of its characteristics. The large blue area represents the Willamette River. The white areas represent land. Some large green areas stand out—these represent parks; a yellow area says "Lloyd Center"; a gray area says "Lonefir Cemetery." Freeways are marked by dark red lines, and smaller roads are marked by thin gray or black lines.

The relationships between locations

The locations of map features reflect more or less accurately their locations on the earth's surface. Because the earth is a sphere and maps are flat, there is necessarily some distortion in the locations of features on maps. We'll discuss the distortion found on maps, how to control it, and the methods used for recording locations of features in chapter 5.

Because features on maps are organized according to relative position or location, maps are particularly good for showing the relationships between feature locations. These relationships, called *spatial relationships,* are important because understanding them helps us solve problems. For example, in order to plan a delivery route, you need to know which streets connect, where they cross highways, and which parts of town they pass through. Selecting a site for a new picnic area might involve finding areas near the river, adjacent to office buildings, and where there are plenty of trees.

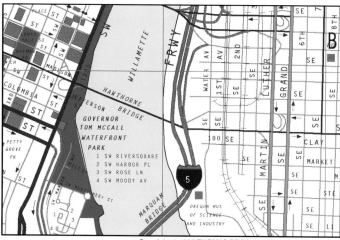

The relationships between feature locations are visible on a map. You can see where highways connect and which ones cross the railroad tracks or the river; you can see which buildings are near the river and also near parks.

Map features have distinct shapes

To represent real-world objects, maps use three basic shapes—points, lines, and areas. Any object can be represented using one of these shapes.

Points represent objects that have discrete locations and are too small to be depicted as areas. On the Portland map, these include schools, churches, train stations, fire stations, and other buildings such as museums and the Department of Motor Vehicles.

ENVIRONMENTAL SYSTEMS RESEARCH INSTITUTE, INC.

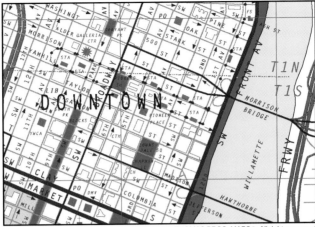

Small buildings, such as train stations, post offices, the YWCA, and the Department of Motor Vehicles, are represented as point features on the Portland map.

Lines represent objects that have length but are too narrow to be depicted as areas. On the Portland map, lines represent freeways and roads of all kinds, railroads, bridges, and creeks.

Freeways, bridges, and roads are prominent line features on the Portland map.

Areas represent objects too large to be depicted as points or lines. The Willamette River, parks of all kinds, Portland State University, the Lloyd Center, Buckman Field, and Lonefir Cemetery are all shown as areas on the Portland map.

The river, parks, and large buildings are area features on the Portland map.

Symbols identify or characterize map features

Shapes alone do not give you enough information. So, maps use graphic symbols to help identify features and provide information about them. There are symbols for points, symbols for lines, and symbols for areas. Symbols for points often look like the features they identify. For example, the symbol for a school may be a little red schoolhouse and the symbol for an airport may be a small plane.

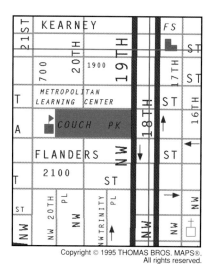

Schools, churches, and fire stations all have distinct symbols on the Portland map.

Line symbols include thick or thin lines, solid or broken lines, and may come in colors.

ENVIRONMENTAL SYSTEMS RESEARCH INSTITUTE, INC.

Red double lines make the freeways stand out and differentiate them from other roads; thick, black lines differentiate major roads from lesser roads (thin, gray lines).

Area symbols include the colors and patterns used to fill in area shapes. Some colors have a natural connection to the objects they represent, such as blue for water and green for parks and forested areas, while others do not.

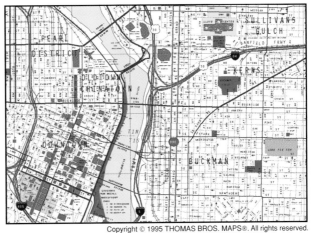

The river is shaded blue, parks are green, the university is pink, the Lloyd Center is yellow, and the cemetery is gray.

Sometimes symbols don't give enough information and so text labels are added to help identify features. For example, you know that the blue area on the Portland map is a river, but you may not know which river; you may know that the green areas are parks, but you need labels to identify them by name.

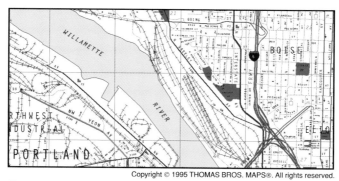

Features of all kinds need labels to identify them.

Map scale determines the size and shape of features

Most features can be represented as more than one shape. The *scale* of a map tells how the size of the map features compares with the size of the geographic objects they represent. The larger the map scale, the bigger the map features will appear. Depending on the map scale, a feature such as a city can appear as a point or as an area, and a feature such as a river can appear as a line or as an area. For example, the Willamette River is represented as an area on the Portland map, but on a map of Oregon State it appears as a line. The city of Portland covers the entire area shown on the downtown Portland map, but the same area appears as a single point on the state map. The buildings that are points on the Portland map would appear as areas on a larger-scale land use map.

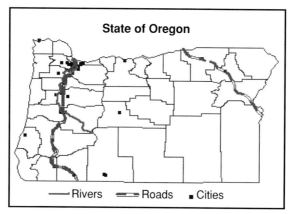

Lines depict roads and rivers alike on this smaller-scale state map; cities are depicted as points.

ENVIRONMENTAL SYSTEMS RESEARCH INSTITUTE, INC.

Buildings appear as areas on this land use map.

What's different about desktop GIS

Desktop GIS links features with lists of attributes

On paper maps, each color, pattern, picture, or label gives you information about the features. But, the amount of information you can get from a paper map is limited to what is shown.

With desktop GIS, you can get an almost unlimited amount of information about what you see on a map. Desktop GIS stores all the information about map features in a GIS database and links the features on the map to the information about them. This means that you can access all the information about a feature by simply clicking on it.

The information that a desktop GIS stores about map features is referred to as *attribute* information, or *attributes*. The attributes of a river, for example, might include its name, length, average depth, rate of flow, water quality, how many dams are on it, and how many bridges cross it. The attributes for a map feature that represents a shopping mall might include the name of the mall, its type, size, the names of its anchor stores, a list of tenants, and the number of available spaces.

Desktop GIS formats attributes in rows and columns, and stores them as *tables*. Each column stores a different attribute and each row relates to a single feature.

Street ID	Length	Surface Material	Resurface Date	Speed Limit	Number of Lanes	Avg. Daily Traffic
66	5.4	asphalt	5/85	40	4	3200
69	9.4	asphalt	6/88	50	4	4000
99	25.3	concrete	7/91	55	6	7900

The attributes of all the streets on a map can be stored in a table like this.

The link between map features and their attributes is the basic principle behind how a desktop GIS works, and is the source of its power. Once the map features and attributes are linked, you can access the attributes for any map feature or locate any feature from its attributes in a table.

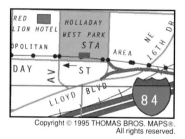

Copyright © 1995 THOMAS BROS. MAPS®.
All rights reserved.

Park Name	Area (acres)	Admin.	Type Code
Waterfront	26	city	2
Holladay	2	city	1
Irvin			

Type	Sq. Feet	# of Floors	Year Built
office	12000	5	1989
office	50000	15	1980
hotel	110000	22	1991

Street ID	Length	Surface Material	Resurface Date	Speed Limit	Number of Lanes	Avg. Daily Traffic
81	1.4	asphalt	6/94	35	2	200
82	19.4	asphalt	10/89	40	4	2400
84	34.5	concrete	2/90	55	8	10100

Pointing at any feature on the Portland map displays the list of attributes linked to that feature. First you see the attributes for a park, then a building, then a road.

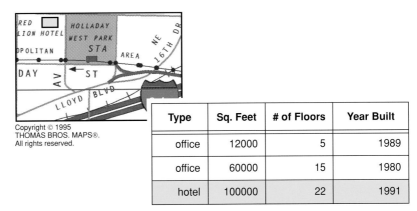

Type	Sq. Feet	# of Floors	Year Built
office	12000	5	1989
office	60000	15	1980
hotel	100000	22	1991

From the table of attributes, you can access the building feature linked to any attribute you choose.

Desktop GIS displays features based on their attributes

Not only can GIS access features from an attribute table and access attributes from a map, it can also display features based on any attribute in the table. Take a look at how this works using the streets of downtown Portland. Suppose you need to move a modular office building across town to the Lloyd Center. You'll need to know which streets are wide enough to carry the extra-wide load. The street features are stored in a desktop GIS and linked to a table of attributes. Recall that one of the attributes is the number of street lanes. You display the streets based on the number of lanes for each street so you can find the widest streets. Then you can trace a path across town that follows these streets.

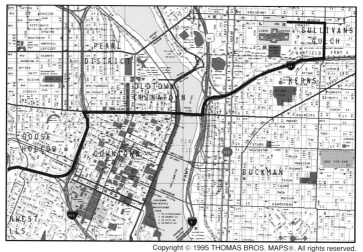

This path follows the widest streets across town.

But wait a minute. Another important variable to consider is the type of traffic you'll encounter. So you display the streets again, this time based on a different attribute, average daily traffic. Now you can trace a different path, one that follows streets with the lowest daily traffic flow.

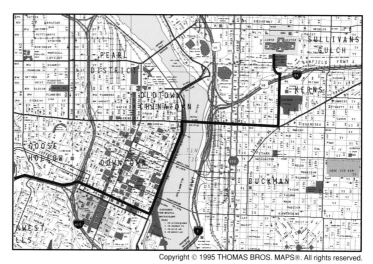

This path follows the streets with the least traffic.

Now you might ask, "What if I want to find streets based on both attributes?" That is, you want to find wide streets that have low traffic flow. Because features and attributes are linked, this is easy to do with desktop GIS. The GIS can locate the features you want based on any number of attributes and display them on a map. In the next chapter, we'll discuss the details of how this works.

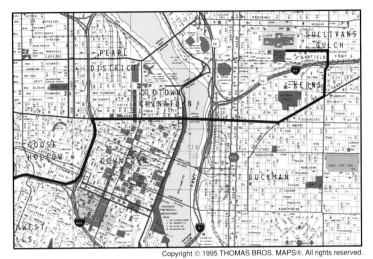

This path follows the widest streets with the least traffic.

The link between features and attributes is dynamic

Because the link between features and attributes is a two-way relationship, changing an attribute in the table automatically results in a change on the map. Here's a hypothetical situation to demonstrate how it works. Say that Fremont Street, located in the northeast portion of downtown Portland, is a major road between Highway 99E and the eastern edge of town. But, west of Highway 99E, it's a minor road.

The change in line symbols from thin to thick shows that Fremont Street changes from a two-lane to a four-lane road as it crosses Highway 99E.

Suppose that the highway department has decided to widen the western portion of Fremont Street, from its current two lanes to four lanes, so both portions will have the same number of lanes. You work in the GIS division, and it's your job to update the attribute table to reflect this change. Since the map symbol for a four-lane road is different than for a two-lane road, the symbol for the western portion of Fremont Street should change once you update the table.

Street ID	Length	Surface Material	Resurface Date	Speed Limit	Number of Lanes	Avg. Daily Traffic
66	5.4	asphalt	5/85	40	4	3200
69	9.4	asphalt	6/88	50	4	4000
99	25.3	concrete	7/91	55	6	7900

In the attribute table, you change the number of lanes from two to four for the western portion of Fremont Street.

The next time you display the road features, the western portion of Fremont Street appears with the same line symbol as the portion east of Highway 99E.

ENVIRONMENTAL SYSTEMS RESEARCH INSTITUTE, INC.

This simple link between features and attributes makes desktop GIS a truly dynamic system.

How desktop GIS manages features and attributes

Themes link features with their attributes

Desktop GIS links sets of features and their attributes and manages them together in units called *themes*. A theme contains a set of related features, such as roads, streams, parcels, or wildlife habitat areas, along with the attributes for those features. Take, for example, the Portland map. It contains many themes. All the interstate freeways could make up one theme, and all railroads, another. City streets might be a separate theme. Parks, buildings, and waterways are examples of other themes.

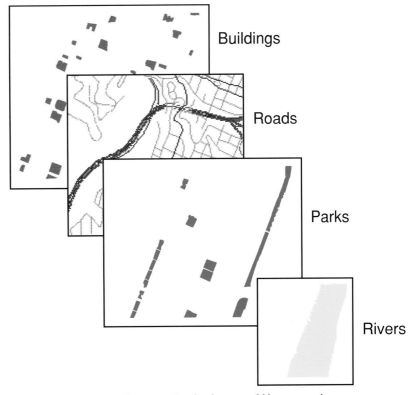

Buildings

Roads

Parks

Rivers

The information on the downtown Portland map could be managed as many separate themes.

Themes are made up of features with a set of common attributes. For example, all the roads have lanes, pavement type, and a route or street name. On the other hand, the railroads have a different set of characteristics in common, such as whether they are main line or branch line railroads, the type of usage they get, and the volume of traffic they bear, measured in tons.

Sometimes features that share common attributes are placed in separate themes for convenience. For example, if you work with and display freeways separately from other roads most of the time, you can keep them in a separate theme.

Collections of themes form a GIS database

All the themes for a geographic area taken together make up a *GIS database*. You can use the themes in a GIS database to analyze multiple situations and solve multiple problems. To determine the best routes for a pickup and delivery service, you could use the freeway and road themes. To plan a tour of the city, you might use the themes for roads, buildings, parks, and points of interest.

The design of a GIS database is strong because it's flexible. You can add new themes to a GIS database or delete old ones; you can separate themes to create more themes, or combine themes if they have common characteristics. What you want to do with a GIS database, and what information you need, will determine the best design for you.

ENVIRONMENTAL SYSTEMS RESEARCH INSTITUTE, INC.

Asking questions; getting answers

*He who asks a question is a fool for five
minutes; he who does not ask a question
remains a fool forever.*

—Chinese proverb

Asking questions; getting answers

At first glance, a GIS map display on a computer screen looks like any other map. The solid black lines are roads, the thin blue ones are rivers; the circles are cities, the small triangles are mountain peaks. But with a GIS map display you can get detailed information about each feature; with GIS you can find features based on their attributes and analyze feature locations to uncover relationships between them.

Finding attributes by selecting features

Suppose that you're a real estate agent. You need information for a client about a piece of property. With desktop GIS, you're only a click or two away from displaying a table of the property's attributes, a photograph of the property, a legal description of it, real estate figures about it, and even a video of the inside of the house located there. Here's how.

Selecting features by pointing

You recall from chapter 2 that desktop GIS links features with their attributes and stores them as a single row in an attribute table. When your clients want to know the attributes of a particular property, like when a house was built or how many bedrooms it has, you need only point to the property on the computer map with a mouse to see its attributes.

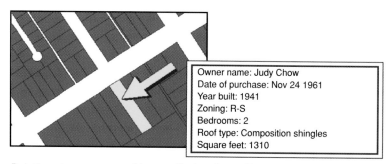

Owner name: Judy Chow
Date of purchase: Nov 24 1961
Year built: 1941
Zoning: R-S
Bedrooms: 2
Roof type: Composition shingles
Square feet: 1310

Pointing at a property on this map displays its attributes.

ENVIRONMENTAL SYSTEMS RESEARCH INSTITUTE, INC.

Now you know who currently owns the property, when it was purchased, how it's been improved, how many bedrooms the house has, and how big it is. Do you need to know more? If so, desktop GIS enables you to access additional information as long as that information is linked to features on a map display.

Legal description:
2ND PREL MAP ADD NO 3 PTN LOT 5
3/4 BLK 1 COM ON SLYL1 FERN AVE
S 56 DEG 20MINW198FT FROM MOST
NLY COR SD LOT TH N 56 DEG 20

Pointing at the property this time displays its legal description and a picture of the house located there.

Selecting features by drawing shapes

Sometimes you need to work with more than one feature at a time, like when your clients want information about all the homes for sale in a neighborhood. Selecting many features individually by pointing is tedious and time consuming. So, to list and compare information about a group of features, you select them by drawing a line through them or a shape around them.

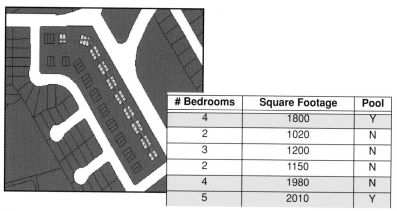

# Bedrooms	Square Footage	Pool
4	1800	Y
2	1020	N
3	1200	N
2	1150	N
4	1980	N
5	2010	Y

Drawing a line selects all the houses the line passes through along with their attributes.

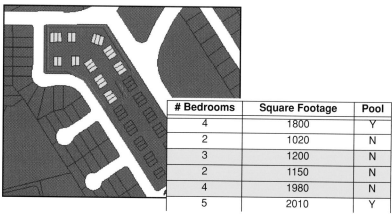

# Bedrooms	Square Footage	Pool
4	1800	Y
2	1020	N
3	1200	N
2	1150	N
4	1980	N
5	2010	Y

Drawing an irregular shape selects all the houses inside the shape along with their attributes.

ENVIRONMENTAL SYSTEMS RESEARCH INSTITUTE, INC.

Finding features by selecting attributes

Pointing at rows

You've seen some ways to select features directly from the map display. But, since features and attributes are linked, you can also select features indirectly by selecting their attributes. By pointing at a row in an attribute table, you can select it, along with the feature it's linked to. You can select one row or as many rows as you like. Features linked to the rows you select are highlighted on the map display. This can be a powerful way to find features while looking over a table of their attributes.

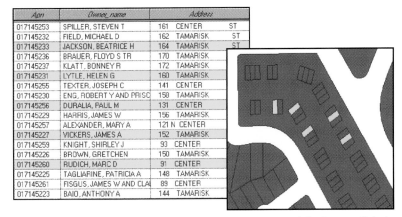

Selecting one or more rows in a table highlights the rows and the features linked to them.

Entering text

Looking for a feature on a paper map can be challenging if the feature is small. With GIS map displays, finding a feature is easy no matter how small it is, because you can find it by requesting any of its attributes. Suppose your client wants to purchase a commercial property. He's seen a For Sale sign in front of a vacant building. He jots down the address and brings it to you on the back of a crumpled business card. You enter the address as a request. Desktop GIS locates the feature linked to the address you enter and shows it to you by highlighting it on the map.

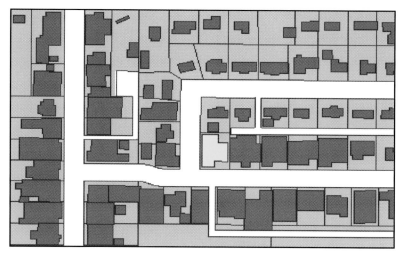

Find: **504 West Main**

By entering a street address, you can find the property at that address.

You could find the same property by entering a different attribute. Suppose your client had written down the building's name, "Bradshaw Building," instead. You can simply enter that name, and the first building found that matches your request will be highlighted on your screen.

Finding features that meet your criteria

You can find one or more features by requesting them based on an attribute they share. For example, you can ask for buildings of a certain type, buildings built in a certain year, or buildings with a certain square footage. All the buildings that match your request are selected and highlighted in both the attribute table and on the map display.

You can find features based on more than one criterion, too. A couple has asked you to look for a house with a tile roof (for fire safety) and five bedrooms (they have four kids). You write a request that asks for houses having both "tile roofs" and "five bedrooms."

The desktop GIS finds and selects all the houses with both of these attributes from all the other houses in the map theme. (Recall that a theme stores all the features of a particular type, such as houses, along with their attributes.) The desktop GIS highlights the selected houses on the map and in the table containing their attributes.

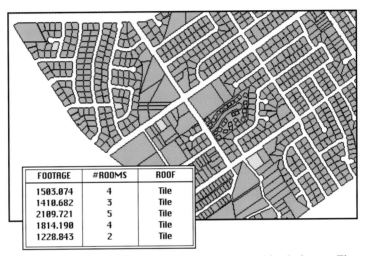

FOOTAGE	#ROOMS	ROOF
1503.074	4	Tile
1410.682	3	Tile
2109.721	5	Tile
1814.190	4	Tile
1228.843	2	Tile

This map highlights the houses that have tile roofs and five bedrooms. The attributes linked to the selected features are also shown in the table.

Performing operations on selected features and their attributes

Once you've selected a group of features, you can perform any operation on them as a separate group, apart from all the other features. For example, you can have the GIS zoom in to see selected features fill the center of your screen, or perform statistical operations on any numeric attribute, or use statistics to summarize the information in a table, or even create a chart comparing attributes of the selected features.

Your clients want to know prices and number of square feet for the selected houses. You have a column for price and one for square footage in the attribute table. The GIS can compute the price per square foot and place the results in a new column you've added to the table. Now that you know the average price per square foot for houses in the selected group, you can combine all the information to display only those houses that meet all your clients' criteria.

This map shows the houses that have tile roofs, five bedrooms, and a price of less than $100 per square foot.

It's the relationships that matter

In chapter 2, we examined the features on the downtown Portland map and the relationships between them—freeways crossing the river, roads intersecting other roads, neighborhoods sharing common boundaries. Some buildings were near the river, others were near the freeways. The parks were on the west side of town. Some features even shared the same geographic space (the Lloyd Center contained several other features).

The orientation of certain features to those around them may be important if you need to know such things as which schools are within a certain distance of properties you're considering, or whether a specific property is next to a commercial zone, inside this fire district or that water district or that flood zone, or underlain by clay soils or a fault zone, or overlapping an endangered species habitat.

When you use desktop GIS to analyze these relationships, you are performing *spatial analysis.* "Spatial" refers to the way information is organized on maps, that is, according to its relative position or location on the surface of the earth. Analyzing spatial relationships is something a desktop GIS is very good at.

ENVIRONMENTAL SYSTEMS RESEARCH INSTITUTE, INC.

How far is it?

One way of analyzing the locations of features is by measuring the distance between them and other features in the area around them. The information you get by clicking on a piece of property will probably show you the dimensions of a lot, but probably not how far the house is from the shopping mall, the distance to the nearest airport, or the closest high school.

Measuring distance on a GIS map is easy. When you enter two points with the mouse that define the distance you want to measure, the desktop GIS calculates and reports the distance between them in any units you choose (e.g., feet, meters, miles, kilometers).

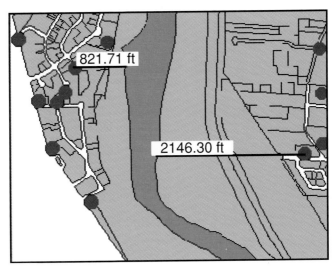

Here, distances from properties to the river are measured and displayed; properties within 1,000 feet of the river have higher insurance rates.

How big is it?

Another way of analyzing the locations of features is by measuring the area around them. Perhaps you need to know the size of a corridor between a property and the soon-to-be-built freeway or the area surrounding a proposed airport that buffers it from the surrounding residential properties. Desktop GIS calculates area as easily as distance. Just draw any shape on a map and the GIS calculates the area inside that shape.

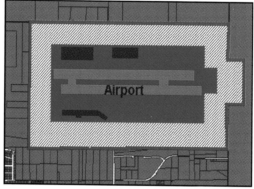

63758328 sq ft

Drawing a closed shape around the airport lets you calculate the size of the area that separates it from surrounding residential properties.

Finding the features nearby

A GIS can find features located within a certain distance of other features you specify. For example, the decision to buy or develop a certain property could depend on its proximity to surrounding features. Parents might want their house close to a particular school. A developer might purchase a property only if it's far enough away from the floodplain. An investor might be interested in a shopping center only if it's near major highways.

Say your clients with the four kids now want you to find all the houses for sale within half a mile of a particular school, so their children can walk to it. The houses and schools are in separate map themes, but you can display both themes at the same time.

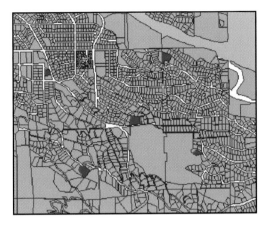

The house and school themes are both displayed.

Then you can select the particular school and find all the houses within a half-mile radius of it. Since you're only interested in the ones that are for sale, you can select only those.

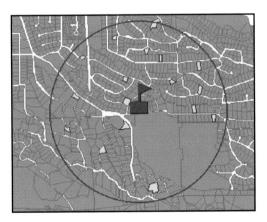

Only houses for sale within half a mile of the school are highlighted on the map.

Finding the features inside

A GIS can find points, lines, and areas that are enclosed within other area features. You might want to find all the fire hydrants in a subdivision containing undeveloped lots. This may be important to clients who want to build their own homes because lots far from fire hydrants may require that you pay to have a hydrant put in or that you install an expensive sprinkler system in your home.

The subdivisions and fire hydrants are stored in separate themes in the GIS database, but this is not a problem because desktop GIS allows you to find features in one theme contained within the boundary of a feature in another theme. First you display the subdivision and hydrant themes together. Then you select the subdivision of interest from the subdivision theme. The desktop GIS finds all the fire hydrants located within the selected subdivision, highlights them on the map, and selects them in the GIS database.

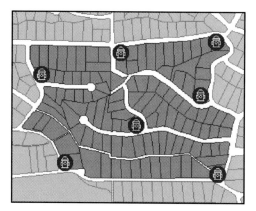

This map shows fire hydrants located within the selected subdivision.

Now you notice that scenic Henderson Creek runs through certain properties in the subdivision, making them highly desirable to people who want to build close to the river. The GIS finds all the properties Henderson Creek crosses and you print out a list.

ENVIRONMENTAL SYSTEMS RESEARCH INSTITUTE, INC.

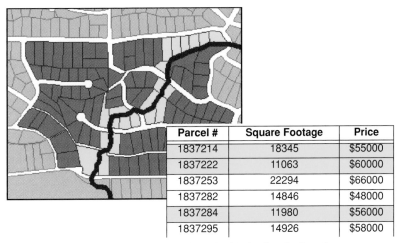

Parcel #	Square Footage	Price
1837214	18345	$55000
1837222	11063	$60000
1837253	22294	$66000
1837282	14846	$48000
1837284	11980	$56000
1837295	14926	$58000

Properties crossed by Henderson Creek are highlighted and selected.

Working with properties is not the exclusive domain of real estate agents. Local governments need land use or land ownership information too. Whenever there is a zoning change, for example, the city must notify the owners of the affected properties. Using the boundary of the new zone, the desktop GIS can identify all affected properties and provide the names and addresses of their owners.

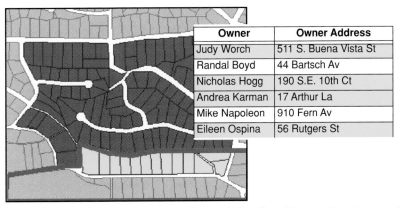

Owner	Owner Address
Judy Worch	511 S. Buena Vista St
Randal Boyd	44 Bartsch Av
Nicholas Hogg	190 S.E. 10th Ct
Andrea Karman	17 Arthur La
Mike Napoleon	910 Fern Av
Eileen Ospina	56 Rutgers St

The desktop GIS selects the properties that would be affected by a zoning change and displays their owners' names and addresses.

Finding the features next to other features

Desktop GIS also locates features that are next to other features you select. This type of analysis is important when selecting sites for businesses. For example, your client wants to purchase a space where she can locate a new store and expand into neighboring spaces if she needs more room. So she wants to know the square footage of the spaces adjacent to the one she wants to buy—those that share walls with her space. Desktop GIS finds adjacent properties, highlights them on the map, and selects them in the GIS database.

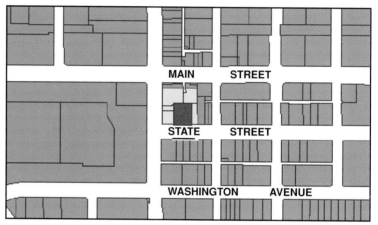

Properties adjacent to the selected business (red) are selected and highlighted on the map (yellow).

ENVIRONMENTAL SYSTEMS RESEARCH INSTITUTE, INC.

Finding where features share space

A property is a certain piece of land. The property is located in a certain land use area and building zone. It is also in a certain school district, fire district, and emergency services district. Not only that, the land is a habitat for certain plants and animals. It is made up of certain soils and certain geology layers, and below it, there may even be groundwater.

A GIS database stores all of these objects as map features in separate map themes, one for properties, one for habitats, one for geology, and so forth. Anytime you want to know which features occupy the same geographic space, you can display the themes on top of one another. This allows you to visually inspect which features share this same piece of the earth.

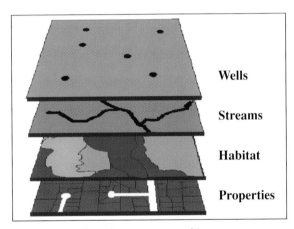

These themes share the same geographic space.

A desktop GIS uses the location information associated with each feature to find the exact intersection of the features, no matter what theme they are in. This process of finding features that share common space is a powerful tool called *spatial overlay.*

Suppose a city needs a suitable site for a landfill. The engineers would have a list of criteria to start with. For example, a landfill must be located on land with a certain type of soil that is rich in clay, to prevent materials buried in the landfill from seeping into the groundwater below.

The landfill must also be located away from airports. This is because birds visiting the landfill might collide with airplanes, causing potentially catastrophic accidents. To prevent the movement of material once it's in the ground, a landfill should not be located in an earthquake fault zone or in a flood zone. To meet these criteria, the engineers would use GIS to find those areas that are not too close to airports and not within a fault or flood zone.

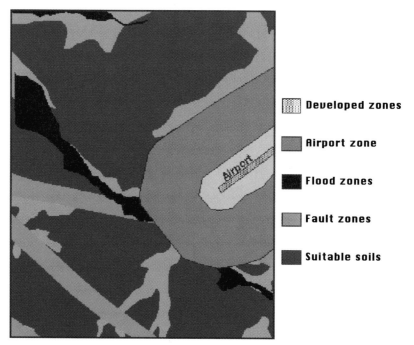

Developed zones

Airport zone

Flood zones

Fault zones

Suitable soils

This map shows areas where soils are acceptable, outside the five-mile radius around the airport, and outside the flood and fault zones.

And since nobody wants a landfill near their house, the engineers will have to find the areas that do not overlap with residential streets. By selecting some areas and avoiding others, they find all the areas that meet all the criteria for a landfill.

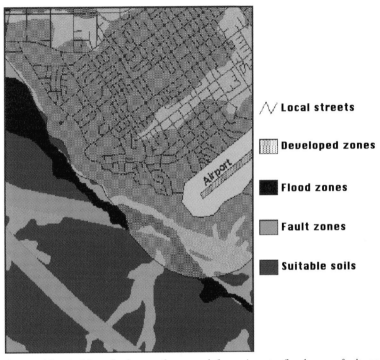

/\/ **Local streets**

Developed zones

Flood zones

Fault zones

Suitable soils

Areas with suitable soils that are far enough from airports, flood zones, fault zones, and residential streets are potentially good sites for a landfill.

You provide the questions; desktop GIS provides the answers

As you work more with desktop GIS, you'll find that it often leads you to ask new questions. Sometimes the answers present new information, even surprises. But no matter how many or how complex the questions, desktop GIS gives you the tools for understanding and analyzing the information so you can get the answers you need.

ENVIRONMENTAL SYSTEMS RESEARCH INSTITUTE, INC.

Making information presentable

> *To envision information—and what bright and splendid visions can result—is to work at the intersection of image, word, number, art.*
>
> —Edward R. Tufte
> *Envisioning Information*

Making information presentable

Now you know how to ask questions and get answers from a desktop GIS. But how do you present the answers you get? Often it's not enough to have the answers yourself. You may have to present the information to others in a way that convinces them that the information you've derived supports your point of view.

Desktop GIS can help because it provides a wide variety of tools for presenting information as quality graphic presentations. These presentations may include maps, charts, and tables, along with graphics you import from other programs or even graphics you draw yourself. The presentations you create can be output to a printer to produce hard copy, or displayed on your computer's screen.

To make information presentable, you need to know your audience. Then you need to decide which information to include in your presentation. If your presentation includes maps, then how much information should be included on each map, and how should the information be organized and displayed? Should you use charts or tables instead of maps or in addition to maps? What other graphics could enhance your presentation?

We'll explore each of these topics separately, and then show you how easy it is to create attractive presentations that accomplish your objectives.

Knowing your audience

Before you sit down to create a graphic presentation that other people will see, ask yourself who they are and how much they already know. Are they a general audience or a group with specific knowledge of the topic you're presenting? Say your presentation includes a map. Knowing who is going to see the map will determine the colors and symbols you choose, the amount of detail you show, and how you organize the information. Only when you know who your audience is can you create the presentation that best conveys your message.

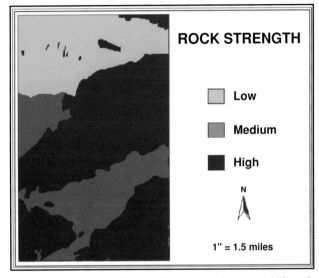

This map was designed for a public meeting. It uses symbols and text that anyone can understand.

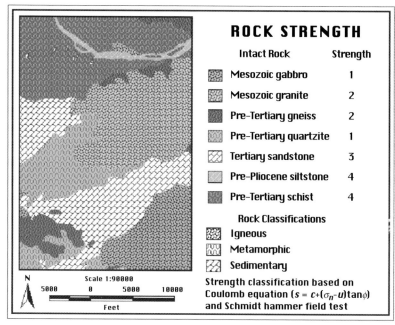

This map was designed for scientists. It presents similar information but with more detail, and uses symbols and text that a person with a technical background understands.

Knowing what information to present

You have a GIS database full of information, and you can access any of it. But, how much of this information should you present on a map? Too much information will confound and overwhelm the audience, and won't get your message across. If you get reactions like these, you've probably botched it: "I don't get it. What are all those lines? Those points on top of each other are confusing. I don't want to look at this map anymore. It makes me dizzy."

Desktop GIS gives you tools for controlling what appears on a map. For example, there are tools for controlling how big or small features appear and for reducing the number of features, so that just the ones you need are displayed. Other tools let you turn entire map themes on or off, or create more than one view of the information.

How much detail do you need?

The scale of the map determines how big or how small features appear and how much detail you can show. If your audience needs to see a lot of detail in a coastline, the scale must be large enough to show it. A sailor needs to see every cove and harbor to stay on course. A wildlife biologist needs to see all the crenulations in the coastline—its inlets and peninsulas—to identify and preserve good habitat areas. On the other hand, a traveler looking for a good vacation spot along the coast wants to see all the scenic overlooks, access roads, and public beaches, and have a map small enough to unfold in the car. (No map folds *back* quite right.)

One way to control the amount of detail is by *zooming in* and *zooming out*.

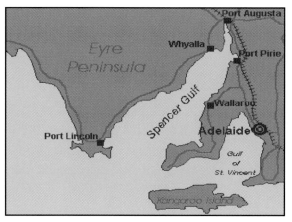

Zooming in enlarges the scale so you can see more detail.

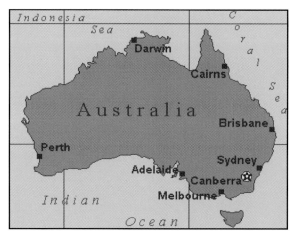

Zooming out decreases the scale and the size of the features. Features like harbors, inlets, and offshore islands become too small to see.

How many features do you need?

No matter how much you zoom in or out, there may still be more features in a theme than you want to show. You don't want to eliminate features, just hide some of them for a while until you need them again. You can do this with a process called *filtering*. For example, you have a theme of cities with populations larger than one million. You want to show only those cities with populations larger than ten million. You simply apply a filter that hides the cities that are too small.

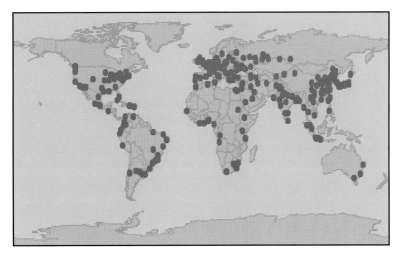

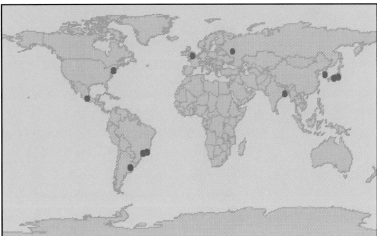

Filtering hides the cities you don't want to show.

Or, suppose you have a theme of properties and you only want to show those that are vacant and zoned for commercial development. Filtering allows you to hide the properties that don't meet your criteria and show the ones that do.

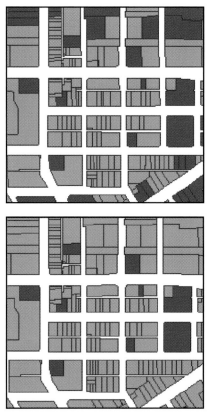

You can display all the vacant properties, or apply a filter to show just those that are zoned for commercial development.

Filtering doesn't remove the features from the map theme. You can display them again, anytime you want, by removing the filter.

How many themes do you need?

GIS databases usually contain many themes of information. You can choose which themes you need to convey your message. To show a citizens' group which streets will flood next time it rains, you might only need to show the streams and the roads they'll overflow onto. However, to present a case for choosing a particular site for a new retail store to potential investors, you'll want to show more themes, including local demographic information, locations of the major roads, the chief competitors, and the best vacant lots.

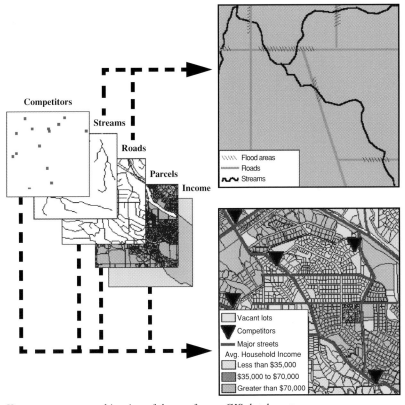

You can use any combination of themes from a GIS database to convey your message.

How many maps do you need?

Sometimes, you really do need to present more information than fits comfortably on a single map. To avoid a cluttered map that's hard to read, you can combine a series of maps in one presentation. This way, you can show separate themes or different portions of the same geographic area, or changes in a geographic area over time.

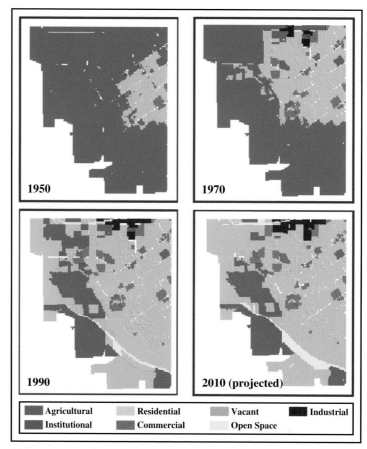

This map series shows past and predicted changes in land use over a 60-year period.

Organizing and displaying information

OK. Now you've figured out the whos and the whats, but you still have to decide *how* to organize the information on a map and the best way to present it. To present information as accurately as possible, you need to choose the most appropriate symbols. Some colors are commonly accepted as appropriate for certain things, green for plants and blue for water, for instance.

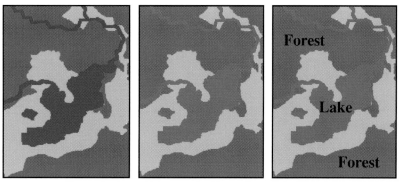

Colors indicate a difference between these area features. Shading the water blue and the forests green conveys more meaning; text labels remove any ambiguity.

On road and topographic maps, a small triangle almost always means a mountain peak. A skull and crossbones likely indicates danger or poison.

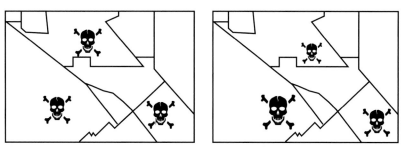

Using a skull and crossbones as symbols to mark toxic spill sites is more meaningful than using plain symbols. Varying the size of the symbol gives more information by indicating that toxic spills come in different sizes.

Line thickness or color can distinguish one type of road from another. A thicker line indicates a wider road; a red line usually indicates a major road.

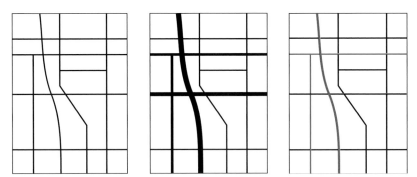

Varying the size or color of these line symbols shows that there is a difference between the roads they represent.

Classifying information

Sometimes you need to present information that has a large number of unique values such as income or population. Since it's too confusing to display each value, you divide them into groups. Each member of a group receives the same symbol. Dividing values into groups, or *classifying,* lets you present a lot of information on a map without overwhelming your audience.

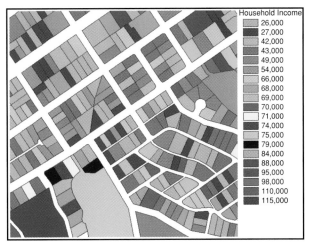

This map shows every unique value for household income with a unique symbol. It's hard for the audience to remember which symbol represents which value and to tell the difference between one symbol and another.

On this map, the household income values are grouped into five classes. Fewer symbols make the information easier to understand.

Some information is more meaningful when you know something about how it ranks, from lowest to highest, such as sales information, housing prices, ages, incomes, temperatures. A *color ramp* uses a range of colors to indicate ranking or order among classes. The colors progress in an orderly fashion from light to dark or from one color to another.

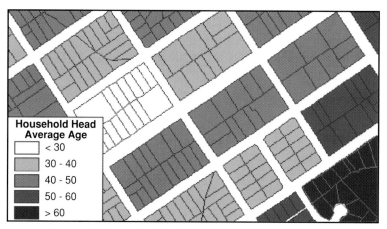

Age classes for households are displayed using a color ramp. The youngest age class (white) progresses to the oldest age class (black).

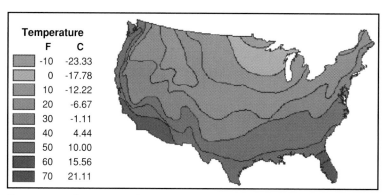

Temperature classes range from the lowest temperatures at the violet end to the highest temperatures at the red end.

Using color ramps to indicate ranked classes makes maps more informative. And the good news: color ramps are easy to create with desktop GIS.

Depending on how you define classes, you can create different maps showing different patterns. For example, if two different methods are used to divide population values into the same number of classes, two different maps would result.

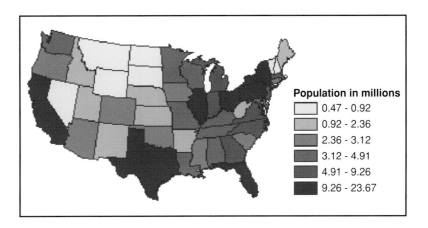

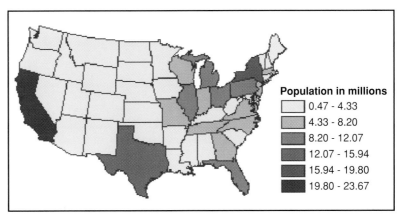

Both of these U.S. maps show population figures for the 48 contiguous states grouped into six classes. Each map tells a different story because each uses a different method to classify the information.

On the top map, each class contains the same number of states (eight). On the bottom map, each class contains the same population (one sixth of the total). The patterns formed by the symbols on each map are different, and so is the message conveyed.

When symbols aren't enough

Text, of course, identifies features with more certainty than symbols alone. Green shading on a map may indicate that those features are parks, but which parks? Text tells you the name. Blue may indicate a body of water, but which body? Text tells you the name.

Some text labels do more than name features. They give you the elevations of mountain peaks, the distances between points along a route, and other attribute values.

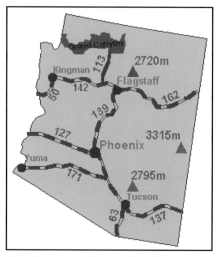

Text labels name features, identify elevations, and indicate distances.

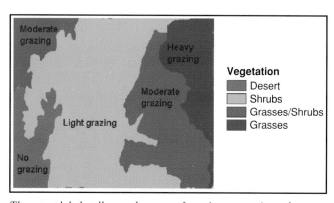

These text labels tell you what type of grazing occurs in each area.

Using charts, tables, and other graphics

Desktop GIS is more than mapping. Using desktop GIS tools, you can create such traditional presentation graphics as pie charts, bar charts, and tables. Not only that, you can include graphics in and add text to the presentation.

Like maps, charts alone are a powerful way of presenting information to others. Used in combination with maps, charts give the audience a different view of the information.

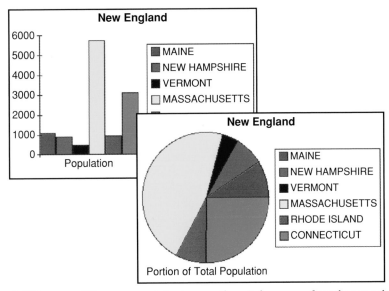

A GIS creates different types of charts as easily as it does maps, from the same data.

Tables can be an effective format for presenting detailed information about a map. You might show selected portions of a table as part of a map presentation or include an entire table in a report.

You may want to enhance your final presentation by adding text and graphics. An arrow here or an explanation there might be just what the audience needs to better understand the message. Placing graphics such as images, scanned pictures, or documents in your presentation adds another dimension.

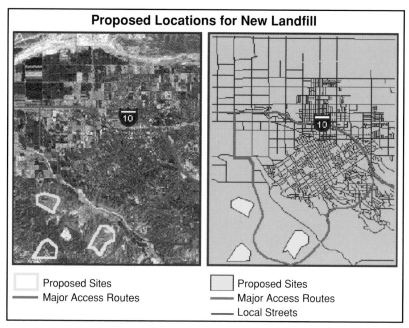

Including an image along with a map of the same area makes a more informative presentation than the map alone.

The dazzling presentation

You know who your audience is, what information to show them, and how to organize and display it. Now you're ready to use desktop GIS to create a presentation that accomplishes your objectives and looks good too.

ENVIRONMENTAL SYSTEMS RESEARCH INSTITUTE, INC.

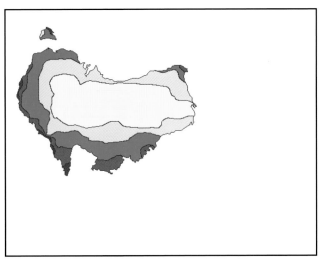

The body of this presentation is a map. It includes the map features you've chosen to show and the symbols used to show them.

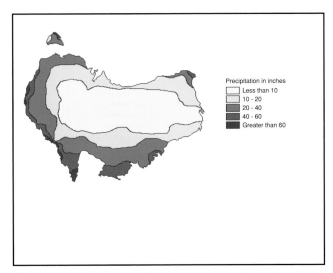

The legend contains a sample of each symbol and describes what each symbol means.

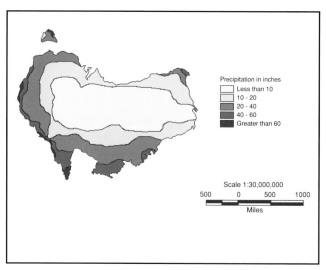

The map scale is traditionally shown in two ways, as a ratio and as a scale bar.

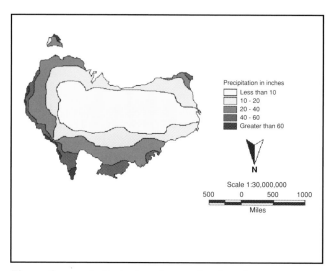

The north arrow indicates how the map is oriented.

ENVIRONMENTAL SYSTEMS RESEARCH INSTITUTE, INC.

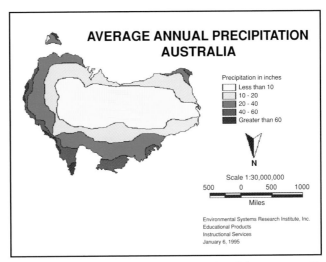

The title identifies the topic of the presentation. Other text can tell who made the presentation and when, as well as where the information was gathered and when.

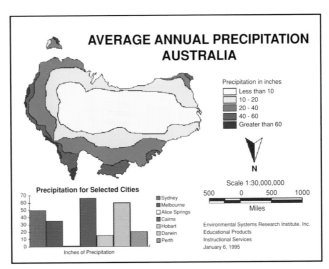

A table, chart, photograph, or document adds information to what's already on the map.

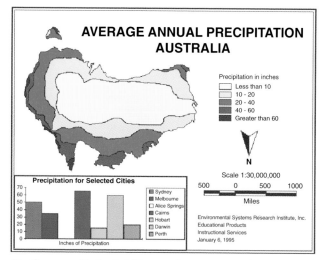

Neatlines provide the finishing touch to a presentation.

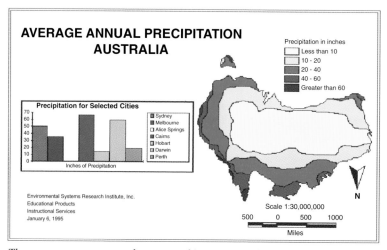

The same components can be arranged in a variety of ways.

The most flexible mapping system

When you create a presentation with desktop GIS, you have the flexibility to change anything, at any stage of the process. You decide what information to present and how much—how much detail, which colors and symbols, and how the final pieces will be arranged. And if your audience or your objective should change, it's easy to make your presentation reflect those changes, without having to start over.

What you need to know about data

A decision is as good as the information

that goes into it.

—John F. Bookout, Jr.

What you need to know about data

Now you know how desktop GIS works. You know that it can help you answer questions and solve problems and present your solutions as dazzling map presentations. All you need now is data.

Deciding what data you need is an important part of any GIS project. Once you know what you need, you need to know where to find it. Once you find it, you need to evaluate it. This chapter gives you information about the types of data you can use with desktop GIS, how to evaluate it, where to get it, and how to make it yourself.

Understanding geographic data

Geographic data refers to information about the earth's surface and the objects found on it. This information comes in three basic forms: spatial data, tabular data, and image data.

Spatial data—what maps are made of

Spatial data is at the heart of every GIS project, or *application.* Spatial data contains the locations and shapes of map features. Also known as *digital map data,* this is the kind of data you need to make maps and study spatial relationships.

Spatial data includes points that represent such things as shopping centers, banks, and physicians' offices, and lines that represent such things as streets, highways, and rivers. It also includes natural areas and political or administrative areas such as the boundaries of countries, states, cities, census tracts, postal zones, and market areas.

Geographic boundaries often come with their areas and perimeters already calculated for you. Street data often includes address ranges along each street.

Tabular data—adding information to geography

Tabular data—the descriptive data that GIS links to map features—is the intelligence behind the map. Tabular data is collected and compiled for specific areas like states, census tracts, cities, and so on, and often comes packaged with spatial data.

You probably have some tabular data that's suitable for use with desktop GIS. If you have customer lists or spreadsheets or databases, you can use the GIS to link that information to map features. For example, you can link a sales database with postal code areas so you can map sales volume by postal code. Then if you add commercially available tabular data such as demographic statistics by postal code, you can profile each community.

Some tabular data contains geographic locations, such as addresses, wildlife sitings, or places where crimes occur. You can use these locations to create map features that can be displayed and analyzed along with other spatial and tabular data. You can use the addresses from a customer list to create points on a street map and display them along with the boundaries of your sales territories.

Images—adding another dimension

Image data includes such diverse elements as satellite images, aerial photographs, and *scanned* data—data that's been converted from printed to digital format.

Images of the earth taken from satellites or airplanes can be displayed as maps along with other spatial data containing map features. You can also use these images as attributes of map features. You could link a satellite image of San Francisco to a map feature so that clicking on the feature would display the image.

© CNES/SPOT Image

A satellite image can be used as a map or as an attribute of a map feature.

Almost any document or photograph can be scanned and stored as an attribute in a GIS database. Photos of houses for sale can be linked to a real estate map; field data forms can be linked to sample sites; and scanned permits can be linked to building sites. Desktop GIS lets you access this information when you need it by simply clicking on a map display.

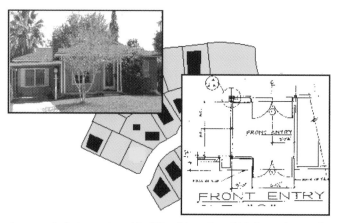

A scanned photograph and building blueprint add information to the map.

ENVIRONMENTAL SYSTEMS RESEARCH INSTITUTE, INC.

Referencing spatial data

The locations of map features are referenced to actual locations of the objects they represent in the real world. The positions of objects on the earth's spherical surface are measured in degrees of latitude and longitude, also known as *geographic coordinates*. On a flat map, the locations of map features are measured in a two-dimensional *planar coordinate system*. Planar coordinates describe the distance from an origin (0,0) along two separate axes, a horizontal *x* axis representing east–west, and a vertical *y* axis representing north–south.

Because the earth is round and maps are flat, getting information from the curved surface to the flat one requires a mathematical formula called a *map projection*. A map projection transforms latitude and longitude locations to x,y coordinates.

Moscow
(Moskva)

Geographic
Degrees
Latitude: 37° 36' 30"
Longitude: 55° 45' 01"

Moscow
(Moskva)

Universal Transverse Mercator
Meters
X: 412,648.41
Y: 6,179,073.07

Locations are expressed as latitude and longitude on the globe and as x and y coordinates on a map.

This process of *flattening* the earth creates distortions in distance, area, shape, and direction. The result is that all flat maps are distorted to some degree in these spatial properties.

Fortunately, there are many different map projections. They are distinguished by their suitability for representing a particular portion and amount of the earth's surface, and by their ability to preserve distance, area, shape, or direction. Some map projections minimize distortion in one property at the expense of another, while others strive to balance overall distortion.

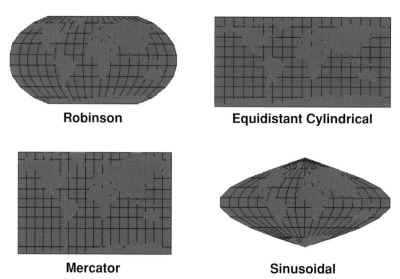

Robinson   **Equidistant Cylindrical**

Mercator   **Sinusoidal**

Each of these world maps uses a different map projection. Different projections cause different distortions.

What to evaluate in data

No matter what the source of the data you use with desktop GIS, you'll need to evaluate the quality and appropriateness of the data for your application. Here are seven issues you need to consider when you select spatial, tabular, or image data for GIS.

Managing distortion

The impact of the distortion caused by a map projection on your work depends on how you will use the data and the size of the area you're covering. If you use measurements to make important decisions, you need to use a projection that doesn't distort whatever you're trying to measure.

ENVIRONMENTAL SYSTEMS RESEARCH INSTITUTE, INC.

If your data covers the entire world, the amount of distortion caused by a map projection may be significant. Knowing the characteristics of the map projection you are using is important, especially when your application involves comparing the shape, area, or distance of map features.

If the data for your area covers a very small part of the earth's surface, such as a small city, then the distortion caused by the map projection you use may be negligible.

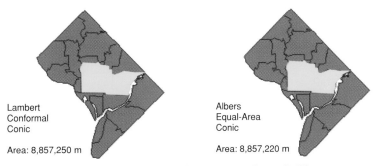

Lambert
Conformal
Conic

Area: 8,857,250 m

Albers
Equal-Area
Conic

Area: 8,857,220 m

When a small area is projected, the distortion may be negligible.

Desktop GIS makes it easy to work with spatial data from a variety of sources at the same time. To do so, all the data in your GIS database needs to be in the same map projection so you can use it and display it together. Because of the distortion inherent in *all* map projections, data won't align properly unless it's in the same projection. You might not even be able to view themes together if they're not in the same projection. For example, if your county boundaries are in one map projection and your rivers are in another, the features might appear shifted from their actual locations when you display both themes at the same time.

Spatial data sets in the same projection can be viewed together.

Spatial data sets in different projections do not display together properly.

A desktop GIS can store feature locations as either unprojected geographic coordinates or as projected x,y coordinates. Buying unprojected data gives you several advantages. Since data stored as geographic coordinates can be displayed in any supported projection, you can combine it with data you already have that may be in a different projection. Also, if you use the same data in different applications, you can change projections according to what's appropriate for each application.

Covering your territory

The more specifically you define the geographic area you need to cover, the more precisely you can define how much data you need. If you're deciding where to open a store, you obviously want to know about the tastes and incomes of the people in the immediate area. But if your store will attract customers from a distance away, the area you cover needs to be larger.

If you're studying wildlife habitat, you may need to consider more than one set of boundaries. For example, the flora probably stays put, but the fauna likely ignores those boundaries. Your data may need to cover the territory of wide-ranging and migrating species. If a river flows through your study area, you may need to consider the area where it starts or the portion of it that passes through a large city before it gets to your area.

On the other hand, you don't want geographic information for areas you don't plan to investigate. This information just takes up space on your computer. And the larger the data set, the longer it takes to process.

Getting enough detail

Cities represented as points don't give you information about their shapes. You can't measure their dimensions or find the features, such as roads and parks, contained within them. Rivers represented as lines don't show anything about contours of their banks or changes in width. Buildings as points don't tell you anything about their shapes, nor can you measure the distance between them or between their walls and their lot boundaries.

On the other hand, if you only want to locate your customers, you really don't need to know the shapes of their houses.

Note that the amount of detail with which geographic objects are depicted also influences their attributes. When an entire forest is depicted as a simple area with a boundary, all of the attributes linked to that feature describe the forest as a whole. If a forest is depicted as a set of districts, each one having its own attributes, the attribute information can be more detailed.

When timeliness counts

While physical features like mountains don't change too often, other geographic objects are in constant flux. If you're tracking safe routes through the shifting sand bars of the Mississippi, you want current information. If your application deals with census tracts or postal codes, you want the most up-to-date boundaries. If your application deals with finding customers based on their street addresses, you won't be able to find an address on a new street if the street doesn't exist in the database. The same goes for attributes. If you use demographic data for marketing, you know that good results depend on having the most recent information about potential customers.

When accuracy matters

Some projects require a higher degree of locational accuracy than others. Data may be accurate enough for one use, but not for another. For example, if a line feature representing a road is mapped to within 40 feet of the road's real-world location, it may not be accurate enough for the transportation engineer, but is more than acceptable to the traveler who uses the map to get from one place to another.

Understanding attribute codes

Attribute data is often stored in abbreviated or even cryptic ways. An attribute name might be abbreviated in a table, or six different types of vegetation might be coded as "a" through "f." A catalog that explains the data is called a *data dictionary.* The data dictionary is where you look up the full names of attributes and the meanings of codes. The data dictionary may also include other useful information, like when the data was gathered, the scale of the original source information, the accuracy of locations, and the map projection used. Data that doesn't come with a data dictionary may not be usable.

Data Layer	Name	Source	Date	Projection	Acc	Item	Code	Defin.
Zoning	ZONE	plan.dpt	1994	Mercator	20°	**ZONE2**	AGR	Agricultural
							RES	Residential
							COM	Commercial
							IND	Industrial
							OS	Open Space
							INS	Institutional
Soils	SOILS	SCS	1990	Robinson	200°	**SOIL_TYP**	01	Alo Clay
							02	Delhi Sand

A data dictionary can be a paper or computer document. It contains information about the data.

ENVIRONMENTAL SYSTEMS RESEARCH INSTITUTE, INC.

Compatibility of formats

The format of the data you choose must be compatible with the desktop GIS you plan to use and with any data you already have. The documentation that comes with your desktop GIS software should tell you what spatial, tabular, and image data formats it supports.

Where in the world can you get data?

Data sources abound and data is getting to be less expensive and more available all the time. Your own company or organization may be a source of data. Finding data may be as easy as loading the sample data that comes with your desktop GIS. The best systems include commonly used spatial and tabular data, such as political boundaries and census statistics, as part of their package.

Governments and all kinds of agencies within them collect spatial, tabular, and image data. In some countries this data is available to the public at minimal or no cost. In the United States, for example, the Census Bureau's TIGER street-centerline data is one of the foremost spatial data sets for businesses, enabling them to locate their customers on a map.

If you work for local government, you may be able to share data with other departments. If the fire department uses a spatial data set containing streets to determine the best route to take when responding to an alarm, the police department could use the same street data to map crime incidents, and the transportation department, to map automobile accident sites.

Buying data

Vendors collect, package, and sell data for a wide range of applications, from business to natural resources. The spatial data sets they sell contain specific features, such as streets and highways, political and administrative boundaries (states and counties), census areas, postal areas, and marketing areas. The tabular data sets they sell contain specific types of attributes. Business establishment data contains the location, number, type, and characteristics of businesses; census data contains the age, sex, race, income, and housing types of potential customers; health care data contains information about hospitals, physicians, other health care providers, the services they provide, and the demand for those services; and environmental data includes measurements of climate, stream flow, water quality, soil type, and more.

Image data includes over three million images of the earth's surface that have been collected from earth-orbiting satellites. Many of the objects found on the earth's surface can be interpreted and mapped using images.

These data sets are available for areas of all sizes—from a small area defined by a circle around a business location to regions, nations, and the entire world. To help you get started, we've provided a list of data resources, including some data providers, in appendix B.

Creating your own data

Even if you buy data, you may want to make some of your own. With desktop GIS, you can create maps from tabular data that contains locational information. For example, you can map customers from a list of street addresses; map shopping centers from a list containing their x,y coordinate locations; or map wildlife from a list containing the latitude and longitude of each wildlife sighting.

In addition to creating maps from tabular data, a desktop GIS lets you create maps by drawing shapes over the top of existing maps or images, or create your own attributes by creating new tables or adding columns to existing ones.

Creating features from files

People often have data they don't know is usable for GIS. Businesses have customer files containing information about what customers bought, when they bought it, and what they paid for it. Police departments have accident files containing information about where accidents occurred, what types of accidents they were, and what conditions existed at the time of each accident. Wildlife biologists have files containing information about where nesting sites are located, how many birds are at each site, and the general condition of the birds. Whenever data sets include locational information, you can use them to generate a map.

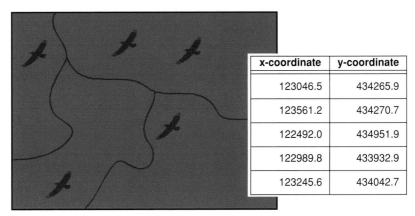

x-coordinate	y-coordinate
123046.5	434265.9
123561.2	434270.7
122492.0	434951.9
122989.8	433932.9
123245.6	434042.7

Desktop GIS can easily map the locations of nesting sites from a file containing their coordinate locations.

Address geocoding

Addresses are actually the most common form of locational information. An address specifies a location in much the same way as a geographic coordinate does. But, addresses are merely text strings containing a house number, street name, and postal code. The GIS needs a mechanism to calculate their geographic location coordinates before you can display them on a map. *Address geocoding* allows you to display tabular data containing addresses as points on a map. To do so, a GIS associates addresses stored in a tabular file with a spatial data set, usually a street network that also contains addresses. The GIS then uses the coordinates of the street features to calculate and assign coordinates to addresses in the file. The result is a map on which each point represents an address location in your file.

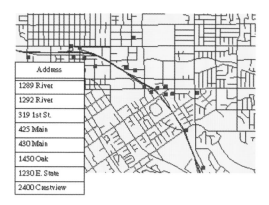

Address
1289 River
1292 River
319 1st St.
425 Main
430 Main
1450 Oak
1230 E. State
2400 Crestview

You can match the restaurant addresses in a file to a street network and show them on a map.

There are countless applications for address geocoding. You can map the addresses of customers, facility sites, club members, retail stores, stops on a delivery route, crime locations, and more. The ability to create map features from files of addresses and other geographic locations is a powerful tool for making better use of the data you already have.

Creating features from shapes you draw

Using desktop GIS tools, you can draw shapes (boxes, circles, points, lines, and polygons) on top of maps and save the shapes as map features. For example, you can draw trade areas on top of a map containing shopping malls. Once you've saved them, you can assign attributes to them and perform desktop GIS operations on them.

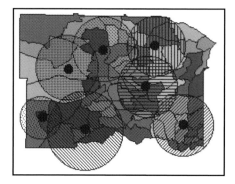

Drawing tools make it easy to define trade areas. Each shape becomes a feature for which you can store such attributes as sales figures and demographics.

Not only can you draw shapes on top of maps, you can also draw shapes on top of images. Images are ideal for creating map features when they have been projected and corrected for photographic distortions. You can trace whatever objects the image contains—rivers, roads, buildings—to create themes of map features. In this way, you can create an entire map database from just one image.

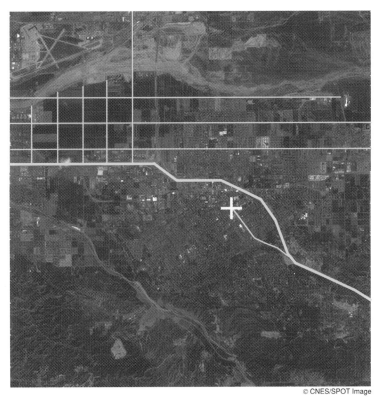

© CNES/SPOT Image

Each object you trace becomes a feature in a map database.

Ready, set, go...

Now you have the information you need to get started with desktop GIS and create your own GIS solutions. In the next chapter you'll see a real application with real data, using a real desktop GIS called ArcView. Enjoy.

ENVIRONMENTAL SYSTEMS RESEARCH INSTITUTE, INC.

Using
desktop GIS

Few things are harder to put up with than
the annoyance of a good example.

—Mark Twain

Using desktop GIS

So far, you've seen examples of what desktop GIS can do, how it works, the kinds of questions it can answer, and how you can use it to present information as maps, tables, charts, and more. Now it's time to see a real desktop GIS session with real data being applied to a realistic problem in a realistic situation. The situation may not be your situation, but you will be able to appreciate the process, the steps involved, and the specific GIS tasks performed.

Finding the right place

Finding the best site for expanding a business requires several types of information—information that can be linked with geographic locations. You need to know who is most likely to need your goods or services, and where these potential customers can be found. Once you know where your best customers are, you want to know where to put your business. It needs to be in a place you can afford, where your customers can get to you easily, and far enough away from your competition so your customers don't go there first.

The situation

Wild Outdoors is a business looking to bring its unique goods and services to the Atlanta area, site of the 1996 Olympics. Wild Outdoors specializes in sales and rentals of equipment, such as equipment for skiing, camping, climbing rocks and mountains, and even walking and running. Their customers are out-of-doors enthusiasts who range in age from 18 to 59. They have attended some college or hold college degrees. They work mostly in white-collar professions, and live in houses they own or for which they pay higher than average rents. All of Wild Outdoor's best customers have incomes above the national average, and most own a greater than average number of vehicles.

The application

Wild Outdoors executives want to find the best site for a new store in the Atlanta area. To do so, they have identified some important criteria. First, the new site must be located in an area where there are people who match the profile of their current customers. The new site should also be located in a shopping center that's easy to get to. The other shops in the center should complement Wild Outdoors without competing with it.

The executives at Wild Outdoors have unanimously chosen Michael, a member of their marketing team, to perform the site analysis. Michael will use their new desktop GIS software, *ArcView*, to perform the analysis. ArcView® software has the tools Michael needs, not only to perform the analysis, but also to present his results. And with ArcView's easy-to-use, point-and-click interface, he'll be able to get results in a hurry.

The data

The first step for Michael is to get the right data for his application. He identifies several types of data that he'll need. First, to locate potential customers in the Atlanta area, he chooses consumer data from Equifax National Decision Systems. This data provides information about distinctive consumer lifestyles called *segments*. Each segment is based on an aggregate of consumer characteristics such as income, age, education, and things like the number of vehicles per household. The data contains the number of households belonging to each segment. It's available in a format that is compatible with ArcView and can be licensed for several different-sized geographic areas, such as cities, counties, census blocks, and census tracts. Michael decides to acquire this data for several counties in the Atlanta area at the census tract level.

Michael also chooses shopping center data from National Research Bureau to see where all the shopping centers in the Atlanta area are and what stores are in each center. It comes in a dBASE®-formatted file that ArcView can read and convert to spatial data. The highway data Michael needs to compare locations of shopping centers with major highways comes with the sample data included with ArcView software.

Getting started with ArcView

Loading the data

To begin the session, Michael starts ArcView.

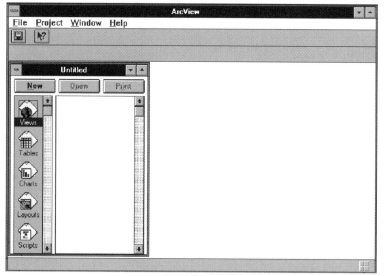

When ArcView opens, it creates an empty container called a project, *where you save your work during the session.*

ENVIRONMENTAL SYSTEMS RESEARCH INSTITUTE, INC.

Michael loads the consumer lifestyle data into a view. A *view* is a window where you can display themes. In ArcView, a *theme* is a set of map features linked to their attributes. The theme in this case contains the census tracts for Fulton County, the county that Atlanta is in, and an adjacent county, DeKalb.

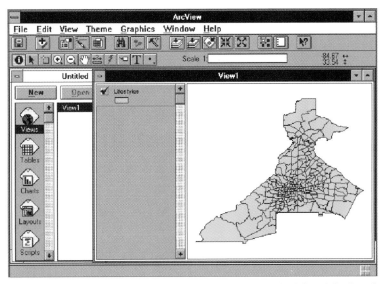

This view *contains one* theme, *called Lifestyles, listed on the left and displayed on the right.*

Displaying the data

When Michael initially draws the theme, the outlines of the census tracts are all displayed with the same symbol. So, he displays the census tracts again based on their county name attribute to differentiate the ones in Fulton County from those in DeKalb.

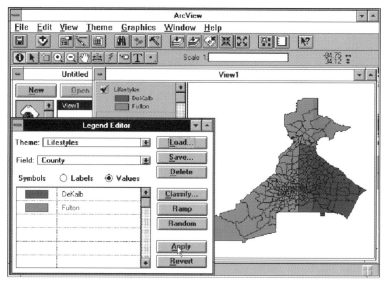

The Legend Editor *lets you choose an attribute and then display the map features based on that attribute.*

Identifying map features

To identify the census tracts and display their attributes, Michael uses ArcView's *Identify* tool. Clicking on a census tract with this tool displays the attributes of that tract in a dialog box.

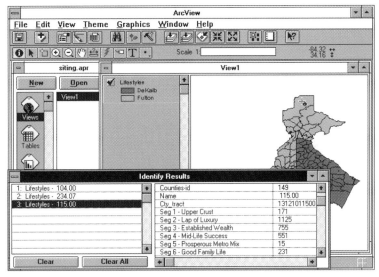

The Identify *tool displays attributes for any feature in an ArcView theme.*

Changing the way information is displayed

As you may recall, the consumer lifestyle data divides households into segments, 50 of them, based on unique consumer characteristics, and stores the number of households per segment for each census tract. By examining the documentation that comes with the lifestyle data, Michael determines that segment number 8, called "Movers and Shakers," most closely matches the profile of the best customers at Wild Outdoors. These customers are over 25 years of age. Many are in two-person households with above-average incomes. They hold college degrees and white-collar jobs or are in professional fields.

In order to visualize the distribution of potential customers like these, Michael displays the census tracts based on the segment attribute containing the number of households characterized as "Movers and Shakers."

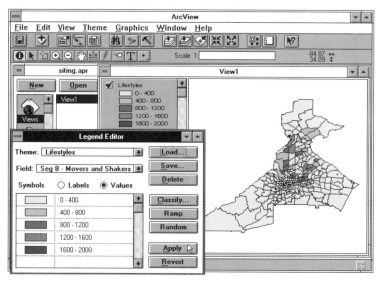

This view shows the distribution of "Movers and Shakers." ArcView lets you classify the values (number of households per census tract) and assign a symbol to each class.

ENVIRONMENTAL SYSTEMS RESEARCH INSTITUTE, INC.

Performing the analysis

The distribution of "Movers and Shakers" gives Michael some idea of the areas where his best potential customers are located. But there are actually three more lifestyle segments that characterize Wild Outdoors customers, segment 4 ("Mid-life Success"), segment 6 ("Good Family Life"), and segment 15 ("Successful Singles"). Michael would like to see where people in all these segments live. Shopping centers located in these areas will be candidates for the new store site.

Finding potential customers

Michael decides that the new Wild Outdoors store must be located where at least 10 percent of the households contain customers from one of these four segments. Based on the average number of households per census tract, Michael has calculated this number to be 500. He uses ArcView's *Query Builder* to find and select the census tracts that meet his criteria.

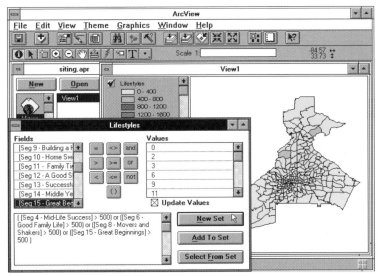

Michael builds a query statement that directs ArcView to search for and select census tracts with at least 500 households in one of four lifestyle segments. Census tracts that meet his criteria are highlighted on the view.

Each census tract shown in yellow has at least 500 households with people from one of the four lifestyles that characterize Wild Outdoors customers. Michael assumes that these people would shop at the new store, were it to be located near them.

At this point, Michael might want to refine his analysis. ArcView has tools he can use to analyze the information in tables, add new information to tables, and then use the new information to display map features. For example, he could rank the four lifestyle segments to reflect the best mix of potential customers and add this information to the database. He could then find all the census tracts that contain 1,000 households of which at least 500 are "Movers and Shakers" and the rest are from the other three segments.

Finding the right shopping center

But, since this is only a preliminary analysis, Michael is ready to add the shopping center data to his view and identify the shopping centers that are located in the selected census tracts. Since the locations and attributes of shopping centers are stored in a dBASE-formatted file, Michael brings this file into ArcView as a table and then creates points for each center based on latitude and longitude information in the table. The shopping centers are added to the view as a theme. Michael draws the shopping center theme to display all the shopping centers on top of the census tracts theme.

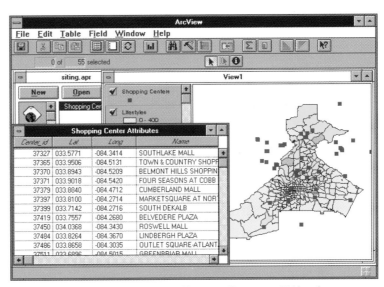

The view now contains two themes: Shopping Centers and Lifestyles.

It's apparent that a number of shopping centers are located in the same areas as potential customers. Michael wants to select only the centers inside the selected census tracts. Although the census tracts and centers are stored in separate themes, ArcView will select features in one theme that are within the selected features of another theme.

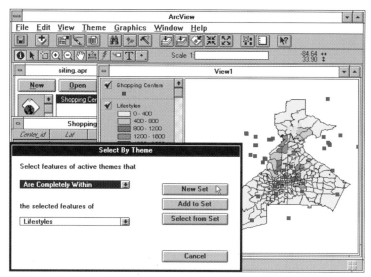

In this case, ArcView searches for and selects the shopping centers that are completely within the selected census tracts.

Selected shopping centers are highlighted on the view. Michael opens the attribute table for the shopping center theme to get information about them.

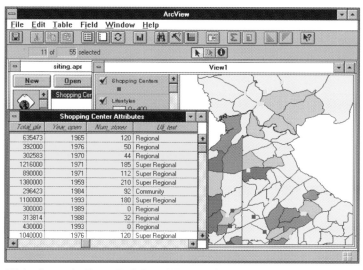

Michael uses the Zoom To Selected Features *button to zoom in to the portion of the view that contains selected shopping centers.*

The 11 selected shopping centers are also highlighted in the table. Michael moves the selected rows to the top of the table with the *Promote* button. Scrolling to the right, Michael can examine all the attributes for these shopping centers, such as gross leasable space, number of stores, type of center, year built, and much more. Michael notices that only some of the centers have available space, so he uses ArcView's *Query Builder* to select only those centers.

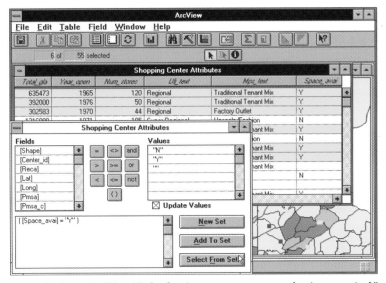

Using the Query Builder, *Michael writes a query statement that instructs ArcView to find and select shopping centers that match his request.*

Only six shopping centers have available space. Since access to the center is another important criterion, Michael adds the highway data to the view so he can determine which centers are located along a major highway.

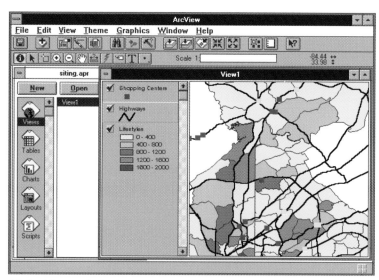

Michael brings the highway data into ArcView as a theme in the view.

Michael can see that each of the six selected shopping centers is easily accessed via a major highway, so none are eliminated at this stage of the analysis.

Evaluating the competition

To further narrow the list, Michael needs to evaluate the competition at each of the six selected shopping centers. Once he determines which centers have the least competition, he can contact a leasing agent to get more information about them, like how much leasable space they have and how much it costs. Then he'll have enough information to make a preliminary presentation to Wild Outdoors' executives.

To evaluate the competition, Michael uses a separate dBASE file that contains the names of anchors (larger stores) and tenants (smaller stores) for each shopping center. Michael brings this file into ArcView as a table. Then he uses ArcView to *link* this table to the Shopping Center Attributes table based on an attribute that both tables contain, the Center_ID attribute. Now when he highlights a center in the Shopping Center Attributes table, all of its anchors and tenants are automatically highlighted in the Tenants table.

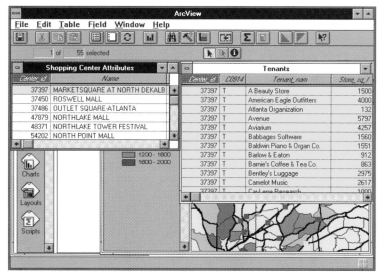

ArcView links tables when there is a one-to-many relationship between them. In this case, one shopping center is linked with many tenants. The two tables are linked based on a column that is common to both, Center_ID.

Michael carefully examines the list of anchors and tenants for each selected shopping center, six in all. As he does so, he notes the number of competitors in each center. Competitors include other outdoor outfitters, sporting goods stores, and stores featuring recreational clothing. Michael would like to compare each center based on the total number of stores and the number of competing stores. So, he uses ArcView to add a column to the Shopping Center Attributes table that contains the number of competitors in each center and uses ArcView's charting capabilities to create a chart comparing the number of stores with the number of competitors.

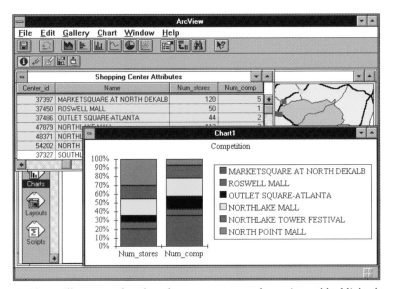

ArcView will create a chart based on one or more columns in a table. Michael identifies two columns for ArcView to chart—the one containing the total number of stores and the one he added containing the total number of competitors.

Not all competitors are created equal

Looking at this chart, Michael can see the balance between the number of stores a center has and the number of competitors it has. But not all competitors are equal. Michael has developed a system to rank competitors, based on how directly they would compete with a Wild Outdoors store. For example, another outdoor outfitter in the same shopping center would provide the most direct competition, while a sporting goods store would provide slightly less direct competition and an outdoor clothing store even less. Michael weights each competitor and calculates a numeric value that represents competition for each of the six shopping centers. The values range from one to nine, where one represents the least amount of direct competition and nine, the most. He adds this information to the Shopping Center Attributes table and then uses it to classify the six shopping centers and display them on a view.

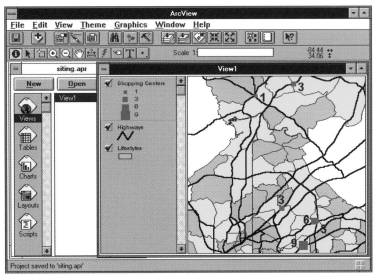

Michael displays the shopping centers along with selected census tracts where potential customers live. The centers are symbolized based on the amount of direct competition they would provide.

Presenting the results

Based on a competition rating of three or less, Michael determines that four out of six shopping centers qualify as potential sites for the new store. However, since one of these centers is adjacent to another one with a higher competition rating, Michael eliminates it, leaving three potential sites. He now has enough information to contact a leasing agent about the size and cost of available spaces and present his preliminary findings to company executives. He would like to show them several pieces of information: a map showing potential sites for the new Wild Outdoors store, along with a chart and a table summarizing the competition at each site. He uses ArcView to create a presentation called a *layout,* which allows him to assemble all the various elements from his analysis to present to company executives. Once the elements are in a layout, Michael can manipulate their size, location, or appearance. Michael can print the layout or use it as an interactive on-screen presentation.

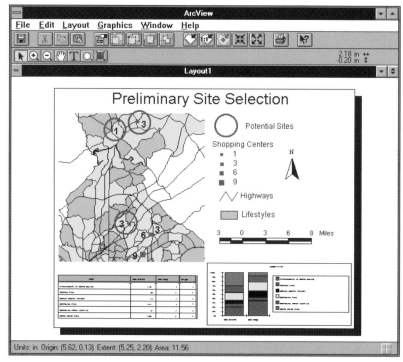

Michael creates a layout that contains a view, a chart, and a table. He adds a number of other elements to aid his presentation, such as a scale bar, a north arrow, and a title.

ENVIRONMENTAL SYSTEMS RESEARCH INSTITUTE, INC.

The outcome

After just one ArcView session, Michael had preliminary results he could present to company executives. The views, tables, charts, and layouts he generated during the session were stored in a single ArcView project that he can reopen and modify any time. Company executives were impressed with the quick results and the opportunity to visualize the data in a variety of ways—as maps, charts, and tables. Although Michael provided each executive with a hard-copy presentation, he also brought his laptop computer with ArcView to the meeting, where executives could make requests and Michael could show them results immediately on the computer screen.

Michael's preliminary analysis gave executives a chance to react and provide additional input. As a result, Michael refined his analysis. The new results gave the company the information it needed to proceed to the next step—an on-the-ground analysis of the best potential sites for a new Wild Outdoors store.

Desktop GIS and you

Desktop GIS. Now you've heard about it. Now you've seen it in action. We hope it will be as valuable to you as it has already been for all sorts of people in all sorts of organizations around the globe.

We've presented only a glimpse of what desktop GIS, and ArcView software, can do. In the remainder of this book you'll see even more applications for desktop GIS, and you'll actually use ArcView to ask questions, get answers, and present your results.

Using ArcView

The next 19 chapters teach you how to use ArcView. Each chapter contains exercises that tell a story and guide you through common GIS tasks. You'll learn the ArcView interface and find out where to get more information about important topics. You'll learn how to load data into ArcView, then use the tools ArcView provides to create meaningful displays, answer questions, make measurements, display data at different scales and in different map projections, modify your GIS database, and perform spatial analysis. In addition, you'll learn how to create charts and presentation-quality maps, and how to create some of your own data. Finally, you'll see how you can customize ArcView with Avenue, ArcView's own programming language.

SECTION 1

ArcView basics

The next three chapters introduce you to the basic tasks you perform over and over again in ArcView. Chapter 7 introduces you to ArcView's point-and-click interface. You'll open an ArcView project and explore its components as well as the menus, buttons, and tools that let you work with each component. In chapter 8, you'll learn how to load data into ArcView from a variety of sources (including images) to create a map display. You'll change the order in which features draw, select a few features directly from the display, then examine their attributes. In chapter 9, you'll display features according to their attributes, change the method and symbols used to classify and display them, and create your own custom classification. Then you'll learn how to label features in a map display.

Introducing
ArcView

How ArcView is organized

Exploring ArcView

Getting help

CHAPTER 7

Introducing ArcView

You saw ArcView in action in chapter 6. Now you're ready for a closer look at what it is, how it's organized, and what it does. ArcView is a powerful desktop geographic information system (GIS) made by Environmental Systems Research Institute, Inc. (ESRI). With ArcView, you can load any data that's linked to geographic locations and display it graphically as maps, charts, and tables. Not only that, you can edit the data, change the way it's displayed, append additional data, create some of your own, perform queries to answer specific questions or meet certain criteria, and analyze the information statistically as well as spatially. Then you can show the results as quality graphic presentations to print out or display on your screen.

It's easy to get started with ArcView, and you don't have to be a GIS expert to use it. ArcView's graphical interface lets you point and click to perform almost every operation. ArcView comes with some ready-to-use data so you can get started immediately. In addition, you can get low-cost, off-the-shelf geographic data sets from ESRI and its business partners via the ArcData^SM Publishing Program (see appendix B). If you already have data containing location information, such as addresses, you can load it into ArcView and display it geographically.

How ArcView is organized

ArcView stores the maps, charts, and tables you create in a *project*. A project is a file for organizing all the information you need to do your work. Projects use five types of components (called *documents*) to organize information: *views, tables, charts, layouts,* and *scripts.* Each displays data differently; each has its own related menus, buttons, and tools organized in a unique interface.

Views display sets of geographic data (called *themes*) as interactive maps. Each view has a display area and a Table of Contents that tells you what is being displayed.

Tables display tabular data. Tables containing descriptive information (called *attributes*) about map features are linked to views containing the features they describe. ArcView lets you access the attributes for a feature from a view or from a table.

Charts display tabular data graphically. ArcView charts are fully integrated with ArcView tables and views so you can choose the information to chart by clicking on it in a table or a view.

Layouts are high-quality, full-color presentations that display views, tables, charts, and images as graphic elements on your screen. Layouts can be sent to a printer or plotter to create a hard-copy product. Because ArcView layouts are linked to the data they represent, any changes you make to the data are automatically reflected in the layout, so it's always up-to-date.

Scripts are programs (macros) written in Avenue, ArcView's programming language and development environment. With Avenue™ software you can customize almost every aspect of ArcView, from adding a new button to run a script you write to creating an entire custom application. The version of ArcView that comes with this book does not include scripts, but you'll get a glimpse of what you can do with Avenue scripts in chapter 25.

Exploring ArcView

Now you'll take a closer look at ArcView by opening an ArcView project and exploring each of its components. The data you'll work with in this project is World data that comes with ArcView. If you haven't yet installed the CD–ROM that comes with this book, see appendix D.

Exercise 7a

1. Double-click on the Getting to Know ArcView program group to open it. Then double-click on the Getting to Know ArcView icon.

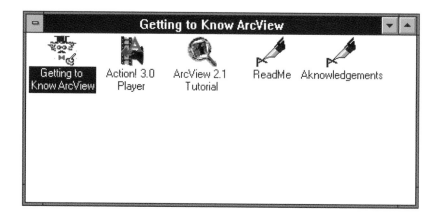

ENVIRONMENTAL SYSTEMS RESEARCH INSTITUTE, INC.

The Getting to Know ArcView window displays.

Now you'll start ArcView.

2. Click the ArcView Tutorial button. The Getting to Know ArcView window disappears. It may take a few moments for ArcView to start, depending on the speed of your computer. You see two windows, a large one entitled ArcView and a small one, the Project window. The title bar for this window displays the name of the current project, in this case, "Untitled." This project is empty because there is no data associated with it yet.

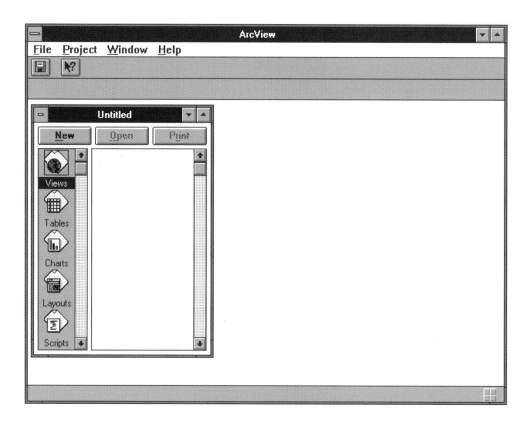

At the top of the ArcView window is a menu bar with four pulldown menus: File, Project, Window, and Help. These menus are available when the Project window is active.

Working with windows in ArcView. Each ArcView project, view, table, chart, layout, and script is contained in its own window. You can have any number of windows open at the same time, but only one window can be active. You make a window active by clicking inside it, clicking on its title bar, or choosing it from the Window pulldown menu. You can resize and move windows using the mouse, using the window icons (to the left and right of the title bar), or using the choices in the Window pulldown menu. For more information, search for this Help Topic: *Working with windows in ArcView.* (You'll learn how to search for Help Topics in exercise 7b.)

Below the menu bar is the button bar. It currently contains two buttons, Save and Help Tool. Buttons offer you quick access to ArcView functions. To find out what a button does, place the cursor over the button. ArcView describes its function in the status bar at the bottom of the ArcView window.

Below the button bar is the tool bar. It doesn't contain any tools yet.

To open an existing project, you'll use the File menu.

3.   Click on the File menu to display its list of choices. One of the choices is Open Exercise. This choice doesn't exist in the standard ArcView interface; it's been added for use with this book. You'll use it to open any of the exercise projects included in this book.

4.   Click on the Open Exercise choice. You see a scrolling list entitled "Exercises." This list contains all the exercises in this book. Each exercise is linked to an ArcView project. Clicking on an exercise in the list opens the project it's linked to.

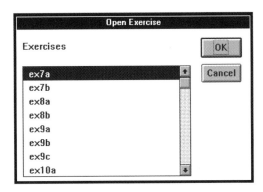

5. In the Exercises list, click on "ex7a" to open a project named
    ex7a.apr. (All ArcView projects have a *.apr* ending, which stands for
    "ArcView Project.") When the project opens, you see that the name
    ex7a.apr replaces the name *Untitled.*

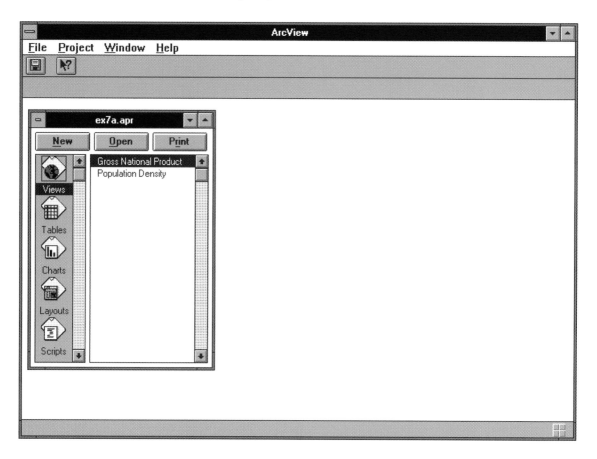

ENVIRONMENTAL SYSTEMS RESEARCH INSTITUTE, INC.

Now take a closer look at the Project window.

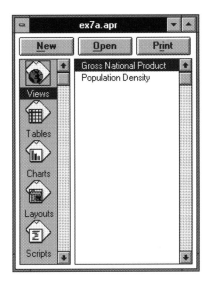

The Project window has icons along its left side, Views, Tables, Charts, Layouts, and Scripts, representing each document type. (You won't see the Scripts icon shown here because the version of ArcView you're using has been modified for this book. The Scripts icon is available when you load a standard version of ArcView.)

Currently, the Views icon is highlighted. The buttons at the top of the window, New, Open, and Print, let you create new views, open existing views, and print a view that's highlighted in the list. These buttons change for each document type.

On the right side of the window, you see the names of the two views currently contained in this project. The Gross National Product view is highlighted.

Next you'll highlight and open both views.

6.   Hold down the Shift key and click on the Population Density view. Now both views in the list are highlighted. Click the Open button at the top of the Project window to open them. Two view windows

open, and ArcView's interface (menus, buttons, and tools) changes to reflect the *view* document type. You can tell the Population Density view is active because its title bar is highlighted and its window is in the foreground.

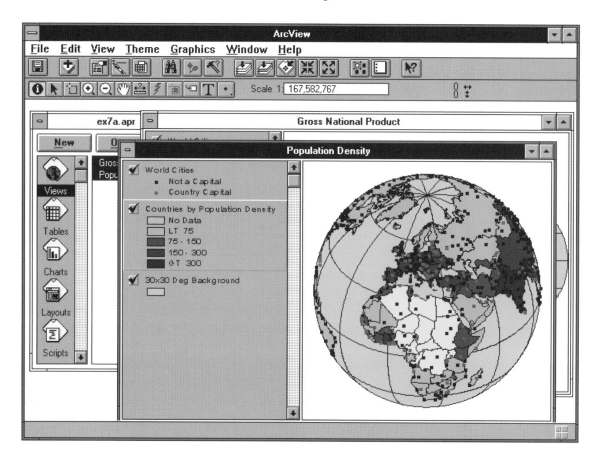

The Population Density view displays three sets of features and attributes, called *themes*. Each theme has a title and a legend that appear in the view's Table of Contents, on the left side of the view window. The World Cities theme represents cities of the world as point features. The Countries by Population Density theme shows countries (area features) divided into five groups, or classes, based on their population values. Each class is displayed using a different symbol. (Notice that some of the countries display in yellow. This indicates that they've been selected as a separate group. By default, ArcView highlights selected features in yellow.)

In the background is a theme showing a grid of latitude and longitude.

7.   Click on the title bar of the Gross National Product view. It becomes the active view.

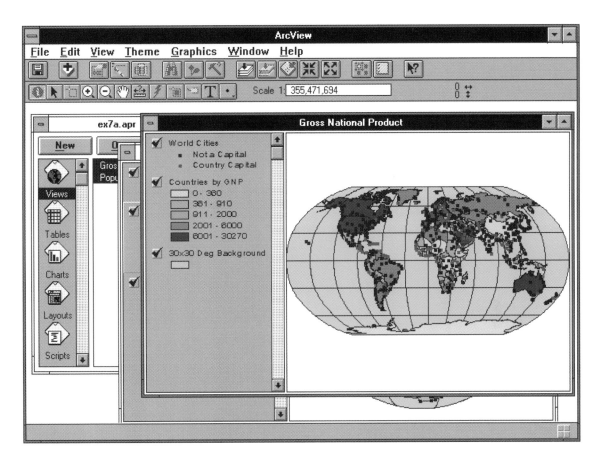

Again you see a theme of world cities, a theme of countries, and a theme of latitude and longitude; however, in this view, the countries are shown according to their gross national product (GNP).

The shape of the world is different in the two views because each view is displayed using a different map projection. In ArcView, you don't have to set a map projection to work with data in a view, although you can choose from a number of different map projections.

You'll close the Gross National Product view and leave the Population Density view open.

8. Click on the icon in the upper left corner of the Gross National Product window and choose Close from the menu. The view window closes.

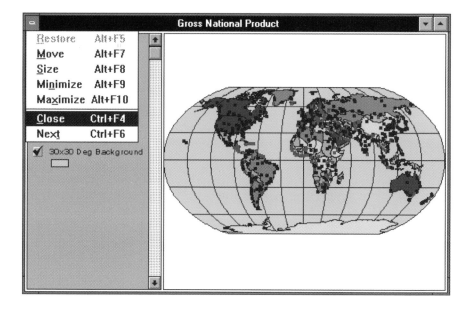

Now you'll look at the attributes that are linked to the features in the Countries by Population Density theme. ArcView stores these attributes in a *theme attribute table* or, simply, *theme table*.

ENVIRONMENTAL SYSTEMS RESEARCH INSTITUTE, INC.

Notice that the gray area containing the name and legend of the Countries by Population Density theme appears raised, indicating that this theme is active. Many of the operations you perform in a view work only on active themes.

Now you'll open the theme table for the active theme.

Opening a theme table. Each theme of geographic data in a view has a table that stores attributes describing the features it contains. To open a theme's attribute table, choose Table from the Theme menu or click the Open Theme Table button on the View button bar. Once you open a theme's attribute table, it appears in the list of tables in the Project window, where it can then be opened using the Open button in the Project window. For more information, see chapter 8 or search for these Help Topics: *Working with tables in a project, Open Theme Table.*

9. Click the Open Theme Table button on the View button bar. The Countries by Population Density table opens.

The table is now the active document, and ArcView's interface changes to display the menus, buttons, and tools you use for working with tables.

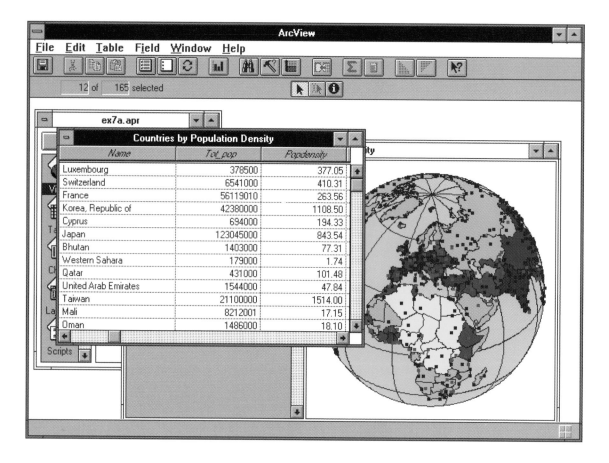

The table contains information about the countries of the world. The information in the column entitled "Popdensity" was used to divide the countries into the five classes shown in the view.

Recall that some of the African countries were highlighted in yellow in the view. The attributes corresponding to those countries are also highlighted in the table, but you can't see them unless you scroll down in the table or use the Promote function to bring them to the top of the table.

10. With the Table window active, click the Promote button. (Or, click on the Table menu to display its choices, then choose Promote.) ArcView moves the highlighted attributes to the top of the table.

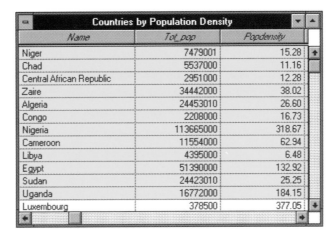

11. Scroll to the right. Notice that the table contains attribute information on birth and death rates (Bir_rate; Dth_rate) for each country. Next you'll open a chart showing the birth and death rates for the highlighted African countries.

12. Click on the title bar of the Project window to make it active, then click on the Charts icon. The Birth/Death Comparison chart is highlighted in the list. Click the Open button. The Birth/Death Comparison chart opens.

The chart is now the active document, and ArcView's interface changes to display the menus, buttons, and tools you use for working with charts.

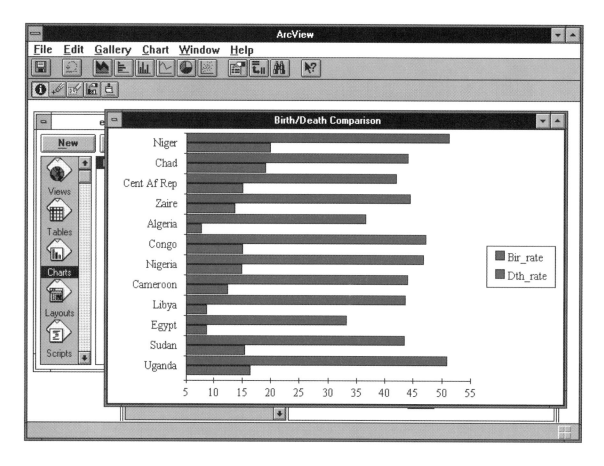

Charts represent tabular data graphically. This chart was created using the values in the Bir_rate and Dth_rate columns (fields) in the Countries by Population Density table. Only the countries highlighted in the view are represented in the chart. You'll learn how to create, modify, and query charts in chapter 20.

Next you'll open an ArcView layout.

13. Click on the Project window's title bar to make it active, then click on the Layouts icon. The Population Growth Rates layout is highlighted in the list. Click the Open button. The Population Growth Rates layout opens.

The layout is now the active document, and ArcView's interface changes to display the menus, buttons, and tools you use for working with layouts.

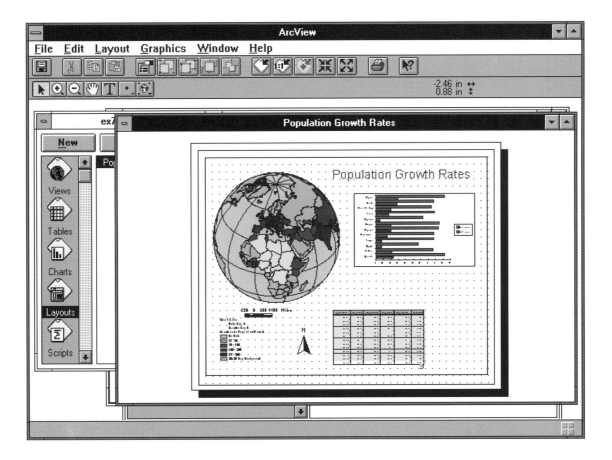

This layout contains the Population Density view and its legend, the Countries by Population Density table, the Birth/Death Rates chart, and additional graphics and text. You can think of an ArcView layout as a canvas or page where you place project components and other graphics to create a presentation-quality display or paper map. You'll learn how to create layouts in chapter 21.

Next you'll close all the windows.

14. From the File menu, choose Close All. Only the Project window remains open and active.

If you want to go on to the next chapter, leave ArcView running. Otherwise, choose Exit from the File menu.

As with any software package, it's important that you save your work regularly. With the version of ArcView that comes with this book, you won't be able to execute a save operation. But you should know how to save, and what happens if you forget to save.

Saving your work in ArcView. In ArcView, you can save the work you do on a view, table, chart, or layout by saving the project that contains it. To save the project, choose Save Project from the File menu, click the Save Project button on the button bar, or press CTRL+S. To save your work to a project with a different name, make the Project window active, then choose Save Project As from the File menu. For more information, search for these Help Topics: *Saving your work, Save Project, Save Project As.*

You've seen an ArcView project and some of the documents it can contain (views, tables, charts, layouts). You've also seen that each document type has its own interface containing menus, buttons, and tools.

In the chapters that follow, you'll perform specific GIS tasks using views, tables, charts, and layouts in a project. After you've worked all the exercises, you'll be ready to tackle your own ArcView project.

Getting help

With ArcView's extensive online help system, you can get answers to most of your questions about ArcView. ArcView offers several kinds of help. For example, you can get context-sensitive help by moving the cursor over a menu choice, button, tool, or document. You can access a Help Topic from the ArcView Help Contents, then navigate from topic to topic by clicking on hypertext links (graphics and text that link to other Help Topics). You can also search for a topic by clicking the Search button, then typing a topic in the dialog box.

Getting Help on Help. To learn how to use ArcView's online help system, click on the Help menu (available on every ArcView interface), then choose Contents to display the ArcView Help Contents menu. Now press the F1 key on your keyboard to display the Contents for How to Use Help. If you are new to Windows Help, choose the "Help Basics" topic (green text) by clicking on it.

ENVIRONMENTAL SYSTEMS RESEARCH INSTITUTE, INC.

SECTION 1:
ArcView basics

Getting data into ArcView

Understanding data sources

Adding themes to a view

Understanding theme tables

Getting data into ArcView

ArcView links sets of features to their attributes in *themes* and manages them in a *view* (chapter 7). You can create an ArcView theme from a variety of geographic data sources, such as spatial data, computer aided design (CAD) drawings, images, and tabular data. In this chapter, you'll create themes from several types of spatial and image data sources.

Understanding data sources

Geographic data sources fall into two categories: feature data sources and image data sources. As you might have guessed from the names, feature data sources contain features, whereas image data sources (which are basically pictures) do not. ArcView supports these data sources for feature-based themes: ARC/INFO® coverages, ArcView shapefiles, and CAD drawings.

Feature data sources

ARC/INFO is GIS software from ESRI, the creators of ArcView. ARC/INFO stores sets of features and their attributes in its own format, called a *coverage*. A coverage can be represented as a theme in ArcView. Some ARC/INFO coverages contain more than one type of feature; ArcView requires a separate theme for each type.

Shapefiles are ArcView's own format for storing features and attributes. You create shapefiles by converting other spatial data sources (such as ARC/INFO coverages), by drawing shapes in a theme you create, or by using tabular data containing location information. (See chapters 22, 23, and 24.) There are a couple of advantages to using shapefiles: they display more rapidly in a view than other spatial data formats, and you can edit a theme that's based on a shapefile. Suppose you want to edit a theme that's based on an ARC/INFO coverage. No problem. Just convert it to an ArcView shapefile.

CAD drawings are another type of spatial data you can use to create themes. A CAD drawing typically contains many entities (feature types) in a single layer. As with ARC/INFO coverages, ArcView requires a separate theme for each entity. To edit a theme based on a CAD drawing, you have to convert it to a shapefile. (Before you create a theme based on a CAD drawing, you must install the optional CAD reader.)

Image data sources

Image data sources include satellite data, scanned data, photographs, and ARC/INFO grids. (An ARC/INFO grid is a spatial data format that represents features as a group of cells in a regular grid or matrix.) ArcView supports images and grids for display only. Because most images don't contain attributes, themes you create from images won't have attribute tables.

Adding themes to a view

Suppose that you work for the City Maintenance Department, which plans to add some utilities and upgrade others in a recently renovated part of town. You've been asked to create a map showing the existing utilities to use for planning the additions and upgrades. There is currently no single map that shows all the utilities. Your task is to locate the necessary data sources and add them to a view as themes so you can display them together.

Exercise 8a

1. If necessary, start ArcView. From the File menu, choose Open Exercise. In the Exercises scrolling list, select "ex8a," then click OK. Because no views have been created yet, you see an empty Project window.

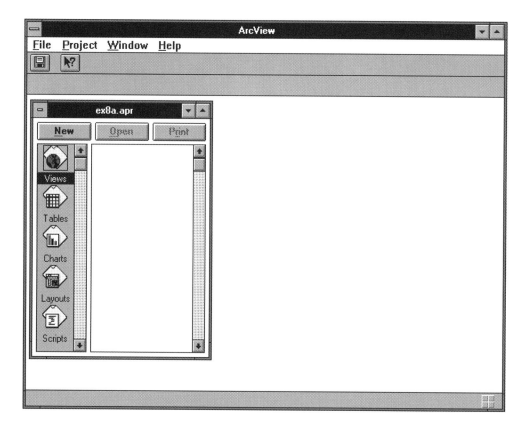

2. With the Views icon highlighted, click the New button. A new, empty view window, View1, opens. (You can resize and reposition this window anytime you need to.)

ENVIRONMENTAL SYSTEMS RESEARCH INSTITUTE, INC.

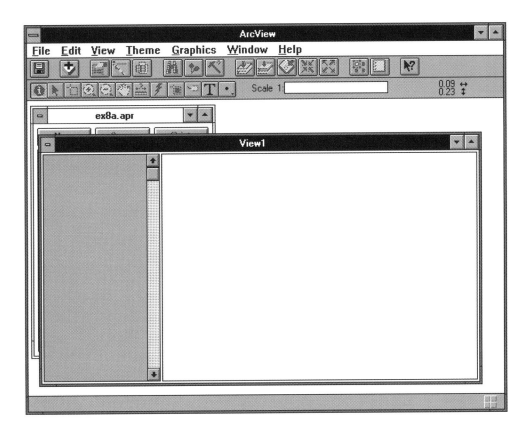

The gray area on the left is the Table of Contents. It's empty now, but when you add a theme to the view, its name, the symbol used to draw it, and a check box indicating whether it's currently displayed will appear there.

3.   From the View menu, select Add Theme. The Add Theme dialog box displays.

4.   From the Drives list (bottom right), select your CD–ROM drive (or the drive where you installed the data for this book), then navigate to *\gtkav\data\ch08* in the Directories list. ArcView lists the geographic data sources available in this directory. When "Feature Data Source" is selected in the lower left drop-down list (Data Source Types), only

data sources containing features (e.g., points, lines, polygons) are listed.

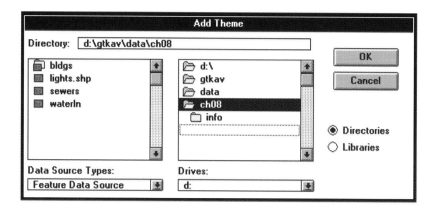

You see four data sources: bldgs, lights.shp, sewers, and waterln. The first of these, bldgs, is an ARC/INFO coverage containing more than one type of feature. It appears with a folder icon in the list. Later, you'll open the folder to see the feature types. The second, lights.shp, is an ArcView shapefile (.shp is the default file extension given to ArcView shapefiles). The other two data sources are ARC/INFO coverages.

Adding a theme from a feature data source. The Add Theme dialog box lets you add a theme from a feature data source. Double-clicking on the name of the data source adds it to the current view as a theme. By holding down Shift, you can select and add more than one data source at once. When a feature data source, such as an ARC/INFO coverage, contains more than one feature type, it appears with a folder icon in the Add Theme dialog box. Single-clicking on the icon lists all the feature types for that data source. You must create a separate theme for each feature type. For more information, search for these Help Topics: *Creating a theme in a view, Add Theme.*

You'll add a theme from the waterln data source.

5.   Double-click on "waterln" to add it to the view as a theme. The theme's name and a symbol appear in the Table of Contents.

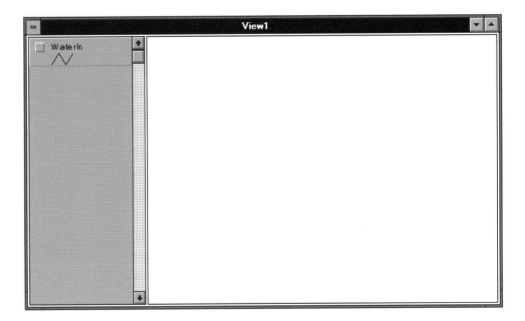

Your view now contains one theme, Waterln. By default, ArcView doesn't draw the theme. To display the theme, you'll turn it on by clicking on its check box.

Turning a theme on just allows it to display. A theme doesn't have to be turned on for you to perform ArcView operations on it. Turning a theme off doesn't remove it from the view.

6.   Click on the check box next to the WaterIn theme name. ArcView draws the features in the theme (lines) using the current symbol.

When you add a theme to a view, ArcView randomly assigns a color to the theme. Therefore, the WaterIn theme may be a different color in your view.

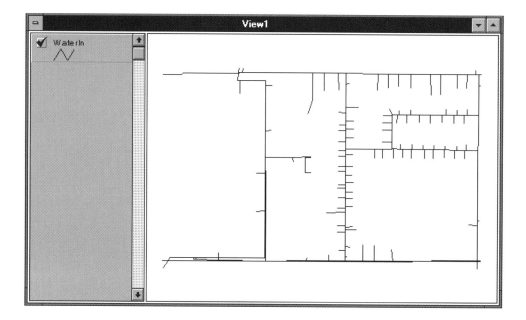

Next you'll add themes based on the bldgs, lights.shp, and sewers data sources.

   7.   Click the Add Theme button to display the Add Theme dialog box. If necessary, select your CD–ROM drive (or the drive where you installed the data for this book), then navigate to *\gtkav\data\ch08* in the Directories list. You see the same list of data sources.

8. Click once on the "bldgs" folder icon to open it.

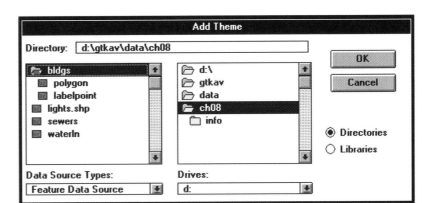

You see two feature types listed, polygon and labelpoint. ("Polygon" is the ARC/INFO term for area feature. A label point identifies a polygon and shares all its attributes.) You want to create a polygon theme to represent buildings, so you'll choose the polygon data source.

9. Click once on "polygon" to highlight it. Then hold down the Shift key and click once on "lights.shp" and once on "sewers." All three data sources are highlighted.

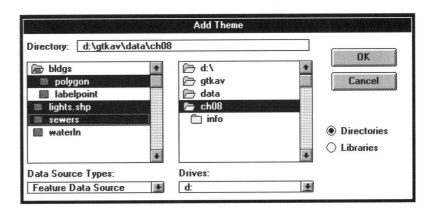

10. Click OK to add these three themes to the view, then click on each check box to draw each theme.

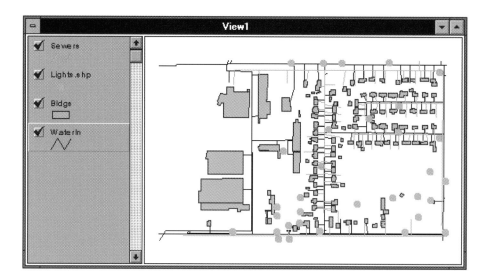

Your view now contains three additional themes, the Sewers theme containing line features, the Lights.shp theme containing points, and the Bldgs theme containing polygons.

Now you can use the themes to plan for upgrading utilities. But first, you'll add an aerial photograph of this part of the city to serve as a backdrop.

11. Click the Add Theme button. If necessary, select your CD–ROM drive (or the drive where you installed the data for this book), then navigate to \gtkav\data\ch08 in the Directories list. Click on the drop-down arrow for the Data Source Types list, then select "Image Data Source." The aerial photograph image source appears in the list on the left side of the dialog box. (The .bil ending indicates a type of image format.)

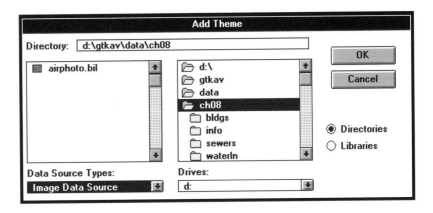

12. Double-click on "airphoto.bil." ArcView adds the aerial photograph image to the view. Click on the check box for the Airphoto.bil theme to turn it on. ArcView draws the photograph as a black-and-white image in the view.

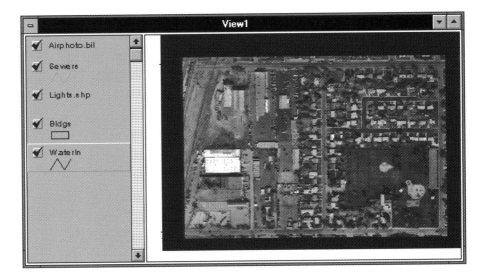

The image draws on top of the other themes. That's because ArcView first draws the theme listed at the bottom of the Table of Contents, then draws each theme listed above it. Thus, the Airphoto.bil theme draws last. You can change the drawing order by dragging themes up or down in the Table of Contents.

You want the image to display in the background (behind the other themes) so you'll drag it to the bottom of the Table of Contents. To do so, you must first make the Airphoto.bil theme active.

> **Understanding active themes.** An *active* theme appears raised in the Table of Contents. Many operations you perform in a view work only on active themes. You make a theme active by clicking on its name or legend symbol in the Table of Contents. To make more than one theme active, hold down the Shift key, then click on the name or legend symbol of each theme you want to make active. For more information, search for this Help Topic: *Making a theme active.*

Notice that the Waterln theme is currently the active theme.

13. Click once on the Airphoto.bil theme in the Table of Contents to make it active. Now it appears raised in the Table of Contents.

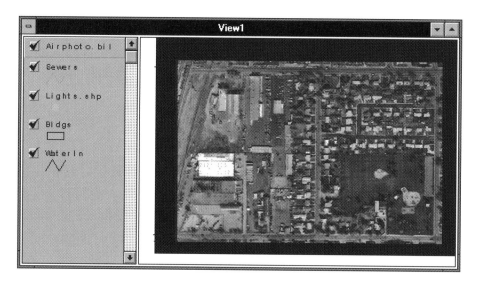

Next you'll drag it to the bottom of the Table of Contents.

14. Place the cursor on the Airphoto.bil theme's name (or the raised gray area surrounding it), hold down the mouse button, move the cursor to the bottom of the Table of Contents, then release the button. ArcView draws the image theme first this time, then draws all the other themes on top of it.

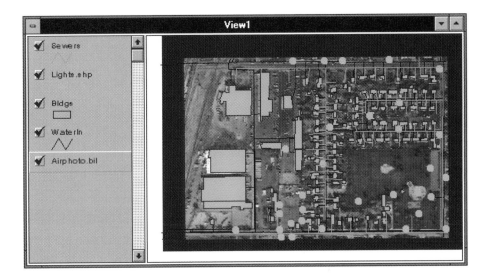

You can see how easy it is to create a view and add themes to it from a variety of data sources. Once you've added themes to a view, you can change the appearance of the view by turning themes on or off and by moving themes up or down in the Table of Contents.

If you want to go on to the next exercise, leave the project open.

Understanding theme tables

When you add a theme based on a feature data source, a *theme attribute table* or, simply, *theme table,* is also added to the project. A theme table contains descriptive information about the features in the theme. The theme table is formatted in rows and columns, called *records* and *fields,* respectively. Each field contains all the values for an attribute; each record represents a single feature in the theme. Because attributes are linked to the features they describe, you can access them by clicking on a feature in the view, or you can find a feature in the view by clicking on its record in the table. (To review the relationship between features and attributes, see chapter 2.)

The City Maintenance Department has decided to dig trenches for sewer lines on some of the properties. Your task is to retrieve the address information for these properties so notification letters can be sent to their owners. The Bldgs theme attribute table contains the address information you need. You'll make this theme active, then open its attribute table.

Exercise 8b

1. If *ex8a.apr* is open, continue. Otherwise, choose Open Exercise from the File menu. In the Exercises scrolling list, select "ex8b," then click OK. When the project opens, you see a view with four feature-based themes, and an image theme in the background.

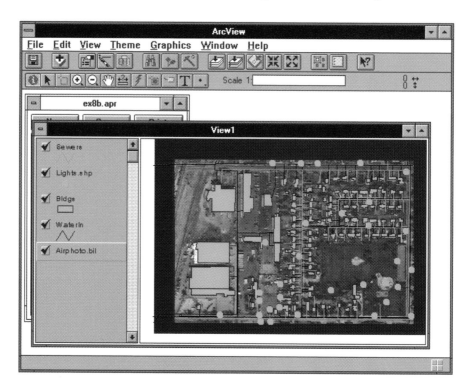

2. Click on the Bldgs name or its legend symbol in the Table of Contents to make it active. The theme appears highlighted in the Table of Contents.

3. Click the Open Theme Table button on the View button bar. A table window opens containing the attributes of the Bldgs theme. When the table opens, you see the first four fields, Shape, Area, Perimeter, and Bldgs#. The Shape field tells you the type of feature (e.g., point, line, polygon) the theme represents.

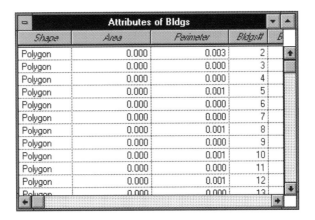

The table also contains addresses and owners for all the buildings in the theme. To see them, you'll use the scrolling bars.

4. Using the scroll bar at the bottom of the table, scroll to the right. The address information is stored in the Address, City, State, and Zip fields; the owner names are stored in the Owner field. (Later you'll resize the table so you can see these fields at the same time.)

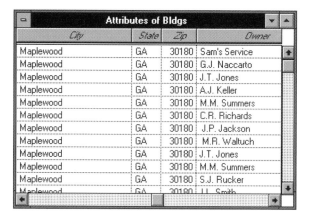

You know that the city plans to dig trenches for sewer lines on the properties of large buildings along the left side of the view. You'll select these buildings by clicking on them in the view.

Before you select the buildings, you'll resize and reposition the view and table so you can see both of them at the same time.

5. Make View1 active by clicking on its title bar. Move it to the upper left corner of the ArcView window, then resize it so it fills the upper portion of this window.

6. Make the Attributes of Bldgs table active. Move it to the lower left corner of the ArcView window, then resize it so it fills the lower portion of this window.

ENVIRONMENTAL SYSTEMS RESEARCH INSTITUTE, INC.

You'll change the table display to show the address and owner information.

7. Using the scroll bar at the bottom of the table, scroll to the right until you see the Address and Owner fields. Your windows should look like this:

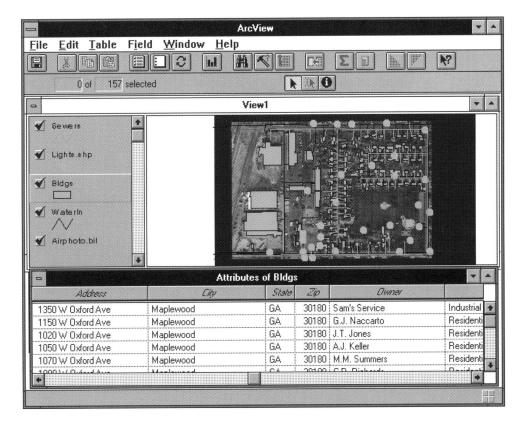

Now you'll use the Select Feature tool to select the large buildings along the left side of the view.

8. Make the view active by clicking on its title bar. In the View tool bar, click on the Select Feature tool, then click on the large building in the upper left corner of the view. The building highlights in the view and the corresponding record highlights in the table. ArcView scrolls the table so the highlighted record displays at the top of the table.

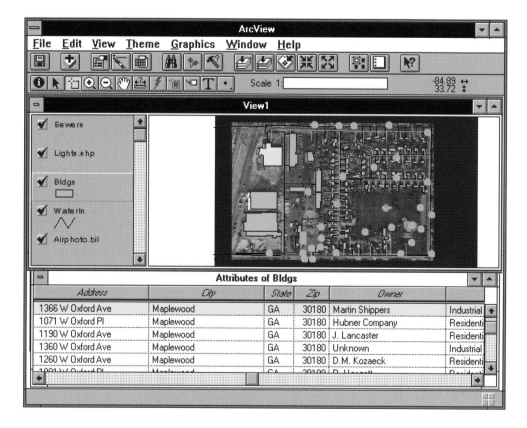

The first building is selected. Now you want to highlight the rest of the large buildings along the left side of the view.

9. Hold down the Shift key, then click on each of the other large buildings along the left side of the view. ArcView selects and highlights the buildings (there are four in all) in the view and their corresponding records in the table.

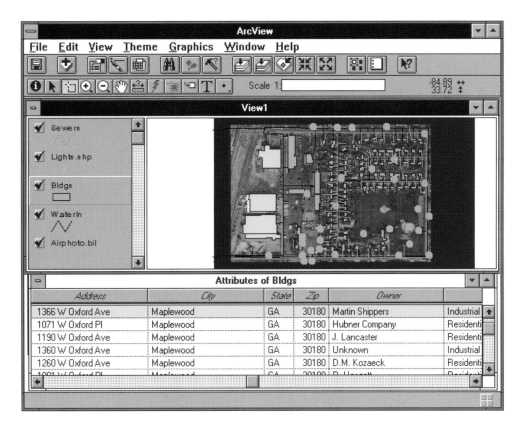

Because the table is large, you can't see all of the highlighted records. To see the highlighted records together in the table, you'll use the Promote function.

10. Make the table window active by clicking on its title bar. Then click the Promote button on the Table button bar. The highlighted records display at the top of the table.

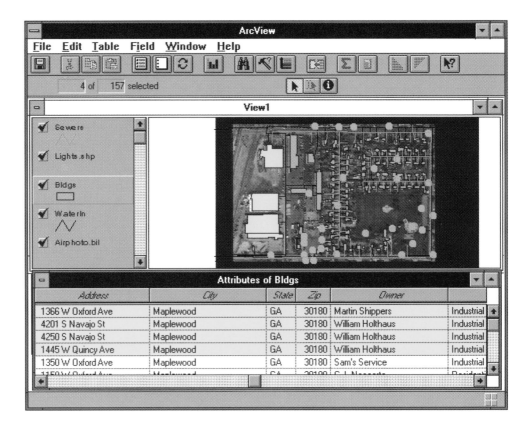

The highlighted records contain address information for the selected buildings. This information can be used to notify owners about the city's plans to put sewer lines in place on these properties.

Selecting features in a view allows you to access their attributes in the theme table. You'll learn other ways to select features and access information about them in chapters 10, 11, and 15.

If you want to go on to the next chapter, leave ArcView running. Otherwise, choose Exit from the File menu.

**SECTION 1:
ArcView basics**

Displaying themes

Displaying features based on their attributes

Labeling features

Displaying themes

In chapter 4, you learned the importance of choosing the most appropriate symbols, classifying information when it contains a large number of unique values, and using color ramps to indicate ranking or order among classes. In this chapter, you'll learn how to actually do all these things in ArcView.

With ArcView's Legend Editor and Symbol Palette, you can choose the best method for displaying a theme. For example, you can specify the attribute a theme will display, choose a method for classifying and symbolizing the features by their attribute values, create your own custom classification and symbolization scheme, and change the symbols used to display features. Once you choose a method for displaying a theme, you can label features interactively, using the Label tool, or automatically, using the Auto-label function.

Displaying features based on their attributes

Imagine that you work for an advertising agency. The agency has a prospective client who wants to market a new product in an 18-county area. The agency has designed a great, but somewhat expensive, newspaper advertising campaign. Knowing that the client has a limited advertising budget, your boss needs to convince him that running a more expensive campaign in the counties with the largest population will get better results than running a cheaper campaign in all the counties. As part of the presentation, your boss asks you to use the agency's desktop GIS, ArcView, to prepare a map of the 18-county area showing how the population is distributed.

Exercise 9a

1. If necessary, start ArcView. From the File menu, choose Open Exercise. In the Exercises scrolling list, select "ex9a," then click OK. When the project opens, you see a view with one theme, Counties.

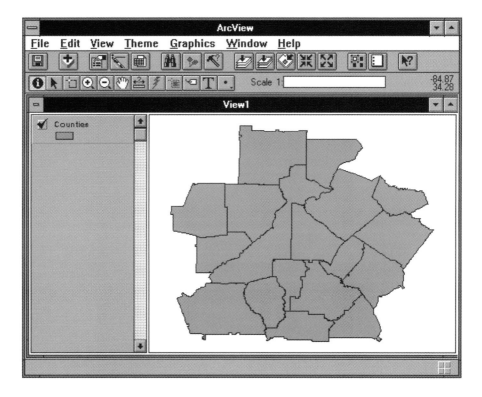

Notice that, by default, ArcView assigns the same color to all the counties. You want to display the counties based on population, so you'll open the Legend Editor, the window in which you change the symbols and colors used to display a theme, and where you assign symbols to features according to their attribute values.

2. Double-click on the Counties theme in the Table of Contents to display the Legend Editor.

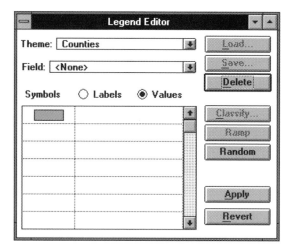

The Theme drop-down list displays the name of the current theme, Counties; the Field list contains the names of all the fields in the current theme's attribute table; the Symbols column displays the symbol ArcView uses to draw the theme.

3. Click on the Field down arrow to display the attributes for the Counties theme. Notice that the first choice, "<None>," is highlighted, indicating that no attribute has been selected for display. Scroll down in the list until you see "Pop_93," then click on it to select it. The Pop_93 field contains the most up-to-date population figures for the 18-county area. This is the field you want to display graphically on the map.

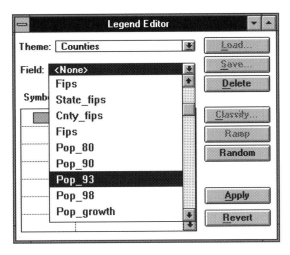

By default, ArcView divides the values in the Pop_93 field into five classes, with an equal number of records in each class, and assigns a symbol to each class ranging from white to black.

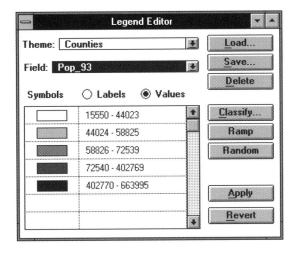

You'll use the Classification dialog box to experiment with different ways to present the Pop_93 data.

4. Click the Classify button in the Legend Editor to display the Classification dialog box. The classification option Quantile, with five classes (the default), is selected.

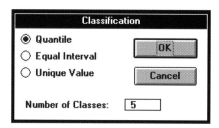

Choosing a classification method. ArcView supports three classification methods: quantile, equal interval, and unique value. *Quantile* groups a field's values into classes containing an equal number of records; *equal interval* groups values into classes with an equal range of values; and *unique value* creates one class for every unique value. You can also classify a field's values manually by clicking the Values button in the Legend Editor and then typing in a range of values for each class you wish to define. For more information, search for these Help Topics: *Classification types, Classifying features with different symbols, Legend Editor.*

You'll use the unique value classification method to display the population data.

5. Click the Unique Value option, then click OK. ArcView creates one class for each unique Pop_93 value.

Now each unique value in the Pop_93 field is a separate class with its own symbol. ArcView uses a random symbol for each class.

ENVIRONMENTAL SYSTEMS RESEARCH INSTITUTE, INC.

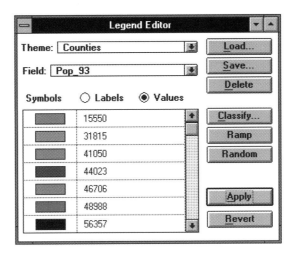

6. Click Apply to create the new legend and display the counties using these symbols.

Changes you make in the Legend Editor aren't reflected in the view until you click the Apply button.

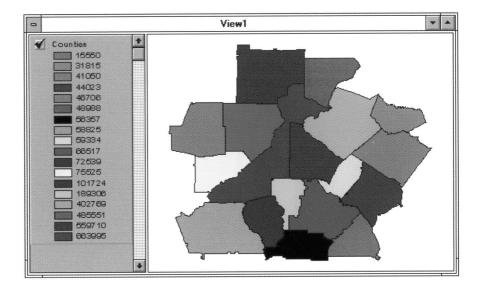

The random colors make a pretty picture, but they don't show which counties have the highest population, which is the map's purpose. You know that your boss won't be happy with this map, so you decide to try a color ramp. In a *color ramp,* the colors change gradually from the first (top) to the last (bottom) symbol in the legend, making it more clear where the population is high or low.

7. Double-click on the first symbol in the Legend Editor. The Fill Palette displays.

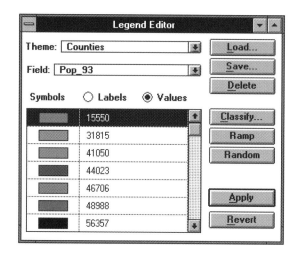

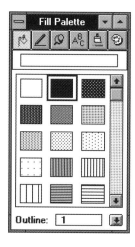

Understanding the Symbol Palette. ArcView provides several different palettes (collectively called the *Symbol Palette*) from which you can change the symbols used to display a theme. Use the Fill Palette for polygons; the Pen Palette for line features; the Marker Palette for point features; the Font Palette for text; the Color Palette to assign colors to fills, pens, markers, and fonts; and the Palette Manager to load, save, clear, and create a palette. For more information, search for these Help Topics: *Symbol Palette, Changing Symbols.*

To switch from one palette to another, you'll use the buttons at the top of the Fill Palette window.

8. Click the Color Palette button at the top of the Fill Palette. The Color Palette displays. In the Color Palette, select the starting color for your color ramp.

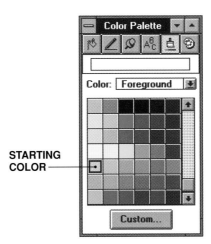

STARTING
COLOR

9. In the Legend Editor, scroll down to the last symbol and double-click on it.

10. In the Color Palette, select the ending color for your color ramp.

ENDING
COLOR —

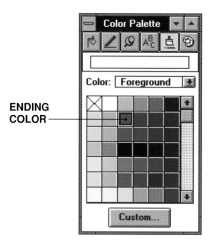

11. Close the Color Palette, then, in the Legend Editor, click the Ramp button to create a color ramp from the top of the classification to the bottom. Click Apply. ArcView creates the new legend and displays the counties with the new symbols.

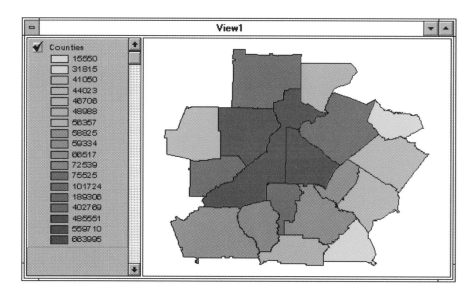

This map is easier to read than the random map, but it's still too complicated for the client to understand quickly. You've learned by experimenting, but you decide to go back to the default (quantile) classification method after all.

12. In the Legend Editor, click the Classify button. Choose Quantile, then click OK. ArcView creates five classes with an equal number of records in each class.

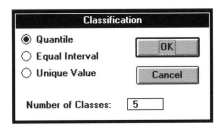

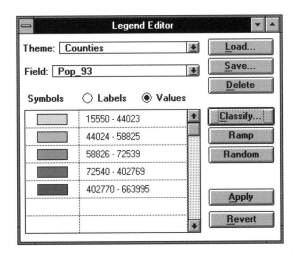

13. In the Legend Editor, click Apply to create the new legend and display the counties with the new symbols.

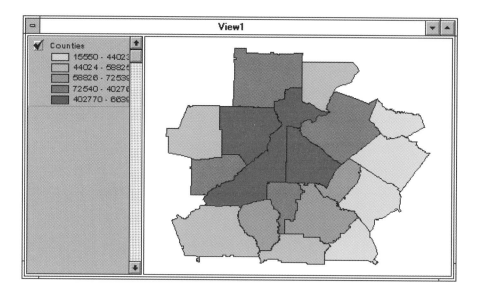

The Table of Contents isn't wide enough to display the entire legend, so you'll make it wider.

14. With the view active, move the cursor over the line that separates the scroll bar from the display area until it becomes a two-headed arrow. Hold down the mouse button and drag the line to the right.

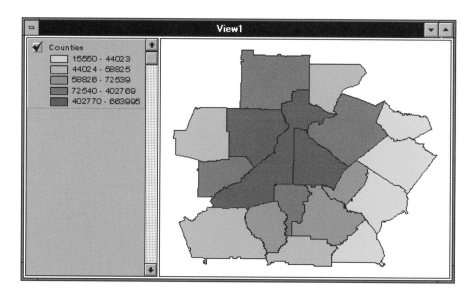

At this point, you decide to show the map to your boss. She's very impressed but says that, from experience, she knows that it won't be worth running an expensive newspaper advertising campaign in counties with a population of less than 50,000, and the optimum county population for this campaign is over 100,000. She wants your map to reflect this.

Based on your boss's comments, you decide to create a custom classification. You'll create three population classes: less than 50,000; 50,000–100,000; and greater than 100,000.

15. In the Legend Editor, click the Classify button and change the Number of Classes from **5** to **3,** then click OK. ArcView creates three population classes with an equal number of records in each class.

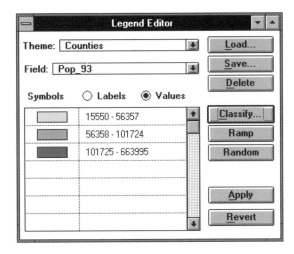

Now you'll change the range of values for each class.

> **Changing values and labels.** When you select the Values choice in the Legend Editor, the text to the right of each symbol gives the range of values in each class. These values govern how ArcView classifies the theme. You can edit the values by clicking on the text and typing your changes, thereby creating your own classification. However, changes you make to the values are not automatically reflected in the labels you see in the Table of Contents. You also have to edit the labels so they match the values. To do so, click on the Labels choice in the Legend Editor, then click on the text and type your changes. The text doesn't affect how ArcView classifies the theme. For more information, search for these Help Topics: *Legend Editor, Classification Types*.

16. With the Values choice selected in the Legend Editor, click on the first (top) value range and change it to **0 - 49999** (without commas), then press Enter on your keyboard. ArcView reclassifies and draws the theme every time you change a value. Now click on the second value range, change it to **50000 - 100000,** then press Enter. Finally, click on the third value range (bottom), change it to **100001 - 663995,** then press Enter. The new classification should look like this:

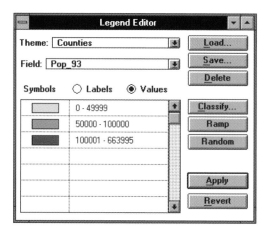

You want the labels in the Table of Contents to reflect the new classification, so you'll edit the labels for each class.

ENVIRONMENTAL SYSTEMS RESEARCH INSTITUTE, INC.

17. Click on the Labels choice in the Legend Editor. Click on the first (top) label, change it to **< 50,000** (with commas), then press Enter on your keyboard. ArcView relabels and draws the theme every time you change a label. Now click on the next label, change it to **50,000 - 100,000,** then press Enter. Finally, click on the last (bottom) label, change it to **> 100,000,** then press Enter. The new labels should look like this:

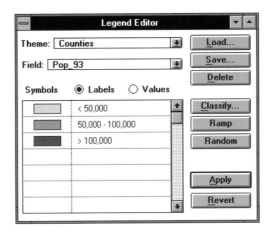

18. Close the Legend Editor.

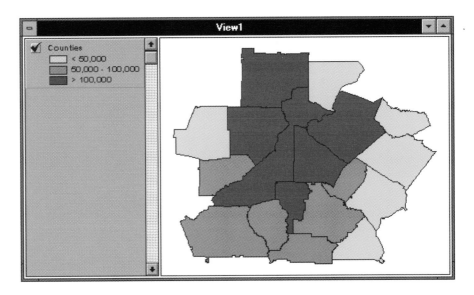

This map clearly shows which counties have the highest population. Your boss is happy with this map, but she would like you to add some finishing touches, such as labels for the counties.

If you want to go on to the next exercise, leave the project open.

Labeling features

You've classified the Counties theme so the legend is easy to read and the display quite clearly shows the areas of highest population—the areas where you want to concentrate your advertising dollars. To make the display more informative, you'll label the counties with their names using Theme Properties and Auto-label.

Exercise 9b

1. If *ex9a.apr* is open, continue. Otherwise, choose Open Exercise from the File menu. In the Exercises scrolling list, select "ex9b," then click OK. You see a view of the Counties theme classified as it was in the last exercise.

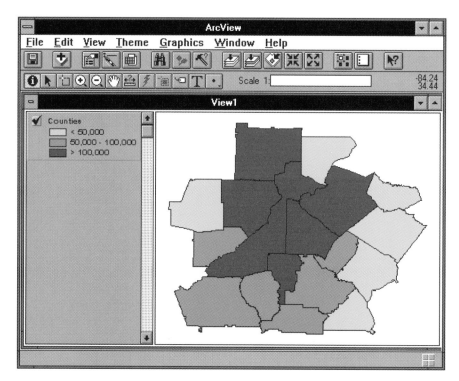

ENVIRONMENTAL SYSTEMS RESEARCH INSTITUTE, INC.

2. With the Counties theme active, choose Properties from the Theme menu. The Theme Properties dialog box displays.

3. Click on the Text Labels icon along the left margin to display the options for labeling features in a theme.

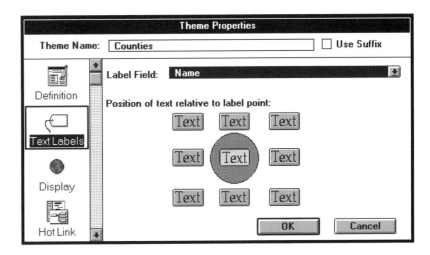

4. In the Label Field drop-down list, choose "Name" as the field to use for labeling. ArcView uses the values in this field to label features.

You'll position the labels at the center of each feature. (This is the default position.)

ArcView labels features relative to a point inside the feature, called a *label point*. When you use Auto-label, the label point is the center of the feature you're labeling.

5. Click OK to set the label properties for the Counties theme.

Now you'll use Auto-label to label the counties using values from the Name field.

6. From the Theme menu, choose Auto-label. ArcView labels the counties with their names. Each label has four selection handles around it, indicating that it's selected.

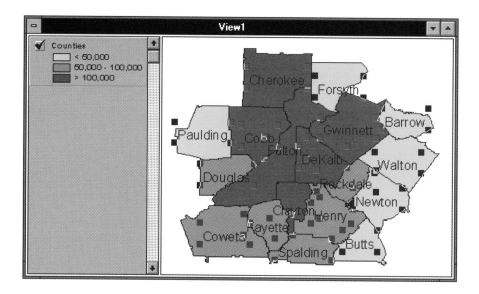

The text is too big! No problem. You can change the font, size, style, and color of the selected text with the Font Palette.

7. From the Window menu, choose Show Symbol Palette. The Fill Palette displays.

8. Click the Font Palette button at the top of the window. In the Font Palette, choose "9" from the Size drop-down list.

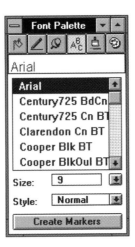

The labels redraw with the new font size.

9. Close the Font Palette.

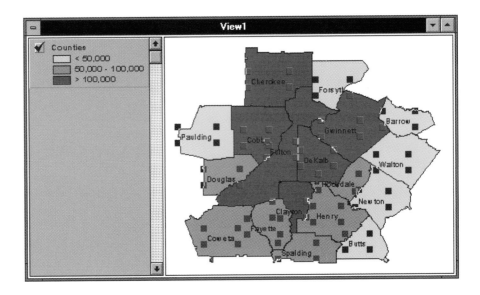

Now you can use the Pointer tool to unselect the labels in the view.

10. Click on the Pointer tool in the View tool bar, then click in the white space (not on a label) in the view. The selection handles around all the labels disappear.

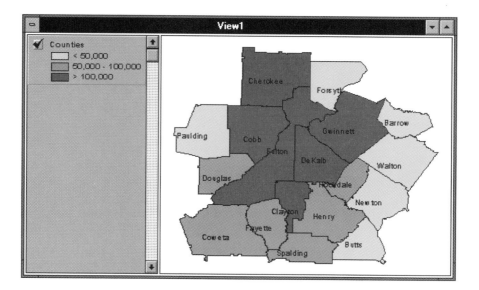

The map is ready. Your boss can use it to help convince the client that he'll get the most bang for his advertising buck by focusing the campaign on counties with the highest population.

If you want to go on to the next chapter, leave ArcView running. Otherwise, choose Exit from the File menu.

SECTION 2

Querying data

The next two chapters introduce you to methods of selecting features and records, and then working with the ones you select. In chapter 10, you'll get information about features, select them directly in a view, then select them according to their attributes, one at a time and in groups. You'll also learn how to select the features you want to show and hide the ones you don't. In chapter 11, you'll select records in a table and work with them by promoting them, getting statistics about them, summarizing them, and charting them.

**SECTION 2:
Querying data**

Selecting map features in a view

Getting information about features

Selecting features based on their attributes

Hiding features

Selecting map features in a view

Sometimes you want to know about a particular feature, or a group of features, rather than about all the features in a theme. With ArcView, you can get information about features by clicking on them one at a time with the Identify tool or by selecting them as a group with the Select Feature tool, then opening their attribute table.

When you want to find features based on their attributes, ArcView lets you find and select them one at a time with the Find button, or as a group using the Query Builder. With Find, you enter an attribute value and ArcView selects the first matching feature it finds. With the Query Builder, you write a statement, called a *query,* specifying an attribute and a value. ArcView selects all the features that match your query.

You can also write a query to define which features in a theme will display in the view. In this case you use the Query Builder in the Theme Properties dialog box to select features. Features that aren't selected won't display in the view.

Getting information about features

In ArcView you can click on a feature in a view with the Identify tool to display its attributes in a dialog box. Identifying features this way is fast. You don't have to select the feature or open the theme's attribute table to see its attributes. But this is only helpful when you want to identify a few features, one at a time. When you want to compare the attributes for a group of features, it's better to select them with the Select Feature tool, then open their attribute table.

When you *select* features, you create a separate set or subset of features. ArcView highlights the selected features in the view and in the theme table. Operations you perform on the theme will affect only the selected set.

Suppose that you're a real estate agent. A family has asked you to show them available properties in your area. They're looking for a tract home, preferably on a corner lot, with three bedrooms.

Exercise 10a

1. If necessary, start ArcView. From the File menu, choose Open Exercise. In the Exercises scrolling list, select "ex10a," then click OK. You see a view with streets, parcels, and a housing tract. The lots in the housing tract are classified into two groups, those that are for sale, and those that aren't.

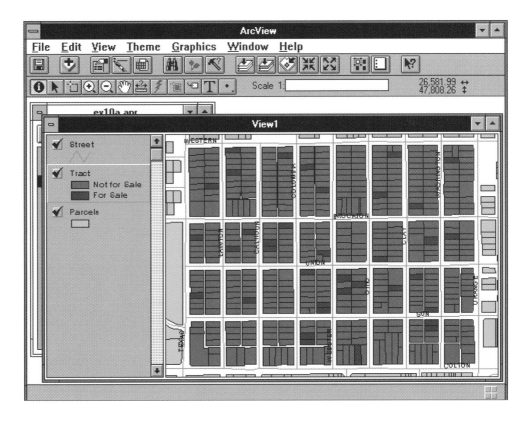

You want to get information about corner lots that are for sale. You'll use the Identify tool.

2. With the Identify tool selected, click on a corner lot that's for sale. The feature flashes in the view and a dialog box displays.

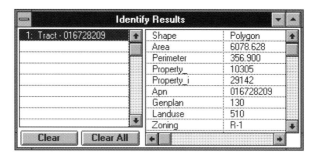

The left side of the Identify Results dialog box lists the feature (lot) you identified and the right side lists its attributes. These are the same attributes that are stored in the theme's attribute table.

3. Scroll down the list of attributes. The Bd_rms field tells you the number of bedrooms the house has.

The next to last field in the table, Status, is set to "Y," indicating that the house is for sale. The Tract theme is displayed based on the values in this field.

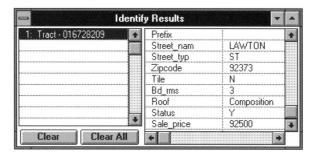

4. Click on a few more corner lots that are for sale. Each one is added to the Identify Results dialog box.

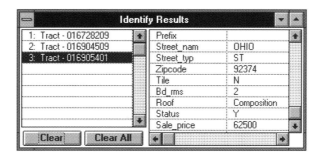

To compare the attributes of all the houses on corner lots, it's more efficient to select them, then open their attribute table. You'll use the Select
Feature tool to select them.

5. Close the Identify Results dialog box, then click on the Select
    Feature tool. Hold down the Shift key and click on each of the green
    corner lots in the view (there are eight in all). ArcView highlights the
    selected lots in yellow.

**If you select the wrong feature, you can unselect it by holding down
the Shift key and clicking on it again.**

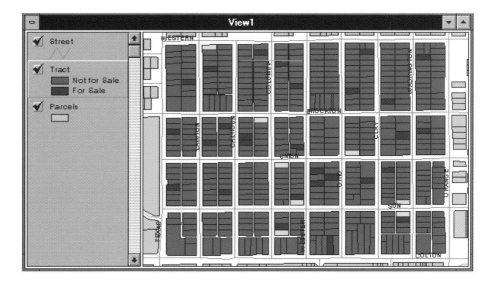

The attributes of the selected lots are also selected and highlighted in the theme's attribute table. To see them, you'll open the table.

6. Click the Open Theme Table button on the View button bar. The Tract theme's attribute table opens.

Shape	Area	Perimeter	Property_
Polygon	7710.413	381.350	3
Polygon	6839.675	374.619	3
Polygon	6709.897	369.130	3
Polygon	6190.391	361.044	3
Polygon	6673.998	365.817	3
Polygon	6286.618	363.021	3
Polygon	6279.261	361.912	3
Polygon	6342.927	363.245	3
Polygon	6332.976	352.558	3
Polygon	6658.709	361.976	3
Polygon	6475.233	355.410	3
Polygon	6549.652	358.291	3

Attributes of Tract

At first, you don't see any highlighted records. To see the entire group of selected records at the same time so you can compare them, you'll use the Promote button to move them to the top of the table.

7. Click the Promote button on the Table button bar. The selected records appear at the top of the table. Now scroll all the way to the right to see the Bd_rms field.

Tile	Bd_rms	Roof	Status	Sale_price
N	2	Composition	Y	62500
N	2	Composition	Y	19000
N	3	Composition	Y	110000
N	2	Composition	Y	73500
N	2	Composition	Y	40500
N	2	Composition	Y	21500
N	3	Composition	Y	92500
N	2	Composition	Y	58000
N	2	Composition	N	0
N	2	Composition	N	0
N	2	Composition	N	0
N	2	Composition	N	0

Attributes of Tract

Now you can see that two of the houses on corner lots have three bedrooms. To find them in the view, you'll use the Identify tool to click on their records in the table. But first you'll arrange the view and table windows so you can see them both at the same time.

8. Click on the table's title bar, then drag it to the upper left corner of the ArcView window. Now click on the view's title bar, drag it to the lower right corner, then make its window smaller.

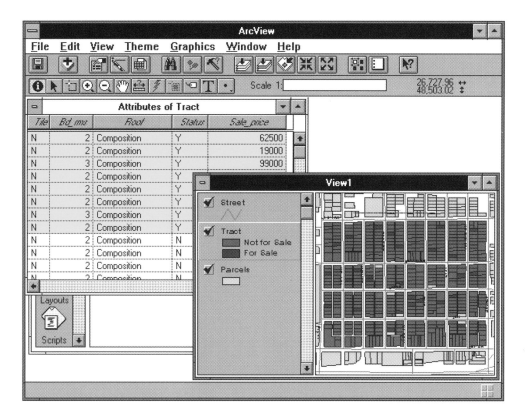

9. Make the table active, click on the Identify tool in the Table tool bar, then click on the first highlighted record with a value of "3" in the Bd_rms field. The Identify Results dialog box displays and the feature you picked flashes in the view. (If you don't see the feature flash, click on the record again.)

10. Move the Identify Results dialog box out of the way so you can see the view. Click on the other highlighted record with a value of "3" in the Bd_rms field. The feature is added to the Identify Results dialog box, and it flashes in the view.

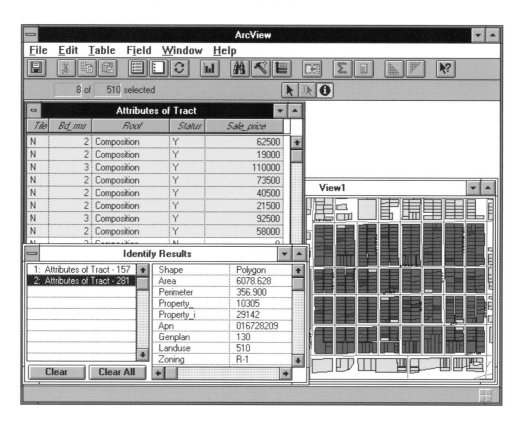

Using the Identify and Select Feature tools, you found two corner lots with three-bedroom houses. You'll show these houses to your clients. Before leaving the office, you'll restore the view to its previous size and clear the selection.

11. Close the Identify Results dialog box, then the theme table. Drag the upper left corner of the View window to enlarge it.

12. Click the Clear Selected Features button to clear the current selection. The previously highlighted features are no longer highlighted.

> **Selecting features graphically.** With the Select Features tool, you select features by clicking on them one at a time or by dragging a box over them. Another way to select features graphically is to use the Draw tool to draw a shape in the view, then use the Select Features Using Shape button to select the features under the shape. For more information, search for these Help Topics: *Selecting features on a view, Select Feature tool, Draw tool, Select Features Using Shape.*

If you want to go on to the next exercise, leave the project open.

Selecting features based on their attributes

Because ArcView links features in a view to their attributes in a table, you can select features by entering an attribute value or by writing a statement, called a *query,* that specifies one or more attributes and the values you're interested in. ArcView searches the attribute table for records that match your request. When you use the Find tool, ArcView finds the first feature that matches your request; when you use the Query Builder, ArcView finds all the features that match your request.

While you were out with your clients looking at the two houses, they noticed another house for sale that interested them, next to the corner on Washington Street. You wrote down the address so you could get more information about it back at the office. You'll use ArcView's Find button to locate the house in your GIS database.

Exercise 10b

1. If *ex10a.apr* is open, continue. Otherwise, choose Open Exercise from the File menu. In the Exercises scrolling list, select "ex10b," then click OK. You see a view with streets, parcels, and a housing tract.

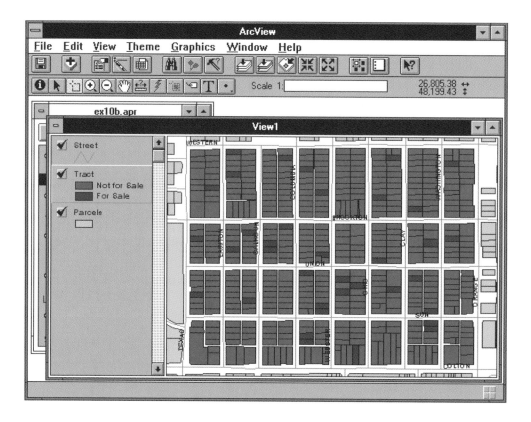

ENVIRONMENTAL SYSTEMS RESEARCH INSTITUTE, INC.

2. With the Tract theme active, click the Find button on the View button bar, then type **831 Washington** in the text box that displays. Click OK.

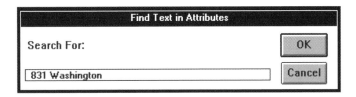

ArcView searches the attribute table for the first occurrence of "831 Washington" and selects it. ArcView highlights the record and the corresponding feature in the view. ArcView also pans the view so the highlighted feature displays in the center.

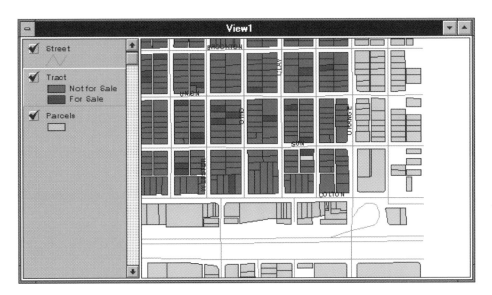

Now that you've found the house, you want to examine its attributes, so you'll open the theme table and promote the selected record.

3.   Click the Open Theme Table button, then the Promote button. ArcView displays the selected record at the top of the table. By scrolling to the right, you can examine its attributes.

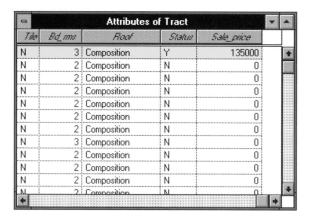

The house has three bedrooms with an asking price of $135,000. Your clients want to see it, but they also want to look at other three-bedroom houses for comparison, even if they're not on corner lots. To find all the three-bedroom houses for sale in the tract, you'll use the Query Builder.

4.   Close the theme table, then click the Query Builder button on the View button bar to display the Query Builder dialog box.

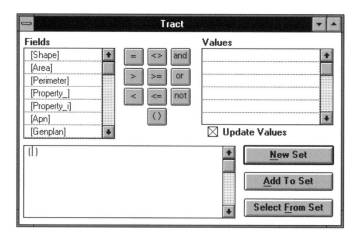

ENVIRONMENTAL SYSTEMS RESEARCH INSTITUTE, INC.

At the top of the Query Builder, you see the name of the active theme, Tract. The Query Builder dialog box contains a list of attribute fields (left), a set of operators (center), and a list of attribute values (right). When you click on a field in the Fields list, all the unique values for that field display in the Values list, as long as the Update Values option is checked (this is the default). To build a query, you double-click on a field, click (or double-click) on an operator, then double-click on a value. As you build the query, it displays in the query text box in the lower left corner of the dialog box. You can also type your query directly in the query text box.

Once you enter the query in the text box, you apply it by selecting New Set, Add To Set, or Select From Set. New Set creates a new set of selected features that match your query. Add To Set adds features that match your query to the existing selected set. Select From Set selects features that match your query from the previously selected set.

With one query, you'll select all the houses for sale that have three bedrooms.

5.   In the Query Builder dialog box, scroll down to the bottom of the Fields list, then click on "[Status]." Two values, "N" and "Y," display in the Values list. (Lots that are for sale have a "Y" value, those that aren't have an "N.") Now double-click on "[Status]" to place it in the query text box.

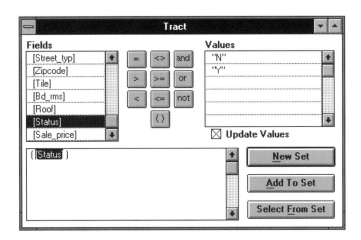

6. Click the "=" button. It displays in the query text box. Then, in the Values list, double-click on "Y." So far, your query should look like this:

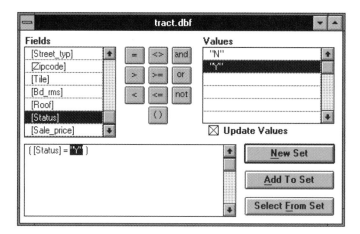

By default, ArcView places square brackets around field names and quotes around strings. The entire query is enclosed by parentheses.

With this query you could select all the houses that are for sale. Then you could build a second query to select houses from this set that have three bedrooms. Instead, you'll build one query to select houses that are for sale and have three bedrooms, at the same time.

Combining queries. You can combine more than one query by using the And and Or operators to connect them. For example, to select houses that are for sale *and* have three bedrooms, you would use this query: ([Status] = "Y") And ([Bd_rms] = 3). ArcView selects all the houses that meet both criteria. To select all the houses that are for sale *or* have three bedrooms, you would use this query: ([Status] = "Y") Or ([Bd_rms] = 3). In this case, ArcView selects all the houses that meet either criterion. For more information, search for this Help Topic: *Query Builder.*

ENVIRONMENTAL SYSTEMS RESEARCH INSTITUTE, INC.

7. Click the "and" button, double-click "[Bd_rms]" in the Fields list, click the "=" button, then double-click "3" in the Values list. Now your query should look like this:

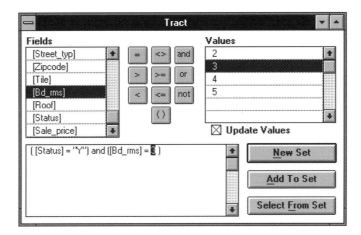

8. Click the New Set button to select those houses that are for sale and have three bedrooms and place them in a new set. ArcView highlights them in the view. (You may need to move the Query Builder dialog box so you can see the view.)

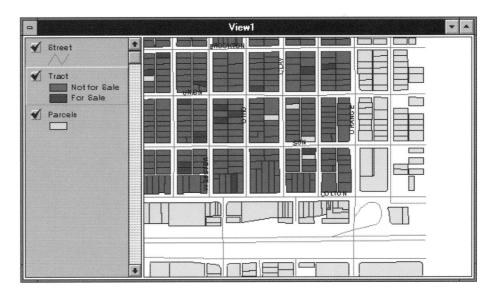

To see all the selected lots, you'll zoom out to them.

9. With the view active, click the Zoom to Selected button. ArcView zooms out so you can see all the selected features.

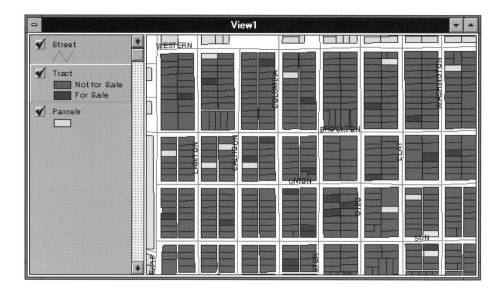

The results are encouraging. There are plenty of three-bedroom houses for sale in the tract to show your clients. Rather than looking at all of them, your clients decide to look at houses priced below $100,000. So, you'll build another query to select houses from the currently selected set, according to the values in the Sale_price field.

10. In the Query Builder's text box, highlight the portion of the query that's between the parentheses, then delete it by pressing the Delete or Backspace key on your keyboard.

11. Double-click "[Sale_price]" in the Fields list, click the "<" button, then type **100000.** Your query should look like this.

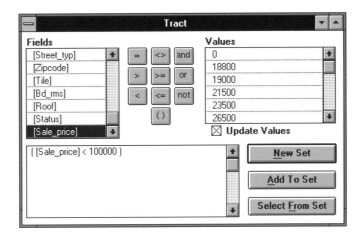

12. Now click the Select From Set button to select houses priced below $100,000 from the currently selected set of houses.

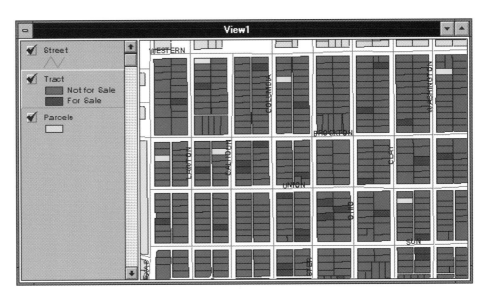

To look at the price of each house, you'll open the theme table.

13. Close the Query Builder. Click the Open Theme Table button, then the Promote button. ArcView displays the selected records at the top of the table.

14. Scroll all the way to the right to see the price of each house that's selected.

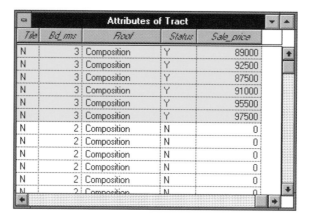

Your clients are satisfied that these houses meet their initial criteria and are ready to look at them.

In this exercise, you used the Find button to locate and select a feature from an attribute value, then the Query Builder to select a group of features by specifying an attribute and the desired value for it. In the next exercise, you'll use the Query Builder from the Theme Properties dialog box to select the features you want to display in the view.

Hiding features

Sometimes you have more features in a theme than you want to work with at a given time. You don't want to delete any data, because you may need it in the future. One way to reduce the size of your data set without deleting any data is through a process called *filtering*. Filtering keeps some of the data visible and hides the rest. To filter data in ArcView, you build a query that selects the features you want to show. Data that's not selected is hidden. When you clear the query, the hidden features return. To build this kind of query, you access the Query Builder from the Theme Properties dialog box, rather than from the View interface.

Filtering helps keep your database manageable. When you filter rather than select data, you reduce the clutter in a view and the time needed to draw it, and make the data easier to interpret and work with. If you have hundreds or even thousands of features in a theme, and you select some of them, it can be hard to distinguish the selected ones from the others. Also, the more records there are in a theme table, the longer it takes ArcView to search for features.

Suppose you're a member of an agricultural commission concerned about the decline of citrus-growing areas due to residential and commercial development. You want to create a map showing the current citrus-growing areas, then use it to track future changes in land use.

Exercise 10c

1. From the File menu, choose Open Exercise. In the Exercises scrolling list, select "ex10c," then click OK. You see a view showing streets and land parcels.

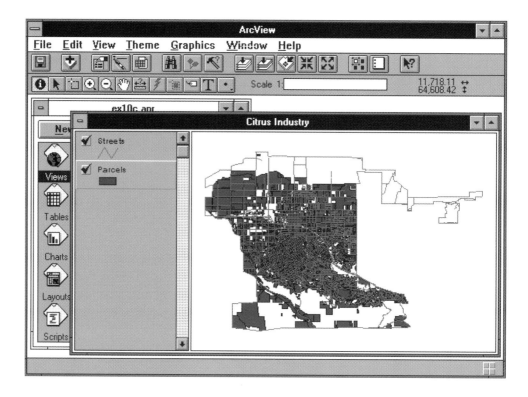

According to the agricultural commission, the land parcels were once used exclusively for growing citrus and other agricultural products, but in recent years they've been converted to residential and commercial land use. Areas where streets are dense (toward the center of the view) have undergone the heaviest development.

For each feature in the Parcels theme, there is a land use code. A code of "732" indicates that the land is used for growing citrus. You'll build a query in the Theme Properties dialog box to filter the Parcels theme so that only the land parcels used for growing citrus will be displayed.

2. With the Parcels theme active, choose Properties from the Theme menu in the View menu bar. The Theme Properties dialog box displays.

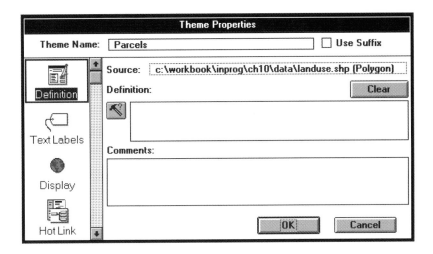

By default, the Definition icon is highlighted on the left. On the right, you see the options for the Definition category of properties.

3. Click the Query Builder button in the Theme Properties dialog box. The Query Builder dialog box displays. It looks like the Query Builder you access from the View interface, but instead of the New Set, Add To Set, and Select From Set buttons, it has an OK button.

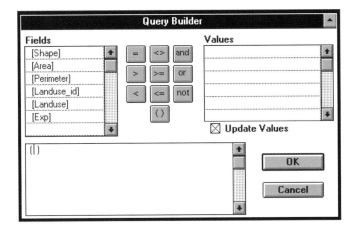

4.   In the Fields list, double-click on "[Landuse]." (Because there are a lot of unique values in this field, it takes a while for them to update in the Values list.)

5.   Click the "=" button, then scroll down in the Values list until you find "732" and double-click on it. Your query should look like this:

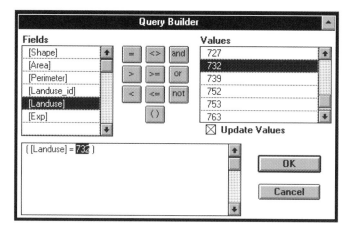

6.   Click the OK button in the Query Builder, then click the OK button in the Theme Properties dialog box to select parcels that match your query. ArcView selects, but doesn't highlight, the features that match your query.

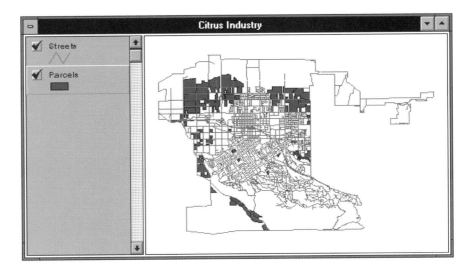

Now the view shows only the parcels that are used for growing citrus; other parcels are hidden from view. You see that the remaining citrus groves are located mainly on the outskirts of the city. Next you'll zoom in to the new Parcels theme.

The area covered by the Parcels theme is defined by the visible features. Features that are hidden in the view are also hidden in the theme table.

7.   Click the Zoom to Active Themes button. ArcView zooms in so the active theme, Parcels, fills the view.

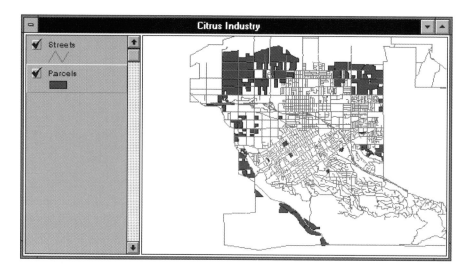

Now you have a theme that shows only the parcels used for citrus. As land use patterns continue to change, you can copy, then update your data to reflect these changes. In this way, you create multiple versions of the data, each one representing a different time period. By filtering each version of the data, you can create a series of maps that show changes in citrus-growing areas over time.

If you want to go on to the next chapter, leave ArcView running. Otherwise, choose Exit from the File menu.

Selecting records in a table

Finding particular records

Working with selected records

Selecting records in a table

So far, you've selected records by selecting features directly in a view; each time you selected features, the corresponding records in the theme attribute table were also selected.

You can also select records directly from a theme table. With the Select tool, you select records by clicking on them. With Find, you type an attribute value in a dialog box and ArcView searches the table for the first matching record. With the Query Builder you specify a value or range of values for one or more attributes and ArcView finds all the matching records.

Once you select a group or *set* of records, ArcView lets you work with them apart from the rest of the features and records in a theme. In this chapter, you'll select records, get statistics about them, summarize them, and present this information in a chart.

Finding particular records

Suppose you're working as a district ranger. It's your job to identify areas in your district that are threatened by drought. In your GIS database, two themes represent rainfall data. One theme contains line features (contour lines) that define the boundaries of areas with given amounts of rainfall. The other theme contains polygons that define the areas between the lines. Each polygon is coded with the highest rainfall value of its two bounding lines. So if a polygon is bounded by the 200-millimeter and 250-millimeter lines, it receives the maximum value of 250 millimeters of annual rainfall.

You'll use the Query Builder to find and select polygons that receive less than 300 mm of rain a year. These areas are considered to be threatened by drought. From the selected set of records, you can derive statistical information and present this information in the form of a chart.

Exercise 11a

1. If necessary, start ArcView. From the File menu, choose Open Exercise. In the Exercises scrolling list, select "ex11a," then click OK. When the project opens, you see an active view with two themes, Contours.shp and Rainfall.shp, and a table, Attributes of Rainfall.shp.

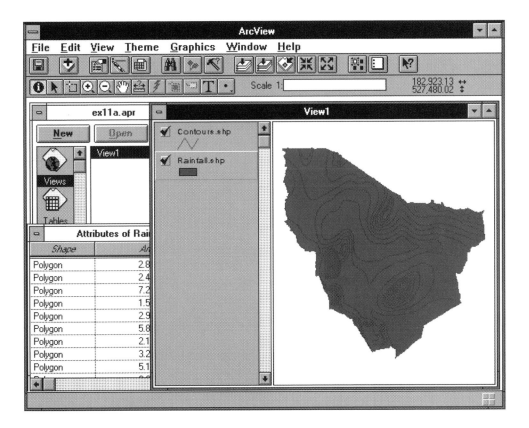

 2. Make the Attributes of Rainfall.shp table active, then click the Query Builder button. The Query Builder dialog box displays with the name of the active table.

The Query Builder dialog box is where you build the statement, or query, that ArcView uses as the basis for selecting records from a table. In this case, you want to find all areas that receive less than 300 mm of rain per year. The next two steps take you through building the query.

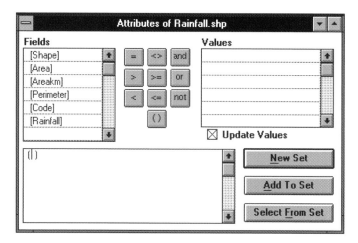

3. In the dialog box, scroll down in the Fields list until you find "[Rainfall]," then double-click on it. Click the "<" button, then double-click on "300" in the Values list. Your query should look like this:

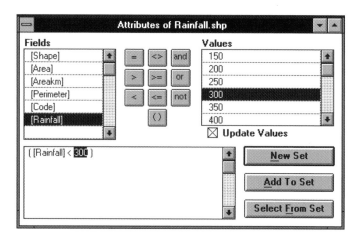

4. Click the New Set button to select all the records that match your query. Close the Query Builder dialog box.

Now you can examine the selected records.

5. Click the Promote button to move the selected records to the top of the table. The selected records are highlighted in yellow, as are the corresponding features in the view.

Attributes of Rainfall.shp		
Perimeter	Code	Rainfall
2.515217e+006	5	250
130373.700000	4	200
1.178831e+006	4	200
488942.600000	3	150
270924.200000	4	200
36947.910000	4	200
418639.300000	4	200
116674.500000	7	350
63488.080000	8	400

You'll work with these records in the next exercise.

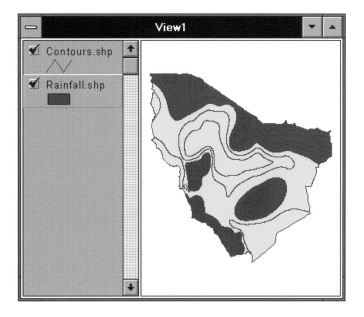

If you want to go on to the next exercise, leave the project open.

> **Selecting records.** ArcView gives you many ways to select records in a table. With the *Select tool,* you can select records one at a time by clicking on them with the mouse. To select more than one record, hold down the Shift key, then click on each record you want to select or drag the mouse cursor over them. With the *Find button,* you can select records by typing an attribute value you want to search for; ArcView searches the table to find and select a record with the value you type. For more information, search for these Help Topics: *Select tool, Find, Selecting records in a table.*

Working with selected records

Once you've selected records in a table you can get statistics about them, summarize them based on a summary field, or create a chart displaying the information contained in them. In the next exercise, you'll use Statistics to calculate the total area of the district that's threatened by drought, and Summarize to determine how this area is distributed between the various rainfall contours. Then you'll create a chart to show the result.

Exercise 11b

1. If *ex11a.apr* is open, continue. Otherwise, choose Open Exercise from the File menu. In the Exercises scrolling list, select "ex11b," then click OK. When the project opens, you see View1 and an active table, Attributes of Rainfall.shp. Records with an annual rainfall of less than 300 mm are already selected.

2. Click the Promote button to move the selected records to the top of the table.

ENVIRONMENTAL SYSTEMS RESEARCH INSTITUTE, INC.

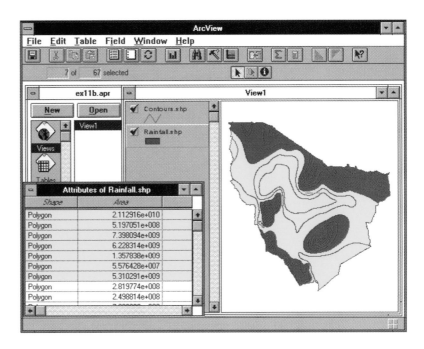

3. In the Attributes of Rainfall.shp table, click on the Areakm field to make it the active field. The field name cell becomes shaded when the field is active.

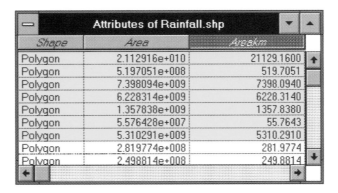

4.   Now select Statistics from the Field menu. A message box displays statistics about the Areakm field's values for the selected records.

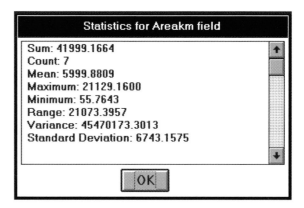

Statistics for Areakm field

Sum: 41999.1664
Count: 7
Mean: 5999.8809
Maximum: 21129.1600
Minimum: 55.7643
Range: 21073.3957
Variance: 45470173.3013
Standard Deviation: 6743.1575

OK

You see that 41999.1664 square kilometers of the district receive less than 300 mm of rainfall annually. Click OK to dismiss the message box.

Now you'll use Summarize to determine how this total area is distributed between the various rainfall contours.

5.   In the Attributes of Rainfall.shp table, click on the Rainfall field to make it active. You'll summarize the selected records based on the values in this field.

Summarizing selected records. You can summarize selected records in a table based on the values in the active field, in this case *Rainfall*. For each unique value in this field, ArcView creates a record in a new table. Each record contains a Count field that specifies the number of records with that value. Additional fields contain any summary statistics (e.g., average, summary, minimum) you requested for fields other than the active field. For more information, search for these Help Topics: *Summarize, Summarizing a table.*

ENVIRONMENTAL SYSTEMS RESEARCH INSTITUTE, INC.

6. Choose Summarize from the Field pulldown menu. The Summary Table Definition dialog box displays.

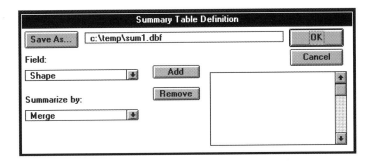

7. From the upper drop-down list (Field), select "Areakm." From the lower drop-down list (Summarize by), select "Sum." Then click the Add button. This adds your selection to the Summary statistics box on the right. Click the Save As button to navigate to the *drive:\directory* where you want to save the new table ArcView creates and call it **rainsum.dbf.** Click OK.

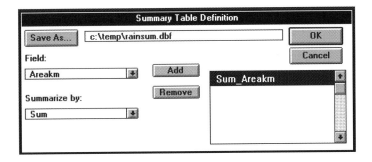

The new table has three records, one for each unique value of *Rainfall*. The Count field tells you how many selected records have each value. For example, five areas receive 200 mm of rain a year. The Sum_Areakm field tells you the total size (in square kilometers) of areas vulnerable to drought, according to the amount of rainfall they receive.

rainsum.dbf		
Rainfall	*Count*	*Sum_Areakm*
150	1	6228.31
200	5	14641.69
250	1	21129.16

You want to share these findings with your district manager, so you'll create a chart showing the information in the Summary table.

A chart is one way of making tabular information graphic, giving it immediate impact. Your audience doesn't have to think about the difference between 6,228, 14,642, and 21,129 square kilometers. They see and understand.

8. Click on the rainsum.dbf table to make it active, then click the Create Chart button. The Chart Properties dialog box displays.

9. Select "Sum_Areakm" in the Fields scrolling list, then click Add. Sum_Areakm appears in the Groups list. This is the field ArcView will plot on the chart.

10. Select "Rainfall" in the Label series using drop-down list. ArcView uses this field to label each set of related values in the chart.

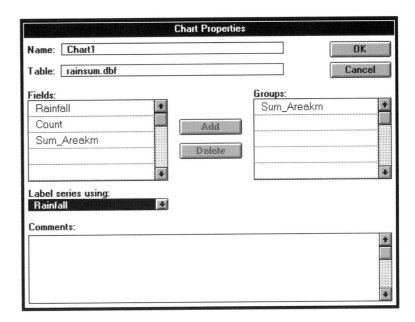

11. Click OK to apply your selections and dismiss the Chart Properties dialog box. ArcView creates the following chart and adds it to your project:

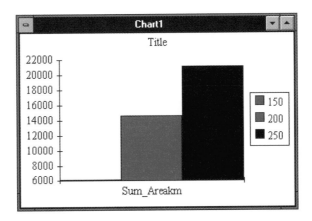

Notice that a red symbol appears in the chart's legend, but you don't see a red column in the chart. That's because ArcView uses the smallest value of Sum_Areakm (6,228.31 rounded down to 6,000) as the minimum value on the y-axis. By changing the values along the y-axis, you could create this chart instead:

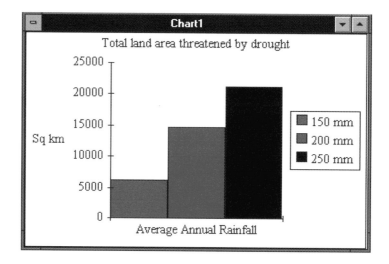

In chapter 20 you'll learn more about creating charts, changing the way they look, and querying and editing them.

Now you know which areas in your district are vulnerable to drought and you know the size of these areas. Armed with maps, tables, and charts, you have the tools you need to plan further studies.

If you want to go on to the next chapter, leave ArcView running. Otherwise, choose Exit from the File menu.

SECTION 3

Working with spatial data

The next two chapters introduce you to how to reference spatial data to the real world. In chapter 12, you'll use ArcView's measuring tools to measure distance and area in a view. You'll also change the map projection used to display a view and witness the effects that different map projections have on distance and shape. In chapter 13, you'll learn how to set the map scale for a view and how to set scale thresholds for individual themes so you can control when they display.

SECTION 3:
Working with spatial data

Measuring distance and area in a view

Measuring distance

Measuring area

Setting a map projection

Working with data that's already projected

CHAPTER 12

Measuring distance and area in a view

In chapter 5, you learned that one of the advantages of a desktop GIS is that you can measure distances and areas on the surface of the earth right at your computer. And the measurements are reported in real-world units, such as feet, meters, miles, or kilometers. You also learned that you can control the distortion in certain properties by using a map projection that preserves the property you're measuring.

In ArcView, you can measure distance and area in a view whether the feature locations are stored as unprojected geographic coordinates or as projected x,y coordinates. All you have to do is tell ArcView what units the coordinates are stored in and what units you want ArcView to use for reporting measurements.

In this chapter, you'll learn how to measure distance and area when the feature locations are unprojected (stored in geographic coordinates), when you set a map projection for the view, and when you use data that's already been projected.

 ENVIRONMENTAL SYSTEMS RESEARCH INSTITUTE, INC.

Measuring distance

You work for a city that's planning to develop a park adjacent to a soon-to-be-developed housing project. The park property has one building on it that will be converted to a rest room. It's your job to make some preliminary measurements that will help the city estimate the cost of developing the park. You'll first consider the cost of bringing water into the park's future rest room, then make some measurements to help determine this cost.

Exercise 12a

1. From the File menu, choose Open Exercise. In the Exercises scrolling list, select "ex12a," then click OK. When the project opens, you see a view containing three themes: Water Lines, Buildings, and Property. All of these themes contain geographic data that's stored in decimal degrees. (*Decimal degrees* are degrees of latitude and longitude expressed as a decimal rather than as degrees, minutes, and seconds.)

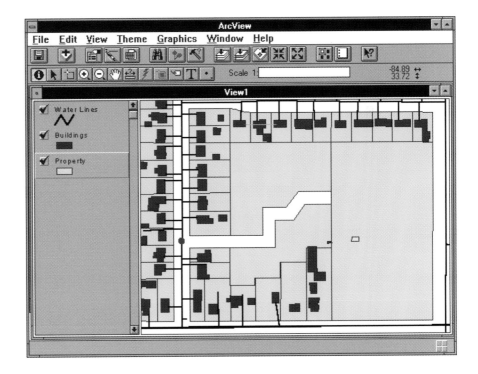

Before you make any measurements in the view, you'll tell ArcView what type of units the data is stored in and what type of units you want to use for measuring.

If you don't know the units your data is stored in, you may need to consult the data dictionary (if your data comes with one), the vendor (if you purchased the data), or the person or agency you received the data from. If the data is an ARC/INFO coverage or grid, it may contain a text file (prj) that describes the coordinate system and units the data is stored in.

2. Select Properties from the View menu to open the View Properties dialog box.

To specify the units in which the coordinates of the data are stored, you'll set the map units.

3. Click on the Map Units down arrow, then choose "decimal degrees" from the list. This indicates that all the data in the current view is stored in decimal degrees.

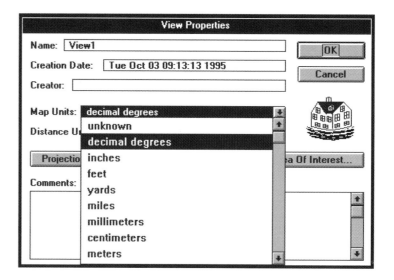

To specify the units ArcView will use to report measurements, you'll set the distance units.

4.   Click on the Distance Units down arrow, then choose "feet."

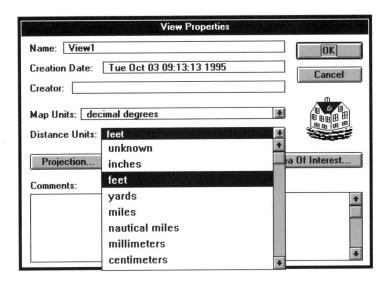

5.   Click OK to apply your settings to the view.

You'll use the Measure tool to determine the distance from the small building (located on the proposed park property) to the nearest water lines.

   6.   Click on the Measure tool (the cursor changes to a ruler), then click on the building (highlighted in yellow). Move the cursor to the water line located directly below the building. Notice that ArcView draws a line segment from the building to wherever you position the cursor in the view and reports the length of this line in the status bar (at the bottom of the ArcView window). With the cursor directly over the water line, double-click the mouse button to end the line. ArcView reports the measurement in feet.

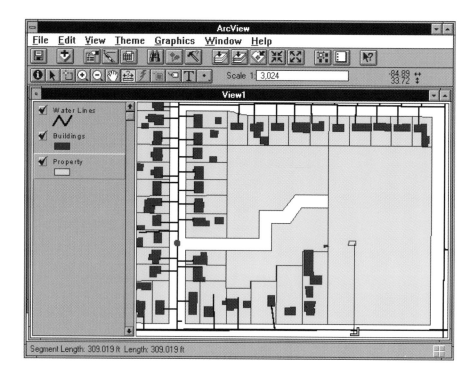

ArcView reports two values, Length and Segment Length. Segment Length is the length of the current line segment and Length is the total length of all segments that comprise the line. In this case, both measurements are the same, 309 feet. (In this exercise, your measurements may vary slightly from those reported.)

7. Click on the same building again, then move the cursor to the water line located to the far right of the building. With the cursor directly over the water line, double-click the mouse button to end the line. ArcView reports the measurement in the status bar.

ENVIRONMENTAL SYSTEMS RESEARCH INSTITUTE, INC.

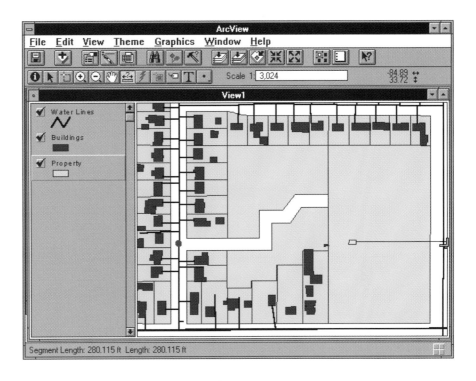

In only a few seconds, and without having to go to the site, you've determined that the water line to the right of the building is approximately 29 feet closer (280 feet) than the water line directly below it (309 feet). You can use this information in calculating the cost of bringing water to the building.

In addition to the proposed park, the city is in the process of approving a housing development on the adjacent property. Before the planning commission gives its final stamp of approval, it needs to estimate the cost of running new water lines into the proposed development.

Because it's common practice for utility companies to use existing rights-of-way to gain access to properties and structures, and the proposed housing development already has a road, you'll use the existing street right-of-way for measuring the new water lines.

8. With the Measure tool selected, click on the red dot located on the street centerline on the left side of the view (this dot indicates where the new water lines will begin).

Now you'll trace the centerline of the street located to the right of the red dot.

9.   Move the cursor along the center of the street and single-click the mouse button each time the street changes direction. (Each time you single-click, ArcView reports a measurement and starts a new line segment.) When you reach the end of the street, double-click to end the line. In the status bar, ArcView reports the length of the last line segment and the total length of all the segments.

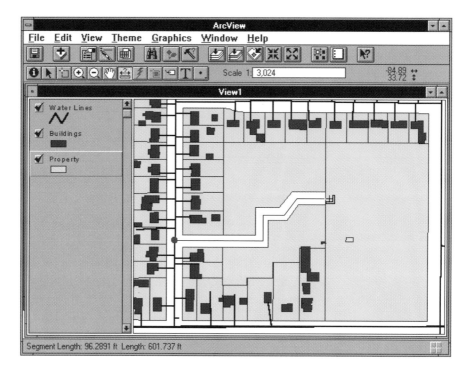

Now you know that the length of pipe needed to bring water to the proposed housing development is nearly 602 feet. Again, you've used ArcView to measure a distance on your computer instead of in the field, saving many hours of labor. Imagine the savings if you needed to run several water lines. You could measure them and estimate their cost in minutes rather than hours.

If you want to go on to the next exercise, leave the project open.

Measuring area

A soccer field is planned for the new park. You're fairly certain it will fit, but you don't want to spend hours at the site trying to determine all the possible locations for it. You'll use ArcView to determine the best locations for a soccer field.

Exercise 12b

1. If *ex12a.apr* is open, continue. Otherwise, choose Open Exercise from the File menu. In the Exercises scrolling list, select "ex12b," then click OK. When the project opens, you see a view with three themes: Water Lines, Buildings, and Property.

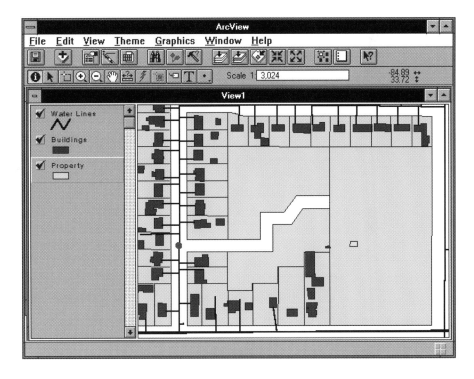

Because a soccer field is measured in meters instead of feet, you need to change the units ArcView uses to report measurements (distance units) to meters.

2. Select Properties from the View menu to open the View Properties dialog box.

3. Click on the Distance Units down arrow, then choose "meters."

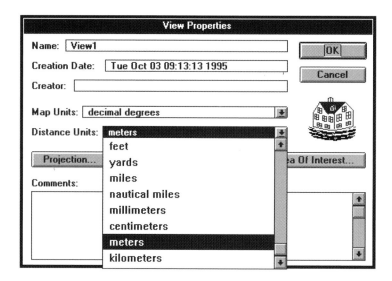

4. Click OK. Your measurements will now display in meters.

You'll use the Rectangle tool to draw the shape of a soccer field, 110 meters by 73 meters.

5. Click on the Draw tool and select the Rectangle tool from the drop-down list of tools.

6. Click inside the proposed park property, hold down the mouse button, and drag a rectangle that measures approximately 110 meters by 73 meters. The status bar indicates the Extent (width, height) and Area of the rectangle as you draw it. When you're satisfied with the rectangle (your measurements don't have to be exact), release the mouse button.

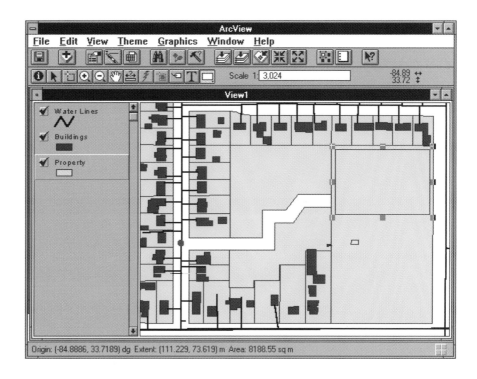

Next you'll use Size and Position to set the exact measurements for the rectangle.

7.   Choose Size and Position from the Graphics menu. The Graphic Size and Position dialog box displays.

8.   In the dialog box, set the width to **110** (meters) and the height to **73.**

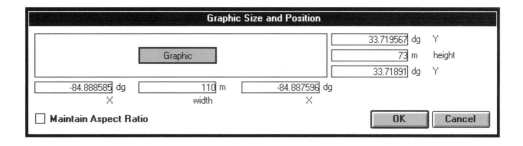

9. Click OK. Now the rectangle has the right dimensions for a soccer field.

To reposition the rectangle, you'll use the Pointer tool.

10. Click on the Pointer tool, then position the cursor over the rectangle (it changes to a four-headed arrow). Now hold down the mouse button and drag the rectangle to any position on the property. In this way you can determine the best locations for the soccer field.

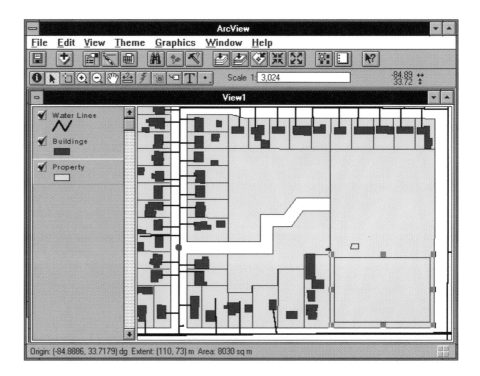

But suppose you want to change the orientation of the soccer field. No problem. Just use Size and Position to change the dimensions of the rectangle.

11. From the Graphics menu, choose Size and Position. Change the width to **73** meters and the height to **110** meters, then click OK.

Now you can use the Pointer tool to reposition the rectangle.

12. Place the cursor over the rectangle, then hold down the mouse button and drag the rectangle to any position inside the park property.

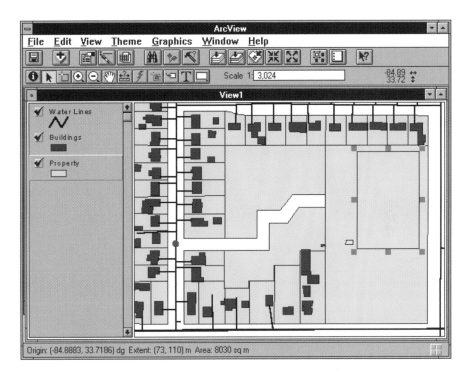

There are many suitable locations for the soccer field. To determine them in the field would take two people, a surveyor's chain or transit, and many hours. ArcView can help you find the possible locations, on your computer, in only a few minutes.

Setting a map projection

You've seen how ArcView lets you work with data that's stored in geographic coordinates without setting a map projection. All you have to do is set the map and distance units for the view. However, when you're working with data that covers a large portion of the earth's surface and you want to preserve a particular spatial property, such as shape, area, distance, or direction, you can choose a map projection that preserves that property and apply it to the view. ArcView provides a wide range of standard and custom map projections to choose from.

You can project a view in ArcView whenever the coordinates of the spatial data (feature locations) are stored in decimal degrees. In other words, the spatial data must be unprojected. You can convert unprojected data from decimal degrees to planar (x,y) coordinates using any projection that ArcView supports.

Suppose you teach a map-reading class at a university. Your lesson for this week is "Understanding Projections." You plan to use ArcView to show students how different projections affect shape and distance. You'll use familiar data (the continental United States) to create a demonstration that shows the changes produced by each projection. To show the distortion of shape, you'll add a circle graphic to the data, then observe how the shape of the circle changes with each projection that's applied. To show the distortion of distance, you'll measure a known distance (the distance from Los Angeles to New York) and compare your measurements.

Exercise 12c

1. From the File menu, choose Open Exercise. In the Exercises scroll-ing list, select "ex12c," then click OK. When the project opens, you see a view with two themes, Cities and 48 States.

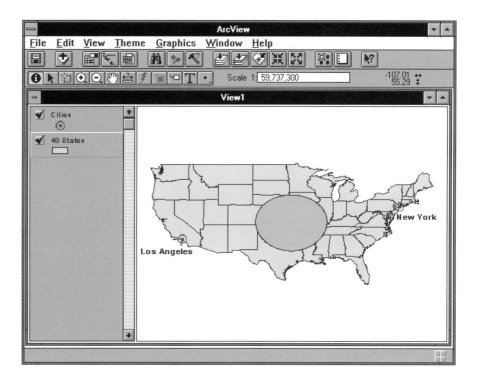

First you'll see how the map units and distance units are set for this view.

2. From the View menu, choose Properties. The View Properties dialog box displays.

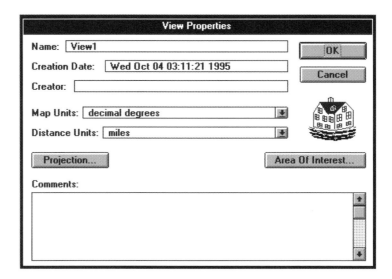

The Map Units are set to "decimal degrees" and the Distance Units are set to "miles," that is, the coordinates of the data in the view are stored in decimal degrees and the measuring units are miles.

3. Click the Cancel button to close the View Properties dialog box.

Now you'll measure the distance from Los Angeles to New York, which is known to be 2,451 miles.

4. Click on the Measure tool, then click on the symbol for Los Angeles. Move the cursor to the symbol for New York, then double-click to end the line. The distance between the two cities displays in the status bar.

ENVIRONMENTAL SYSTEMS RESEARCH INSTITUTE, INC.

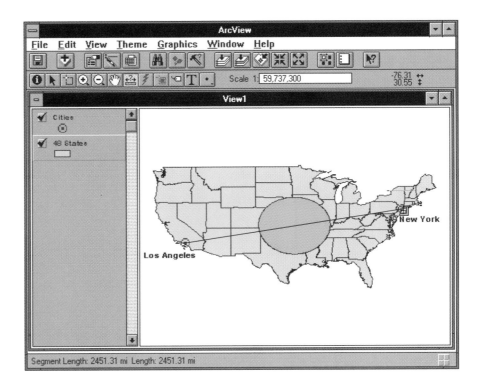

Even though the shapes of the individual states are distorted (note the elliptical distortion of the circle), the distance measurement is accurate. That's because ArcView uses a custom projection that produces accurate distance measurements for data that's stored in decimal degrees.

Now you'll choose a projection for the view and see how it affects distance and shape.

5. Select Properties from the View menu, then click the Projection button. The Projection Properties dialog box displays.

6. Click on the Type down arrow, then choose "Mercator" from the list.

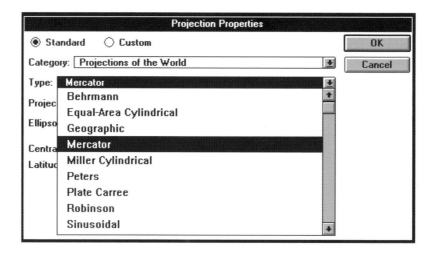

7. Click OK, then click OK in the View Properties dialog box to apply the Mercator map projection to the view.

8. With the Measure tool, measure the distance from Los Angeles to New York.

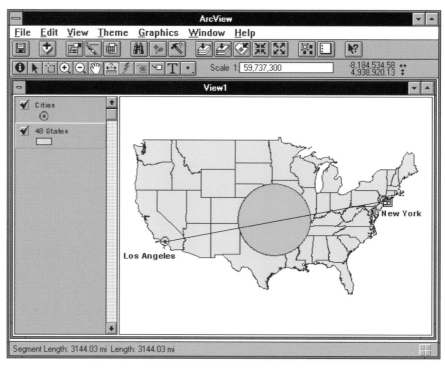

The new measurement is larger than the previous measurement, by approximately 683 miles.

The ellipse is now a circle (its true shape). The Mercator map projection preserves the property of direction and the shape of features, but sacrifices accurate distance and area.

You'll change the projection again.

9. Select Properties from the View menu and click the Projection button.

10. In the Projection Properties dialog box, select "Peters" from the Type drop-down list.

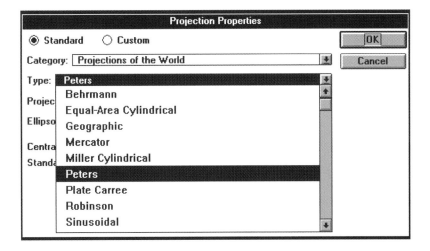

11. Click OK, then click OK in the View Properties dialog box to apply the Peters map projection.

12. With the Measure tool, measure the distance between the two cities.

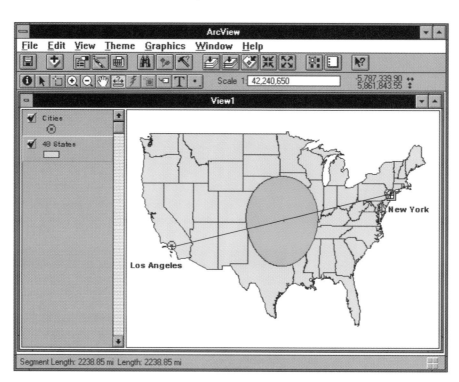

The new measurement (approximately 2,239 miles) is smaller than the original measurement (2,451), by about 212 miles.

The circle is now egg-shaped. The Peters projection preserves accurate area but sacrifices the properties of shape, distance, and direction.

The two previous projections, Peters and Mercator, are most suitable for regions near the equator. Next you'll use a projection that's suitable for the continental United States.

ENVIRONMENTAL SYSTEMS RESEARCH INSTITUTE, INC.

13. From the View menu, choose Properties, then click the Projection button to display the Projection Properties dialog box. Click on the Category down arrow, then select "Projections of the United States."

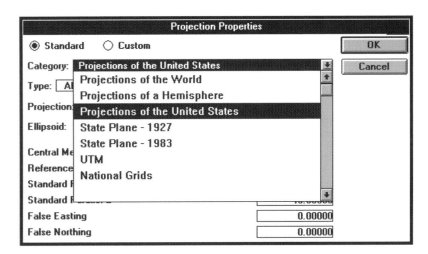

14. Click on the Type down arrow to display a list of projections for the United States, then select "Lambert Conformal Conic (Conterminous U.S.)."

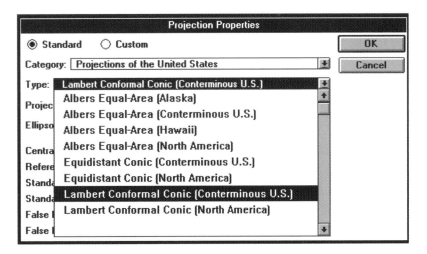

15. Click OK, then click OK in the View Properties dialog box to apply the new projection.

Now you'll measure the distance between Los Angeles and New York again.

16. Click on the Measure tool and measure the distance between Los Angeles and New York.

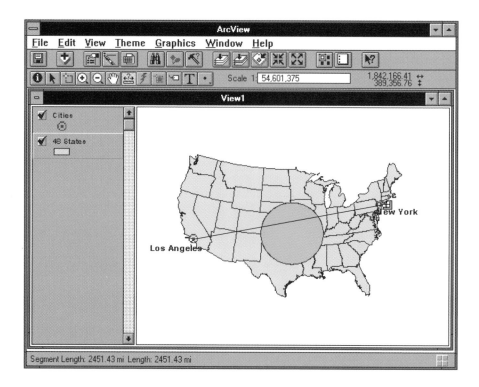

This time, the distance (2,451 miles) is almost the same as the unprojected measurement in step 4.

The ellipse is now a circle. The Lambert Conformal projection preserves shape and maintains accurate distance in the East–West direction for the lower 48 states. However, these qualities are achieved at the expense of direction and area.

ENVIRONMENTAL SYSTEMS RESEARCH INSTITUTE, INC.

With this ArcView demonstration, your students will be able to see how shape and distance change from one projection to another.

Learning more about projections. ArcView provides lists of standard and custom projections. From these lists, you can access more detailed information about any of the projections ArcView supports. For more information, search for these Help Topics: *Standard Projections, Custom Projections, Setting the map projection.* See also *Map Projections: Georeferencing spatial data,* an ESRI publication.

Working with data that's already projected

Much of the data you buy is stored in geographic coordinates, usually decimal degrees. As you've seen in this chapter, you can work with this data without projecting it, or you can apply any of the standard or custom projections ArcView supports. This is the most flexible data.

If you use data from a governmental or international agency, chances are this data is stored in a projection. You can work with this data successfully in ArcView if you remember a few things. First, you can't change the projection of this data or convert it to geographic coordinates (unprojected data). Second, before you can perform measurements on this data or display its scale (see chapter 13), you must go to the View Properties dialog box and specify the units the data is stored in. That's because ArcView has no way of knowing what these units are until you specify them.

Finally, you can't display themes in the same view if they're stored in different projections or use projected data in the same view with data that's not projected. That's because in ArcView, a projection is applied to the entire view, not individual themes. To work with data in different projections successfully, you must store each theme in a separate view.

If you want to go on to the next chapter, leave ArcView running. Otherwise, choose Exit from the File menu.

SECTION 3:
Working with spatial data

Managing scale

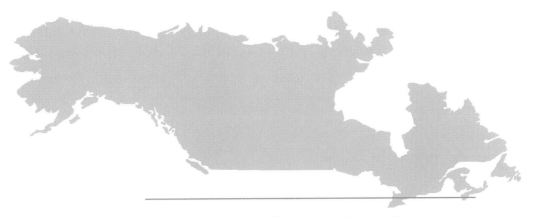

Changing the scale of a view

Setting scale thresholds for themes

Managing scale

Each time you zoom in and out in a view or resize a view's window, its scale automatically changes. ArcView reports the scale in a box located on the right side of the View tool bar. You can set a scale for the view by entering a value in this box. ArcView redraws the view at the new scale. For ArcView to calculate the scale correctly, all you need to do is specify the units the data is stored in.

You can also control the scale at which a theme displays by setting a scale threshold for it. In this way, you can specify that a theme will display only when you zoom in or out to a certain scale. In this chapter you'll learn how to set a scale for a view and how to set scale thresholds for themes.

Changing the scale of a view

Your company is interested in opening a new international sales office in Italy. As the European market analyst for your firm, you've been asked to study potential sites, among them Milano, Genova, Roma, Napoli, and Palermo. After much research, you've concluded that Milano is the best site for the new office. You want to present your arguments to upper management. Some of them aren't familiar with your market region, so you want to use maps at the beginning of your presentation to orient them to the European sales region and the potential sites you considered. Then you want to zoom in on Milano as you describe why it's the best site for the new international sales office. For your presentation, you'll use several of the World data themes that come with ArcView. With these themes and ArcView's zooming tools, you'll create the various scenes for your presentation.

Exercise 13a

1. If necessary, start ArcView. From the File menu, choose Open
    Exercise. In the Exercises scrolling list, select "ex13a," then click
    OK. When the project opens, you see a view of the world from space
    showing the European sales region, the country of Italy, and the
    proposed sites (not distinguishable at this scale).

**During this exercise, don't maximize or resize the view window,
since this alters the view's scale. Your scale values may vary
slightly from those reported, depending on your screen's resolution, font size, and other factors.**

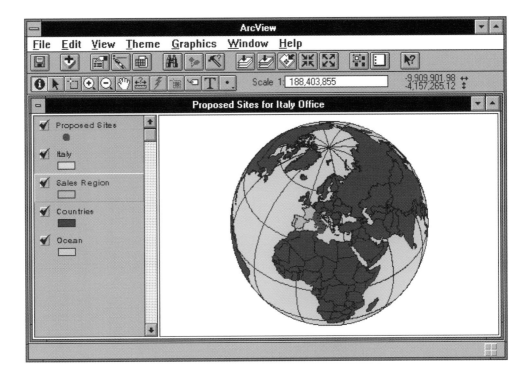

This is the scene you want to show at the beginning of your presentation.
Notice that the Scale box on the right-hand side of the View tool bar
shows a value of 1:188,403,855. This value is the *scale fraction* or *scale*

ratio. It tells the relationship between the size of the area in the view and the size of the same area in the real world.

> **Understanding scale.** The number that ArcView displays in the Scale box describes the relationship between the dimensions of the view and the dimensions of the earth. For example, if the Scale box displays the number 100,000, then one unit of measurement on the view equals 100,000 of the same unit on the earth, or the features you see in the view are 100,000 times smaller than they are in the real world. The scale is commonly expressed as a fraction (1/100,000) or as a ratio (1:100,000). For more information, search for these Help Topics: *Map scale and accuracy, Setting view scale.*

ArcView calculates a view's scale using the current map units. To determine how the map units for this view are set, you'll display the View Properties dialog box.

2.   From the View menu, select Properties. The View Properties dialog box displays.

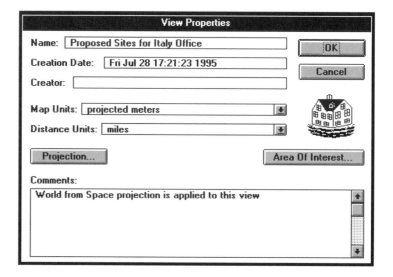

You see that the map units are set to "projected meters" (this means a map projection is applied to the view). The Comments section tells you that the map projection for this view is The World from Space. (See chapter 12 for a discussion of map projections and map units.)

3. Click the Cancel button to dismiss the View Properties dialog box.

For your next scene, you want to show a more detailed view of the European sales region, so you'll zoom in to that theme.

4. With the Sales Region theme active, click the Zoom to Active Themes button. ArcView zooms in so that features in the Sales Region theme fill the view window.

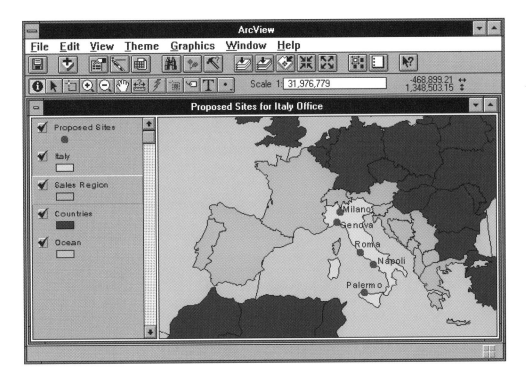

Note that the value in the Scale box changes to 1:31,976,779. This is the scale ArcView calculated based on the size of the view window and the size of the real-world area shown. Notice that the denominator of the scale fraction, 31,976,779, becomes smaller as you zoom in.

For the next scene, you want to zoom in to the Italy theme to look more closely at the proposed office sites.

5.   Make the Italy theme active and click the Zoom to Active Themes button. ArcView zooms so that features in the Italy theme fill the view window. The value in the Scale box changes to 18,407,341.

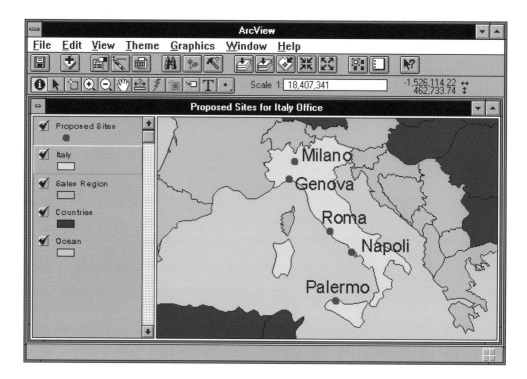

When you present your arguments for siting the new sales office in Milano, you want to show Milano at the center of the view. So, you'll select it, then zoom in to it.

6.   Make the Proposed Sites theme active. Click on the Select Feature tool, then click on the feature (point) that represents Milano. ArcView selects and highlights it.

7. Click the Zoom to Selected button. ArcView pans the view so Milano appears in the center of it. In this case, ArcView doesn't zoom in any further so the scale remains the same.

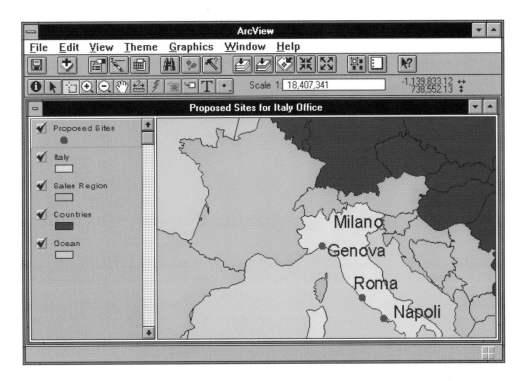

At any time during the presentation you're planning, you may want to return to a view of the entire sales region. You could make the Sales Region theme active, then click the Zoom to Active Themes button. Instead, you'll enter a value in the Scale box.

In step 4, you zoomed in to show all the features in the Sales Region theme. The value in the Scale box was 31,976,779. You'll use this value (rounded off) to set the scale directly.

8. Click in the Scale box, drag the cursor to highlight the current value, then type **32,000,000** and press the Enter key on your keyboard. The view redraws at this scale.

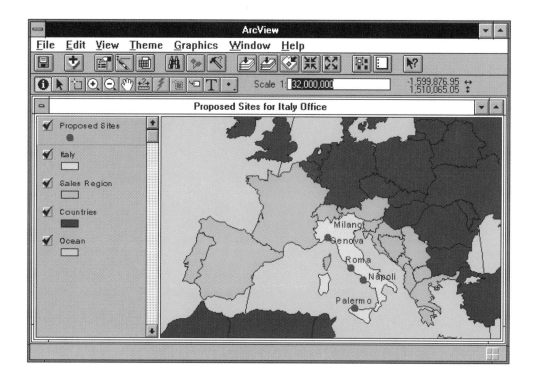

Notice that the view is still centered on Milano, causing part of the Sales Region theme to be cut off. You'll shift the display using the Pan tool.

9. Click on the Pan tool, then move the cursor (now a hand) anywhere over the display. Hold down the mouse button and drag the display (slightly) up and to the left, then release the button. ArcView redraws the view, filling in any blank areas.

ENVIRONMENTAL SYSTEMS RESEARCH INSTITUTE, INC.

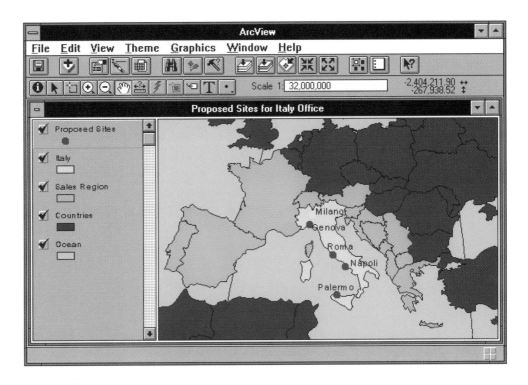

You're ready for your presentation. You've practiced several different ways of zooming in and out and you've set the view scale directly. Your presentation using ArcView's World data and zooming tools will help your audience visualize your sales region and the site you're proposing for the new sales office.

Zooming in and out in a view. ArcView gives you even more ways to zoom in and out. With the Zoom In and Zoom Out *buttons,* you can zoom from the center of the view; with the Zoom In and Zoom Out *tools,* you can zoom from a position or area you define. For more information, search for these Help Topics: *Zooming in and out on a view, Zoom In, Zoom Out, Zoom In tool, Zoom Out tool.*

Setting scale thresholds for themes

With ArcView, you can control the scale at which a theme displays by setting a scale threshold for the theme. When the scale of the view is not within the limits you set, the theme won't display.

Suppose you're a traffic controller for a metropolitan area. You need to display the location of each accident that occurs. In the past, police officers "radioed in" the location and time of each confirmed accident. This information was then relayed to your office and you manually plotted the accidents on a map.

Your agency has been selected to test a new method of registering accidents as they occur. Each time police officers respond to an accident, they use a GPS (Global Positioning System) to record the location of the accident. (A GPS uses the signals sent by satellites to precisely determine a location.) ArcView uses the coordinate information from the GPS to map the accidents as they occur.

Your task is to come up with a way to store all the themes you need in the same view and be able to work with them at different scales. For example, when you examine accidents along city streets, you need to zoom in more than when you examine accidents along major highways. At each scale, you want to display certain themes and not others. To support the different scales you'll be working at, you'll use ArcView's display theme property to set scale thresholds for drawing themes.

Exercise 13b

1. From the File menu, choose Open Exercise. In the Exercises scrolling list, select "ex13b," then click OK. When the project opens, you see a view containing five themes.

ENVIRONMENTAL SYSTEMS RESEARCH INSTITUTE, INC.

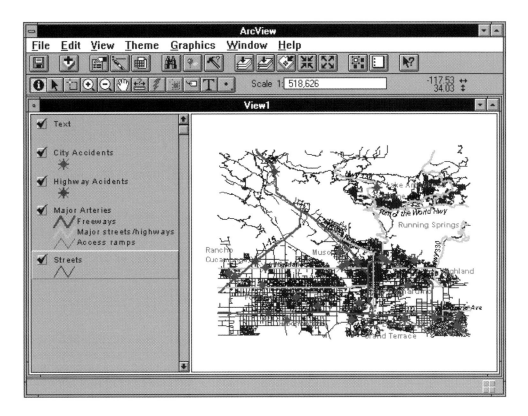

During this exercise, don't maximize or resize the view window, since this alters the view's scale. Your scale values may vary slightly from those reported, depending on your screen's resolution, font size, and other factors.

The Text theme contains the names of towns and major highways; the City Accidents theme contains the locations and times of traffic accidents that occur on city streets; the Highway Accidents theme contains the locations and times of traffic accidents that occur on major highways; the Major Arteries theme contains alternate routes crucial to commuters during rush hour; the Streets theme contains all the city streets for the metropolitan area.

Right away you see that this view is cluttered. At this scale, you can't interpret the information each theme presents without manually turning each theme off and on. To see the highway accidents better, you'll turn some themes off.

2.   Click on the check box for the City Accidents and Streets themes to turn them off.

Now you can easily see where the highway accidents are, which highways they're on, and which cities they're near.

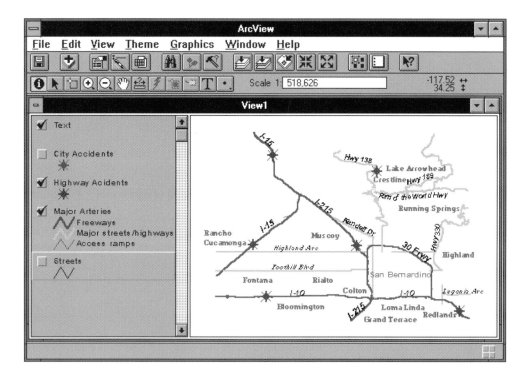

ENVIRONMENTAL SYSTEMS RESEARCH INSTITUTE, INC.

To see the city accidents instead, you'll turn on different themes.

3. Click on the check boxes for the Text, Highway Accidents, and Major Arteries themes to turn them off; do the same for the City Accidents and Streets themes to turn them on.

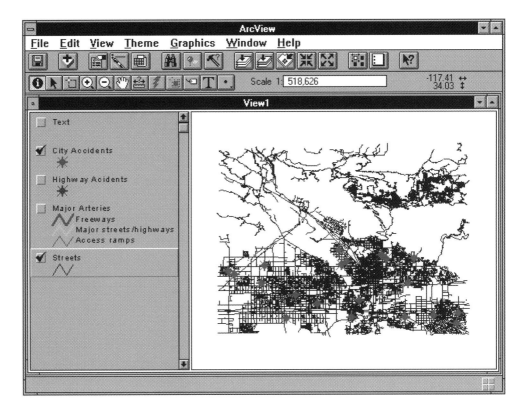

Now you can see the city accidents, but at this scale, you don't clearly see which streets they're on. To zoom in enough to see which street each accident is on, you'd have to click the Zoom In button about six times. Because of the density of the streets, the view takes a long time to draw, so you won't use this method of zooming in. Instead, you'll set a scale directly in the Scale box.

4. Click in the Scale box, drag the cursor to highlight the current value, then change the value to **150,000** and press Enter on your keyboard.

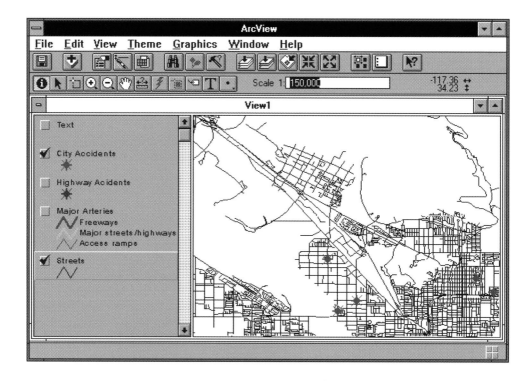

At this scale, you can see the city accidents and the streets they're on. You'll use ArcView's display theme property to set a scale threshold that prevents the streets from drawing until you've zoomed in enough to see them clearly (about 1:150,000 scale).

You'll return to the original view scale.

 5. Click on the check boxes for the themes that are turned off to turn them on, then click the Zoom to Full Extent button. ArcView zooms out so you can see all the features in all the themes.

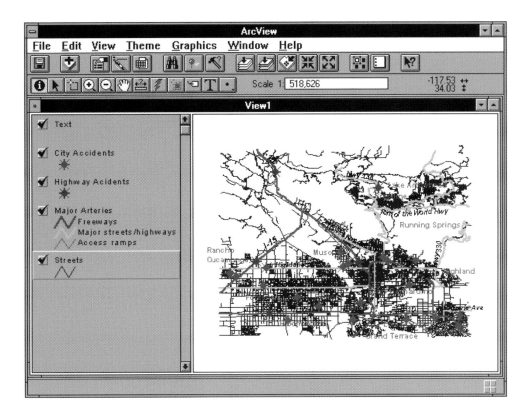

Next you'll set a scale threshold for the Streets theme.

6. With the Streets theme active, select Properties from the Theme menu to display the Theme Properties dialog box.

7. Click on the Display icon along the left margin, then enter **150000** in the Maximum Scale input field. (Don't enter a value in the Minimum Scale input field.)

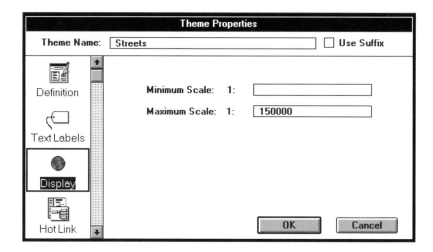

8.   Click OK. Because the value in the Scale box is larger than 150,000, the Streets theme no longer draws in the view, even though it's turned on in the Table of Contents.

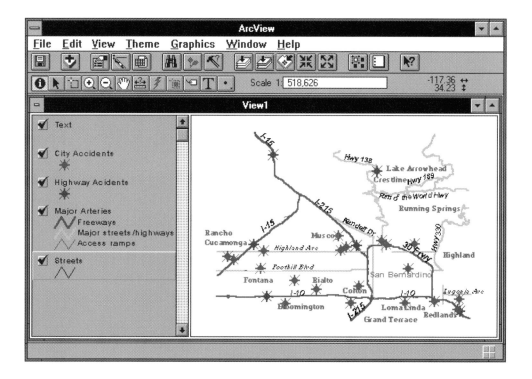

ENVIRONMENTAL SYSTEMS RESEARCH INSTITUTE, INC.

9. Click in the Scale box, drag the cursor to highlight the current value, change the value to **149,999,** then press Enter on your keyboard. When the Scale box contains a value smaller than 150,000, the Streets theme draws.

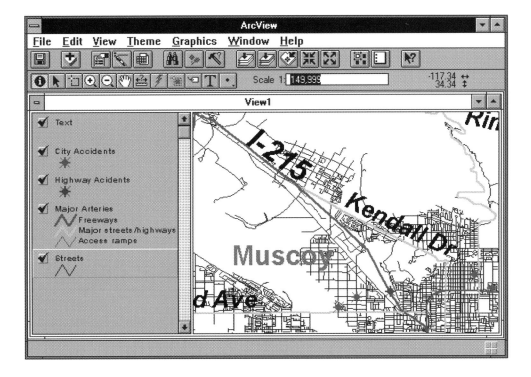

Notice that some of the text labels for the cities and highways cover up accident sites. You don't want them to display when you zoom in to the city streets, so you'll set a scale threshold for the Text theme. First, you'll zoom out again.

10. Click the Zoom to Full Extent button.

11. Make the Text theme active, then select Properties from the Theme menu.

12. Click on the Display icon along the left margin, then enter **150000** in the Minimum Scale input field.

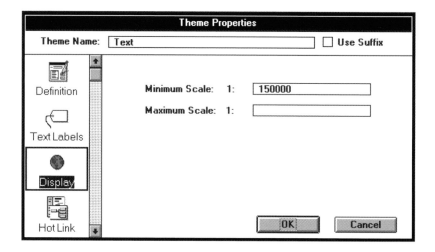

13. Click OK. Now the Text theme won't draw if the value in the scale box is smaller than 150,000.

14. Click in the Scale box, drag the cursor to highlight the current value, enter **149,999,** then press Enter on your keyboard. The Streets theme draws and the Text theme doesn't.

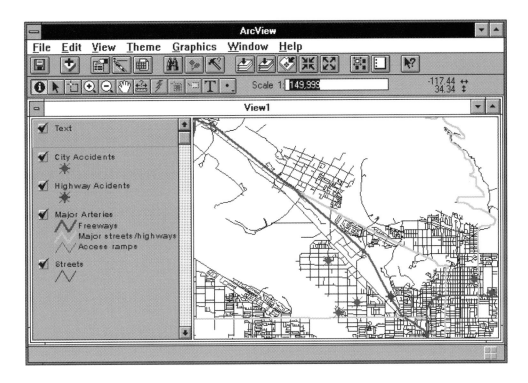

The city accidents are no longer covered up by text and you can see the streets they're on.

Setting maximum and minimum scale thresholds. You can set a range of scales for displaying a theme. For example, if you set a minimum scale threshold of 50,000 and a maximum scale threshold of 100,000, the theme will display only when the value in the Scale box is between these two values. For more information, search for this Help Topic: *Setting a theme's display properties.*

You've completed your task of creating a way to display daily accidents along with other important themes at different scales. Now when you display accidents on major highways, your view won't be cluttered by city streets. Likewise, when you zoom in to see city accidents, they won't be covered up by unnecessary text. By setting scale thresholds for themes, you can display the information you need at the right scale, allowing you to work effectively with a lot of themes in the same view.

If you want to go on to the next chapter, leave ArcView running. Otherwise, choose Exit from the File menu.

ENVIRONMENTAL SYSTEMS RESEARCH INSTITUTE, INC.

SECTION 4

Managing tabular data

The next two chapters introduce you to working with tabular data in ArcView. In chapter 14, you'll learn how to hide fields, assign alias names to fields, add fields, and calculate the values for a new field based on existing fields. You'll also learn how to get statistics for a field and summarize a table based on the values in a particular field. In chapter 15, you'll learn how to add tabular data to an ArcView project, then join or link the data to the theme table, depending on the relationship between records. You'll also learn how to access additional data by setting up hot links.

SECTION 4:
Managing tabular data

Working with fields and records

Modifying fields

Adding fields and calculating values

Analyzing fields and records

Working with fields and records

A valuable feature of ArcView is its ability to store and display attributes linked to map features. ArcView stores attributes as tables made up of fields and records. As you work with tables, you'll want to know how to make fields invisible when you don't need to see them, how to assign new, more descriptive names to fields, and how to widen fields so you can see all the data in them. You'll also want to know how to create new fields and assign values to them.

Modifying fields

Suppose that you work for Consumer Marketing, Inc., a firm that specializes in analyzing consumer behavior and targeting specific markets. You've been hired by a luxury car dealer looking to open a new dealership in Clayton County, Georgia. Your task is to find out if there is a market to support the new dealership. The first thing you'll want to do is use ArcView to analyze the characteristics of people who live in Clayton County. What is their income? Are they married? Do they have children? Do they fit the profile of the luxury car buyer?

Your data contains information about distinctive consumer lifestyles called *segments*. Fifty segments are defined based on consumer characteristics such as income, age, education, and things like the number of vehicles per household. Each segment occupies a field in the attribute table. To tailor the data to this project, first you'll modify it.

ENVIRONMENTAL SYSTEMS RESEARCH INSTITUTE, INC.

Exercise 14a

1. If necessary, start ArcView. From the File menu, choose Open Exercise. In the Exercises scrolling list, select "ex14a," then click OK. When the project opens, you see a view with one active theme, Clayton.shp. This theme shows the census tract boundaries for Clayton County.

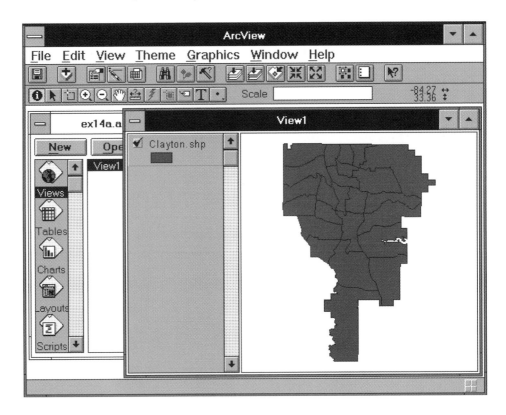

2. Open the attribute table for the Clayton.shp theme by clicking the Open Table button on the View button bar.

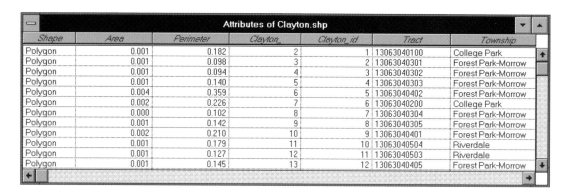

Shape	Area	Perimeter	Clayton_	Clayton_id	Tract	Township
Polygon	0.001	0.182	2	1	13063040100	College Park
Polygon	0.001	0.098	3	2	13063040301	Forest Park-Morrow
Polygon	0.001	0.094	4	3	13063040302	Forest Park-Morrow
Polygon	0.001	0.140	5	4	13063040303	Forest Park-Morrow
Polygon	0.004	0.359	6	5	13063040402	Forest Park-Morrow
Polygon	0.002	0.226	7	6	13063040200	College Park
Polygon	0.000	0.102	8	7	13063040304	Forest Park-Morrow
Polygon	0.001	0.142	9	8	13063040305	Forest Park-Morrow
Polygon	0.002	0.210	10	9	13063040401	Forest Park-Morrow
Polygon	0.001	0.179	11	10	13063040504	Riverdale
Polygon	0.001	0.127	12	11	13063040503	Riverdale
Polygon	0.001	0.145	13	12	13063040405	Forest Park-Morrow

Examine the fields in the table by scrolling to the right. Each record corresponds to a different census tract and each field contains a different attribute. By default, all fields in the table are visible but you may not be interested in all of them. For example, the Shape, Area, Perimeter, (Theme name)_, and (Theme name)_id fields are standard to all shapefiles, but may not contain information that's useful in your analysis. You'll hide these fields so they don't appear in the table.

3. With the table document active, select Properties from the Table menu.

The Table Properties dialog box displays with a list of field names and a column indicating which fields in the table are visible.

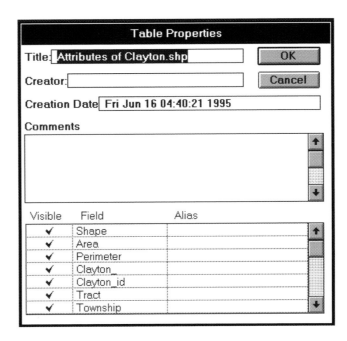

4. Click on the check mark next to the following fields to turn them off and make them invisible: Shape, Area, Perimeter, Clayton_, and Clayton_id. The check marks for these fields disappear.

The table also contains 50 fields of consumer lifestyle data. The name of each field starts with *Hh_seg* followed by a number (from 1 to 50) for each lifestyle segment. Two of the fields, *Hh_seg2* and *Hh_seg3*, represent consumers whose income, age, education, and other characteristics match the customer profile of a luxury car buyer. The data dictionary that comes with the data describes these fields as "Lap of Luxury" and "Established Wealth," respectively.

You can also use the Table Properties dialog box to assign a more descriptive name, or *alias*, to any field. ArcView then uses the alias instead of the field name when displaying the table.

5. Scroll down in the Field list until you find the Hh_seg2 and Hh_seg3 fields. Click in the Alias column to the right of Hh_seg2 and type the words **Lap of Luxury.** Then click in the Alias column beside Hh_seg3 and type the words **Established Wealth.**

6. Click OK. Now Lap of Luxury and Established Wealth appear as field names in the table. (You may have to scroll to the right to see them.)

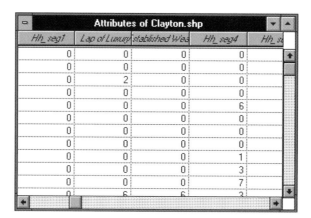

ENVIRONMENTAL SYSTEMS RESEARCH INSTITUTE, INC.

Notice that you can't see the complete field names, *Lap of Luxury* and *Established Wealth,* because the fields are too narrow. You'll widen them in the table.

7. Position the cursor over the field divider (the vertical line to the right of the field name) until it becomes a two-headed arrow, then drag to the right to widen the field.

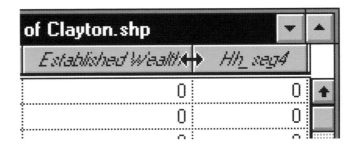

When you resize a field, the new size is saved when you close the table or the project that contains it. The next time you open the table, ArcView displays the field at the saved size.

By hiding fields, assigning aliases, and widening fields, you've tailored the data to your project. Next you'll add a new field to the table.

If you want to go on to the next exercise, leave the project open.

Adding fields and calculating values

The Lap of Luxury and Established Wealth fields contain households that match the profile of a luxury car buyer. You want to know how many potential luxury car buyers live in Clayton County, so you'll use ArcView's Calculate function to add these fields together and place the values in a new field. First, you'll add the new field.

Exercise 14b

1. If *ex14a.apr* is open, continue. Otherwise, choose Open Exercise from the File menu. In the Exercises scrolling list, select "ex14b," then click OK. The Clayton.shp theme is active and its attribute table open.

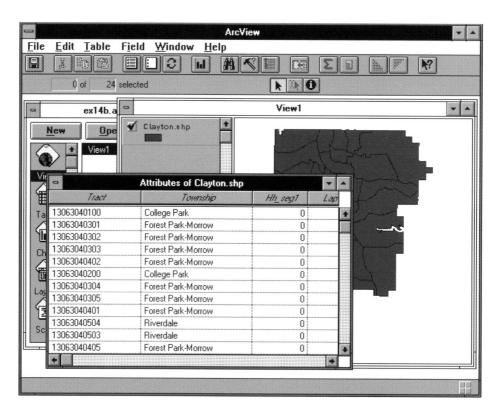

Before you add a field to the attribute table, you must enable editing.

2. With the Attributes of Clayton.shp table active, select Start Editing from the Table menu. Notice that the field names in the table become non-italic when editing is enabled.

3. Select Add Field in the Edit menu. This displays the Field Definition dialog box, where you define the field you want to add. In the Name field type **Luxury and Wealth.** The default values for Type, Width, and Decimal Places are correct.

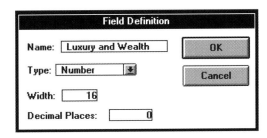

4. Click OK. The Attributes of Clayton.shp table automatically scrolls all the way to the right to display the new field, which is active.

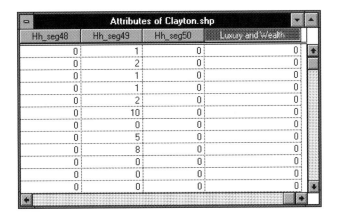

Now you'll calculate the values for this field.

5. Click the Calculate button to display the Field Calculator dialog box. This is where you define the mathematical expression that ArcView will use to calculate values for the active field.

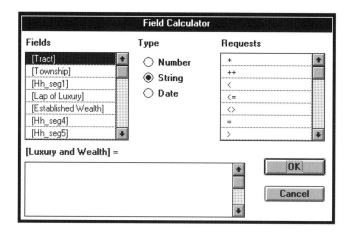

You want to know the total number of households in the Lap of Luxury and Established Wealth fields.

6. In the Fields list, double-click on "[Lap of Luxury]," then in the Requests list, double-click on the "+" sign. Finally, in the Fields list, double-click on "[Established Wealth]." Your mathematical expression displays in the text box (lower left) as you define it.

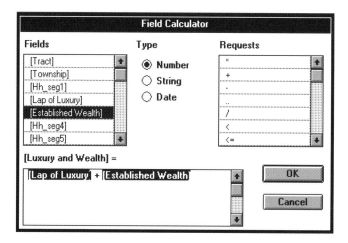

7. Click OK. ArcView uses this expression to calculate the values for the new field, Luxury and Wealth.

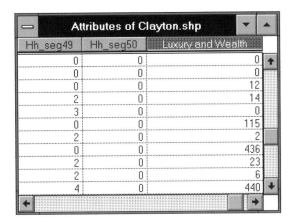

8. Scroll down in the table to see the calculated values. This field represents consumers who are most likely to buy luxury cars. In the next exercise, you'll analyze the information in this field.

Because you have no more edits to make to the table, you'll end your editing session.

9. Choose Stop Editing from the Table menu.

If you want to go on to the next exercise, leave the project open.

Analyzing fields and records

The Luxury and Wealth field represents consumers most likely to buy luxury cars in each census tract in Clayton County. You'll use ArcView's Statistics function to determine the total number of households in this field, then the Summarize function to see how they're distributed in the townships of Clayton County.

Exercise 14c

1. If *ex14b.apr* is open, continue. Otherwise, choose Open Exercise from the File menu. In the Exercises scrolling list, select "ex14c," then click OK.

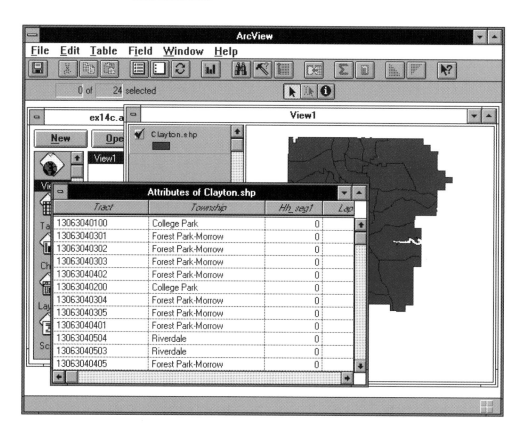

ENVIRONMENTAL SYSTEMS RESEARCH INSTITUTE, INC.

2.   With the Attributes of Clayton.shp table active, click on the Luxury
and Wealth field to make it active.

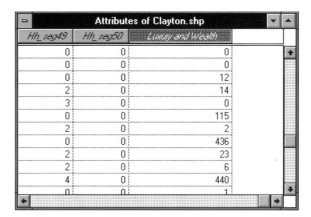

3.   Choose Statistics from the Field menu. ArcView displays a box containing statistics for the Luxury and Wealth field's values.

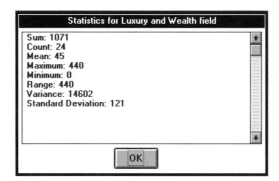

Notice that there are a total of 1,071 households in the Luxury and
Wealth field, representing potential luxury car buyers in Clayton County.

4.   Review this information, then click OK to dismiss the Statistics window.

Your luxury car dealer client is more familiar with townships than with
census tracts, so you'll use Summarize to determine how these potential
luxury car buyers are distributed in the four townships of Clayton County.

Summarizing a table. You can summarize an entire table based on the values in a particular active field. ArcView creates a new table with one record for each unique value of the active field. Each record contains a count showing how many records in the original table have this value. Each record also contains the result of any summary statistics you request for any other field in the original table. For more information, search for these Help Topics: *Summarizing a table, Summarize.*

5. In the Attributes of Clayton.shp table, click on the Township field name to make it active. ArcView will create a new table with one record for each unique value in this field.

6. From the Field menu, select Summarize. The Summary Table Definition dialog box displays.

7. From the upper drop-down list (Field), select "Luxury and Wealth." From the lower drop-down list (Summarize by), select "Sum." Then click the Add button. This adds your selection to the Summary statistics box on the right. Click the Save As button to navigate to the *drive:\directory* where you want to save the new table ArcView creates and call it **luxsum.dbf.**

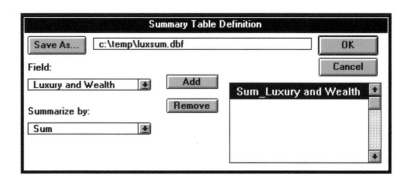

ArcView adds the new table to your project.

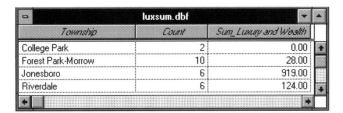

Township	Count	Sum_Luxury and Wealth
College Park	2	0.00
Forest Park-Morrow	10	28.00
Jonesboro	6	919.00
Riverdale	6	124.00

The Count field shows the number of census tracts in each township; the Sum_Luxury and Wealth field shows the total number of households in each township. You can see that Jonesboro Township contains the greatest number of households characterized as potential luxury car buyers.

Now you know which township can best support a luxury car dealership. You might want to present this information to your client as a chart or a map. To show the distribution of potential luxury car buyers by township on a map, you could *join* the summary table, luxsum.dbf, to the Attributes of Clayton.shp table based on the common field, Township. Once the tables are joined, you can use the Legend Editor to display the Clayton.shp theme based on the Sum_Luxury and Wealth field (now a field in the attribute table). You'll learn how to join tables in the next chapter.

If you want to go on to the next chapter, leave ArcView running. Otherwise, choose Exit from the File menu.

ENVIRONMENTAL SYSTEMS RESEARCH INSTITUTE, INC.

SECTION 4:
Managing tabular data

Accessing tables and other data

Joining tables

Linking tables

Defining hot links

Accessing tables and other data

A theme attribute table contains records, one for each feature, and fields, one for each attribute. While the number of possible attributes for a theme is unlimited, it isn't efficient to store all of them in the theme table. Instead, you can store them in separate tables, then *join* or *link* them to the theme table when you need to.

Whether you use Join or Link depends on the relationship between records in the theme table and the other table (one-to-one or many-to-one). In either case, once a table is joined or linked to the theme table, you can work with it as if it were part of the theme table. All that's required to perform either a join or a link is a field that's common to both tables.

To access data that's pertinent to a particular feature in a theme, rather than the entire theme, you can use ArcView's *hot link* function. This function allows you to link a text file, image, document (i.e., view, table, chart, layout), or another project to a feature, then display it by clicking on the feature with the Hot Link tool.

Joining tables

Suppose you're a staff writer for a monthly magazine about California. You've just been assigned to write a feature article on the best counties to live in. You hope this means lots of travel and visits to the best spots in California, like Marin and Klamath. But your editor wants county-by-county rankings, based on hard data and geographic analysis. It looks like you'll be spending the next few weeks at your desk—but at least you've got ArcView.

Exercise 15a

1. If necessary, start ArcView. From the File menu, choose Open
    Exercise. In the Exercises scrolling list, select "ex15a," then click
    OK. When the project opens, you see a view of the state of
    California with county boundaries.

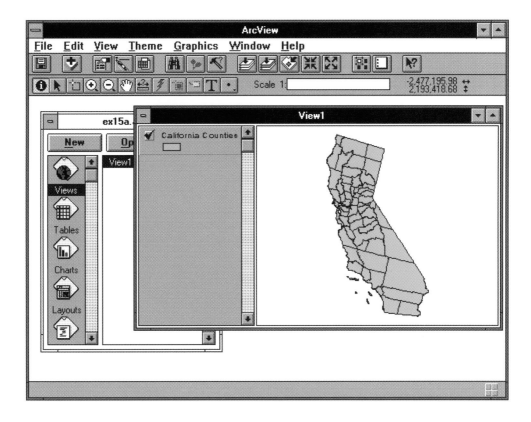

To begin your analysis, you'll evaluate two criteria, economic status and
recreational opportunities. Your data includes a table of per capita
income values (by county) and a table containing the names of recreation
areas (such as national parks) in each county. You want to create two displays, one showing the counties according to per capita income, the other
showing the counties based on the number of recreation areas they contain.

To begin, you'll copy the California Counties theme to a new view.

2. With View1 and the California Counties theme active, select Copy Themes from the Edit menu. The theme is copied to the clipboard, ready to be pasted into a new view.

3. Make the Project window active and select the Views icon. Click the New button to create a new (empty) view, then select Paste from the Edit menu. The California Counties theme is pasted into View2 and ArcView draws the theme.

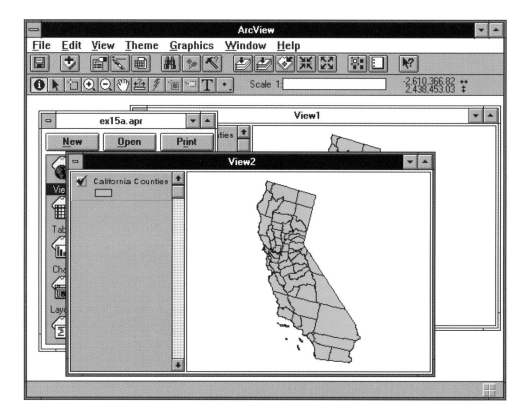

Now you have two views containing the California Counties theme. In this exercise, you'll use View1 to display the counties according to per capita income. In the next exercise, you'll use View2 to display the counties according to the number of recreation areas each county contains.

4. Close View2. Make View1 active, then click the Open Theme Table button to display the theme table.

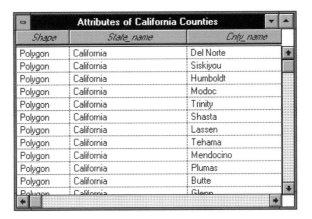

You'll add a table containing per capita income data to the project, then join it to the theme table. Then you'll be able to display the counties based on per capita income.

5. Make the Project window active. With the Tables icon selected, click the Add button to display the Add Table dialog box.

6. In the dialog box, select your CD–ROM drive (or the drive where you installed the data for this book), then navigate to *\gtkav\data\ch15* in the Directories list. Click on the "income.dbf" file to select it.

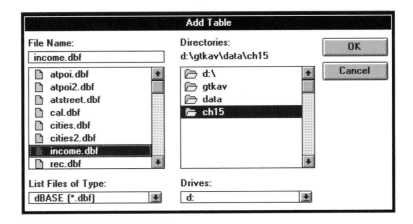

7. Click OK to add the income.dbf table to your project.

When it opens, you see that the last field contains per capita income values for each county. The Cnty_name field contains the same data as the Cnty_name field in the theme table. You'll use this field to join the two tables.

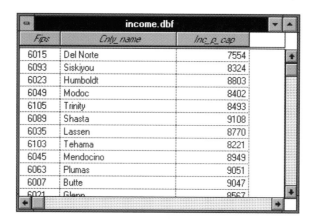

Fips	Cnty_name	Inc_p_cap
6015	Del Norte	7554
6093	Siskiyou	8324
6023	Humboldt	8803
6049	Modoc	8402
6105	Trinity	8493
6089	Shasta	9108
6035	Lassen	8770
6103	Tehama	8221
6045	Mendocino	8949
6063	Plumas	9051
6007	Butte	9047
6021	Glenn	8557

Joining tables. Joining tables lets you attach your tabular data to the themes in a view. In this exercise, when you join the data in the income.dbf table to the data in the theme table, *income.dbf* is the source table and the theme table is the destination table (the table to which fields are appended). Tables are joined based on a field that is common to both tables, in this case, *Cnty_name*. The name of the field doesn't have to be the same in both tables; only the values must be the same. For more information, search for these Help Topics: *Joining tables, Join.*

ENVIRONMENTAL SYSTEMS RESEARCH INSTITUTE, INC.

To see both tables during the join, you'll reposition them.

8. Move the income.dbf table to the upper left corner of the ArcView window, then click on the Cnty_name field to make it active.

9. Now make the theme table (Attributes of California Counties) active, move it to the lower right corner of the ArcView window, then click on the Cnty_name field to make it active.

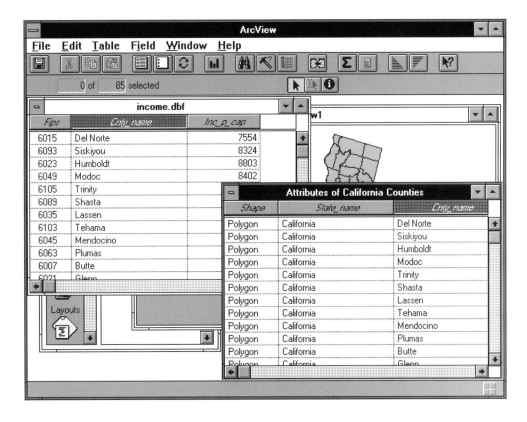

10. Click the Join button. ArcView appends the fields in the income.dbf table to the theme table and closes the income.dbf table.

Records in the theme table have a *one-to-one* relationship to records in the income.dbf table. That is, for each county in the theme table, there is only one per capita income value.

11. Scroll to the right in the theme table and notice that it now contains fields from the income.dbf table.

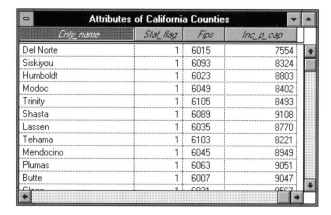

Attributes of California Counties			
Cnty_name	*Stat_flag*	*Fips*	*Inc_p_cap*
Del Norte	1	6015	7554
Siskiyou	1	6093	8324
Humboldt	1	6023	8803
Modoc	1	6049	8402
Trinity	1	6105	8493
Shasta	1	6089	9108
Lassen	1	6035	8770
Tehama	1	6103	8221
Mendocino	1	6045	8949
Plumas	1	6063	9051
Butte	1	6007	9047

Now you can display the counties based on the joined data. First you'll classify it.

12. Close the theme table, then with View1 active, double-click on the theme name in the Table of Contents to open the Legend Editor. (You may want to move the Legend Editor so it doesn't obscure the view.)

13. In the Legend Editor, select "Inc_p_cap" from the Field drop-down list. By default, ArcView groups the values in this field into five classes using the quantile method (see chapter 9) and assigns a symbol to each class using a white-to-black color ramp. You'll change the colors.

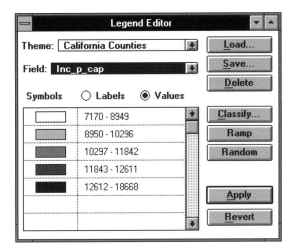

 14. Double-click on the white symbol to open the Symbol Palette, then click the Color button at the top of the window to display the Color Palette. In the Color Palette, choose a light blue color square. The symbol changes in the Legend Editor.

15. In the Legend Editor, click on the black symbol, then in the Color Palette choose a dark purple color square. Close the Color Palette.

16. In the Legend Editor, click the Ramp button. The color symbols are now graded from light blue to dark purple. Apply your changes to create the new legend, then close the Legend Editor.

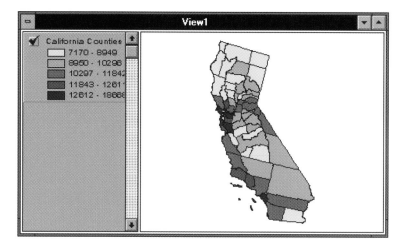

The view shows the counties of California classified according to per capita income, but part of the legend is hidden. You'll widen the Table of Contents, then change the name of the view to reflect what it shows.

17. Move the cursor over the border between the Table of Contents and the display area (the cursor changes to a two-headed arrow), then drag to the right to widen the Table of Contents.

18. Select Properties from the View menu to open the View Properties dialog box. In the Name text box, change **View1** to **Income per Capita.**

ENVIRONMENTAL SYSTEMS RESEARCH INSTITUTE, INC.

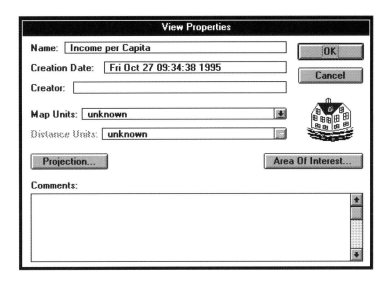

19. Click OK to apply the new name to the view.

The counties with the highest per capita income are symbolized in dark purple. To identify a few of them, you can use the Identify tool.

 20. With the Identify tool selected, click on a county to display its attributes in the Identify Results dialog box. Notice the county's name, then compare its Inc_p_cap value to the theme's legend. When you're finished, close the Identify Results box.

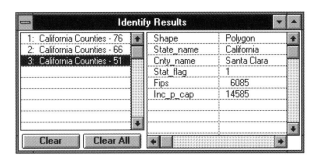

Linking tables

In the last exercise, you used Join to relate each county to an income value. Now you want to relate each county to the recreation areas it contains. You'll add another table to the project containing recreation areas by county. Because many of the counties have more than one recreation area, there's a *one-to-many* relationship between records in the theme table and records in the recreation table. When this type of relationship exists between records, you use Link instead of Join to relate them.

Exercise 15b

1. From the File menu, choose Open Exercise. In the Exercises scrolling list, select "ex15b," then click OK. When the project opens, you see the Income per Capita view.

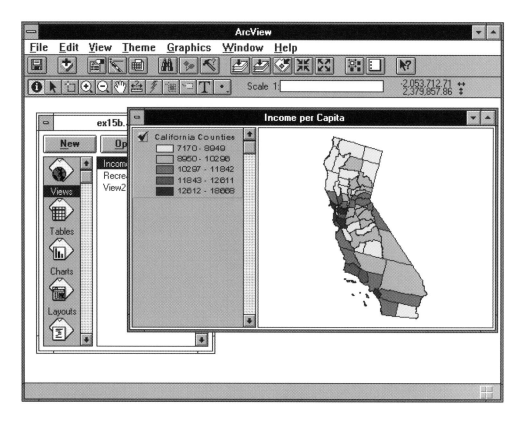

ENVIRONMENTAL SYSTEMS RESEARCH INSTITUTE, INC.

You'll use View2 to show the distribution of recreation areas.

2. Close the Income per Capita view. In the Project window, with the Views icon selected, click on "View2" in the list, then click the Open button. (A Recreational Resources view appears in the list. You'll open it at the end of this exercise.)

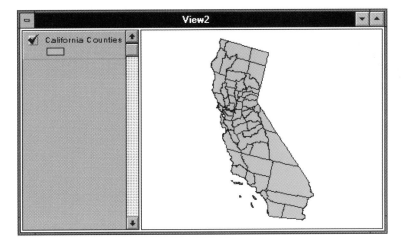

Next you'll add the recreation table to the project, then link it to the theme table.

3. Click the Open Theme Table button to open the theme table.

4. Make the Project window active. With the Tables icon selected, click
    the Add button. In the Add Table dialog box, select your CD–ROM
    drive (or the drive where you loaded the data for this book), then find
    \gtkav\data\ch15 in the Directories list. Click on "rec.dbf" to select
    it, then click OK to add it to your project.

Cnty_name	Feature	Type
Plumas	Almanor, Lake	reservoir
Santa Clara	Anderson Lake	reservoir
Los Angeles	Angeles National Forest	forest
San Bernardino	Arrowhead, Lake	lake
San Diego	Barrett Lake	reservoir
Madera	Bass Lake	reservoir
San Diego	Batiquitos Lagoon	lake
Napa	Berryessa, Lake	lake
San Bernardino	Big Bear Lake	reservoir
Los Angeles	Big Dalton Reservoir	reservoir
Humboldt	Big Lagoon	lake
Shasta	Big Lake	lake

When the table opens, you see three fields. The Feature field lists the
major recreation areas (e.g., national parks, national forests, lakes) in
California; the Type field tells you what type of recreation area each one
is. Because some counties have more than one recreation area, they
appear more than once in the Cnty_name field. This field and the
Cnty_name field in the theme table contain the same data (county
names), so you'll use them to link the two tables.

Linking tables. Unlike joining, linking simply links records in the
source table to those in the destination table. In the current
example, the recreation table (source table) has a field that contains the name of each recreation area. You can link this table to
the theme table (destination table) using the county name field.
Then, when you select a county in the theme table (or in the
view), all of the recreation areas in that county are selected in
the recreation table. For more information, search for these Help
Topics: *Linking tables, Link.*

5. Move the rec.dbf table to the lower right corner of the ArcView window. Click on the Cnty_name field to make it active.

6. Make the California Counties theme table active, move it to the upper left corner of the ArcView window, then click on the Cnty_name field to make it active.

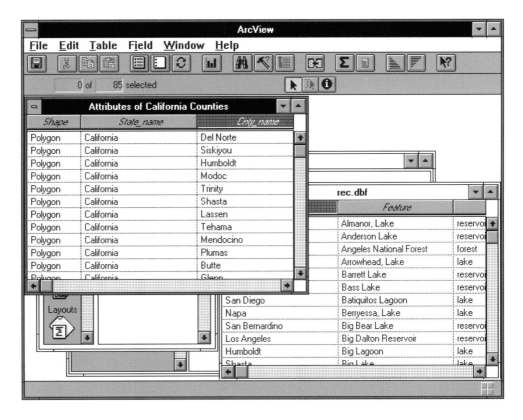

The relationship between each record in the theme table and the records in the rec.dbf table is *one-to-many*. This means that for each county in the theme table, there may be zero, one, or *many* recreation areas. If you were to use Join, ArcView would find the first recreation area belonging to each county, ignoring any additional recreation areas. To preserve the one-to-many relationship between records in the two tables, you'll use Link instead.

7. From the Table menu, select Link. A one-way link is established from the theme table to the rec.dbf table.

8. In the theme table, click on the record for Modoc County (it's the fourth from the top). All Modoc County records are selected in the rec.dbf table.

9. Make the rec.dbf table active, then click the Promote button to move the selected records to the top of the table.

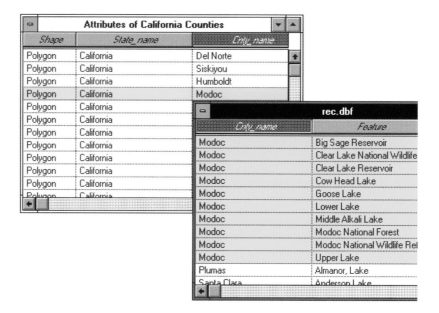

You see a list of recreation areas located in Modoc County.

To display the counties based on the number of recreation areas, you would need to perform some additional steps. First, you would summarize the rec.dbf table based on the Cnty_name field. This would create a new table with a "Count" field containing the number of recreation areas for each county. (For a review of the Summarize function, see chapter 14.)

Next you would use Join to append the summary table (source table) to the theme table (destination table), using the Cnty_name field as the common field. (For a review of the Join operation, see exercise 15a in this chapter.) After the tables are joined, you would use the Legend Editor to display the counties based on the values in the Count field (see steps 13–16 in exercise 15a). The resulting view would show the counties according to the number of recreation areas in each.

Now you'll open a view in which the above steps have already been performed.

10. Close the two open tables, Attributes of California Counties and rec.dbf, then close View2.

11. In the Project window, select the Views icon. Click on the "Recreational Resources" view, then click the Open button. When the view opens, you see the counties of California classified according to the number of recreation areas per county.

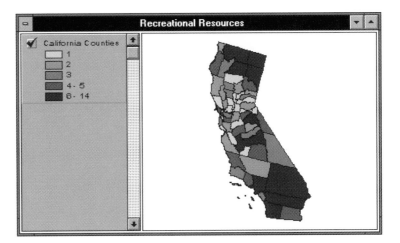

Next you'll display the Income per Capita view along with the Recreational Resources view.

12. Make the Project window active. With the Views icon selected, click on the "Income per Capita" view, then click the Open button.

Now that both views are open, you'll display them side by side. First you'll minimize the Project window.

13. With the Project window active, click on the minimize icon (down arrow) in the upper right corner of the window, then choose Tile from the Window menu. ArcView tiles the two open views.

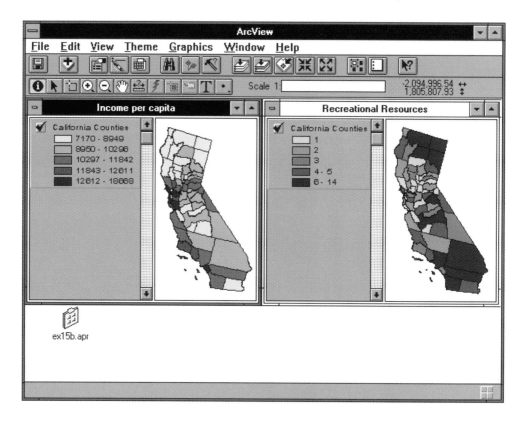

14. Double-click on the Project window icon to restore the Project window. (When the Project window is minimized, you don't have access to the File menu and can't proceed to the next exercise.)

You're part way to your goal of finding the best counties to live in California. You've evaluated two criteria, income and recreation. You can evaluate additional criteria (e.g., educational opportunities, employment, housing prices) by joining or linking different tables of attributes to the theme table and mapping these attributes.

Defining hot links

With ArcView's *hot link* feature, you can access a text file, display an image, open an ArcView document (view, table, chart, layout) or project, or run a program simply by clicking on a feature in a view. To define a hot link, you add a field to the theme's attribute table. In this field, you specify the name and location of the text file, image, document, project, or program you want to access when you click on the feature. Next, you use Hot Link Theme Properties to specify the name of this field and the type of action you want ArcView to perform (e.g., display a file, open a project). Now when you click on the feature using the Hot Link tool, ArcView accesses the specified data and performs the specified action automatically.

Suppose you work in the GIS department of an Atlanta-based firm with offices around the United States. The president of your company has asked you to develop a presentation to show to visitors from other offices (and other companies) to familiarize them with the city of Atlanta and some of its points of interest. You decide to use a series of maps and photographs, along with ArcView's hot link feature, to create the presentation.

Exercise 15c

1. From the File menu, choose Open Exercise. In the Exercises scroll-
    ing list, select "ex15c," then click OK.

The view shows a map of the United States and the cities where your
company has offices. Atlanta, the headquarters, is circled in yellow. The
Cities theme is active.

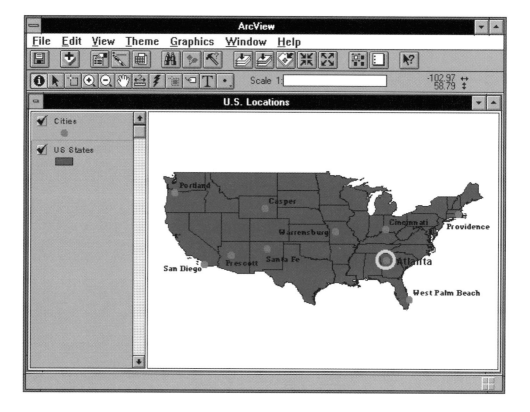

ENVIRONMENTAL SYSTEMS RESEARCH INSTITUTE, INC.

2. From the Window menu, choose *ex15c.apr* to make the Project window active.

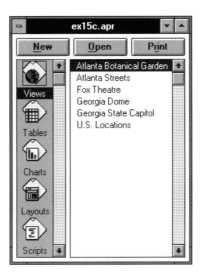

In addition to the view that's already open, the project contains a number of other views, including one of Atlanta Streets. You want to create a hot link that opens the Atlanta Streets view when you click on the feature representing Atlanta in the U.S. Locations view.

3. With the U.S. Locations view and the Cities theme active, click the Open Theme Table button to open the theme table.

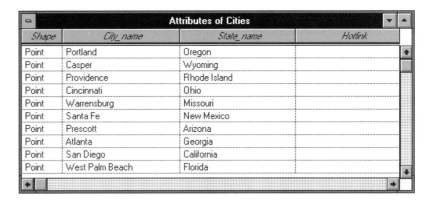

A field called *Hotlink* is already added to this table. You'll use this field to specify the name of the view (Atlanta Streets) you want to hot link to the Atlanta feature. First, you must enable editing.

4.   From the Table menu, choose Start Editing. The field names become non-italic, indicating that the table is now editable.

5.   Click on the Edit tool on the Table tool bar. In the Hotlink field, click in the cell for the Atlanta record (third from the bottom) and type **Atlanta Streets.** Press Enter on the keyboard to commit your edit, then choose Stop Editing from the Table menu.

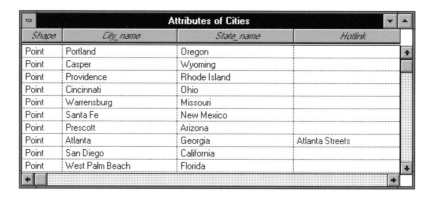

Shape	City_name	State_name	Hotlink
Point	Portland	Oregon	
Point	Casper	Wyoming	
Point	Providence	Rhode Island	
Point	Cincinnati	Ohio	
Point	Warrensburg	Missouri	
Point	Santa Fe	New Mexico	
Point	Prescott	Arizona	
Point	Atlanta	Georgia	Atlanta Streets
Point	San Diego	California	
Point	West Palm Beach	Florida	

Attributes of Cities

6.   Close the theme table.

Next you'll set the properties for the hot link.

Understanding hot link theme properties. The Hot Link Theme Properties dialog box is where you specify what happens when you click on a feature in a theme with the Hot Link tool. ArcView uses a value you specify in the theme's attribute table as input to perform an action. The available actions are: display a text file, display an image, open a document (must exist in the current project), open another project (ArcView imports the project into the current project), or run a program (script). In this example, the action is to open a view, and the value is the name of the view. For more information, search for these Help Topics: *Hot Link Theme Property, Defining a hot link property for a theme.*

7. From the Theme menu, select Properties to open the Theme Properties dialog box. Click on the Hot Link icon (along the left margin) to display the hot link property options.

8. In the Field drop-down list, choose "Hotlink." This specifies the field in the theme table that contains the name of the view to hot link. In the Predefined Action drop-down list, choose "Link to Document" (in this case, the document is a view). A script (program) with the instructions ArcView needs to open the view is automatically selected.

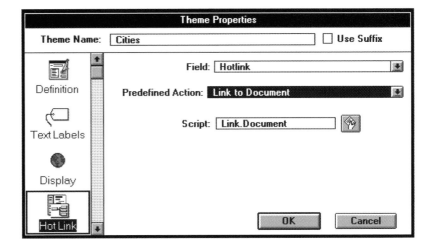

9. Click OK to set the hot link properties.

Now you'll test the hot link you just defined.

10. Click on the Hot Link tool. The cursor changes to a lightning bolt as you move it over the view. Place the lightning bolt on the city of Atlanta feature and click. The Atlanta Streets view opens.

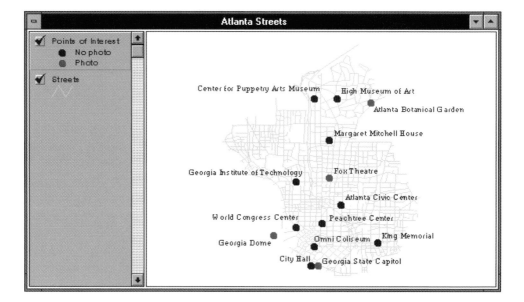

The Atlanta Streets view displays the streets of Atlanta and local points of interest. You want to be able to click on a point of interest and display a scanned photograph of it. Three points of interest (Fox Theatre, Georgia Dome, and Georgia State Capitol) already have hot links defined. You'll add a hot link that links the Atlanta Botanical Garden point of interest to a photograph of it.

11. With the Atlanta Streets view and the Points of Interest theme active, click the Open Theme Table button to open the Attributes of Points of Interest table.

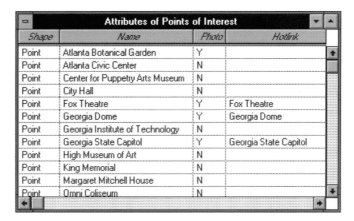

The Hotlink field contains the names of views that contain photographs of specified points of interest. You'll add the name of a view that contains a photo of the Atlanta Botanical Garden to this field. First, you'll enable editing.

12. From the Table menu, choose Start Editing, then click on the Edit tool.

13. In the Hotlink field, click in the cell for the Atlanta Botanical Garden record (first record) and type **Atlanta Botanical Garden** (the name of the view that contains a photograph of this point of interest), then press Enter on the keyboard.

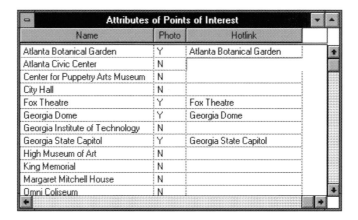

14. From the Table menu, choose Stop Editing, then close the theme table.

15. With the Atlanta Streets view and the Points of Interest theme active, select Properties from the Theme menu to open the Theme Properties dialog box.

16. Click on the Hot Link icon. In the Field list, select "Hotlink" as the field containing the name of the view to hot link. In the Predefined Action list, select "Link to Document." A script (program) with the instructions ArcView needs to open the view is automatically selected.

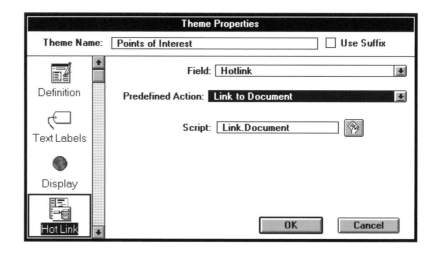

17. Click OK to set the hot link properties.

You're ready to test your hot link.

18. Select the Hot Link tool, place the cursor (now a lightning bolt) on the Atlanta Botanical Garden point of interest, and click. A view opens displaying a scanned photograph of the feature you selected.

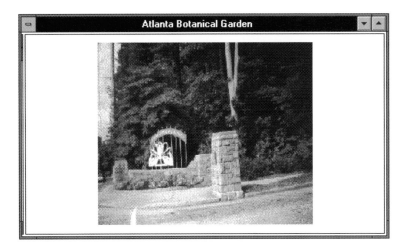

To see scanned photos of other features, you'll use the Hot Link tool again.

19. Close the Atlanta Botanical Garden view, then click on another red point of interest with the Hot Link tool. A photograph of the feature you click on displays in a view window.

To complete your presentation, you can add more hot links until all the points of interest have photos linked to them. Then you'll have a presentation that your company can use to familiarize visitors with Atlanta and its points of interest.

If you want to go on to the next chapter, leave ArcView running. Otherwise, choose Exit from the File menu.

SECTION 5

Analyzing spatial relationships

In the next four chapters you'll learn how to analyze features based on where they're located in relation to other features. In chapters 16, 17, and 18, you'll use theme-on-theme selection to find features that are nearby, adjacent to, inside, or intersecting other features in the same theme or in different themes. In chapter 19, you'll use spatial join to append the attributes of features in one theme to features in another theme based on their locations.

SECTION 5:
Analyzing spatial relationships

Finding the
features nearby

Finding points near lines
Finding points near other points
Finding adjacent features

Finding the features nearby

When you analyze the relationships between map features, you might need to know which features are within a certain distance of other features or are adjacent to other features. ArcView uses *theme-on-theme selection* to analyze the locations of features in relation to other features, whether in the same theme or in different themes. In this chapter, you'll focus on two types of feature relationships, *proximity* (the distance between features) and *adjacency* (features that share the same boundary).

Finding points near lines

Suppose you're interested in buying a gas station near Interstate 40 in Old Town, New Mexico. One of your requirements is that it must be within 1,000 feet of the interstate so you can attract as many of the freeway drivers as possible. Using ArcView's theme-on-theme selection, you can find out which gas stations meet your criteria.

Exercise 16a

1. If necessary, start ArcView. From the File menu, choose Open Exercise. In the Exercises scrolling list, select "ex16a," then click OK. When the project opens, you see a view with two themes: a line theme, Streets, and a point theme, Stations.

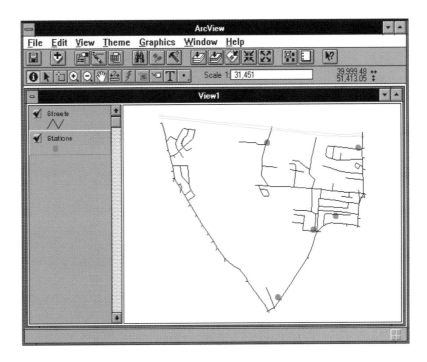

The Stations theme is active and the I-40 freeway is selected (shown in yellow) in the Streets theme. You'll use this feature to select gas stations within 1,000 feet of it.

The Stations theme is the *target* theme. Features in this theme will be selected by features in the Streets theme. (The target theme must be active to perform a theme-on-theme selection.)

The Streets theme is the *selector* theme. That is, features in this theme will be used to select features in the Stations theme.

If features are selected in the selector theme, ArcView uses them to find and select features in the target theme.

2. From the Theme menu, choose Select By Theme. The Select By Theme dialog box displays.

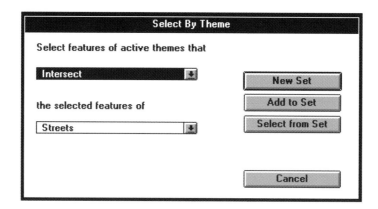

Understanding the Select By Theme dialog box. The Select By Theme dialog box is where you specify the type of spatial relationship you want to analyze with theme-on-theme selection. ArcView supports these types of spatial relationships: *Are Completely Within, Completely Contain, Have their Center In, Contain the Center Of, Intersect,* and *Are Within Distance Of.* For more information, search for these Help Topics: *Select By Theme, Spatial relation types, Theme on theme selection.*

Because the selector theme's feature type determines what types of spatial relationships you can analyze, you'll choose the selector theme first.

3. In the Select By Theme dialog box, select "Streets" from the lower drop-down list, unless it's already selected. Then choose "Are Within Distance Of" from the upper drop-down list. Your selections form this sentence: Select features of active themes that are within distance of the selected features of Streets. Type **1000** feet as the Selection distance.

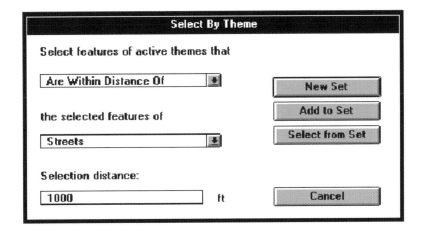

4. Click New Set. ArcView finds two gas stations within 1,000 feet of the I-40 freeway.

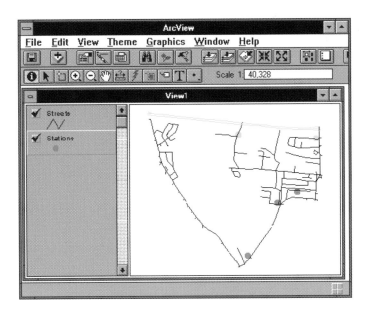

To find out more about the selected stations, you'll use the Identify tool.

5. Click on the Identify tool if it's not already selected. Then click on each selected station to display its attributes in the Identify Results dialog box.

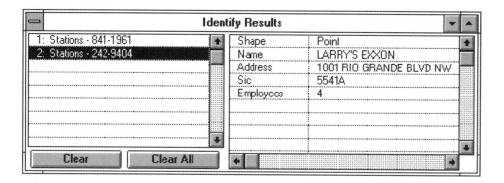

The selected stations are Larry's Exxon and Ann's Mart Station #1963. You'll analyze these locations in the next exercise.

6. Close the Identify Results dialog box.

If you want to go on to the next exercise, leave the project open.

Finding points near other points

Now you know that two gas stations, Larry's Exxon and Ann's Mart Station #1963, are within 1,000 feet of I-40. But, neither is currently for sale. You'd like to make a tempting offer, but first you must know the market potential of each station. Because you'd like to sell gasoline to business customers and employees as well as freeway travelers on I-40, you'll use theme-on-theme selection to find out which gas station is closer to more businesses.

ENVIRONMENTAL SYSTEMS RESEARCH INSTITUTE, INC.

Exercise 16b

1. If *ex16a.apr* is open, close View1 and open View2 from the Project window. Otherwise, choose Open Exercise from the File menu. In the Exercises scrolling list, select "ex16b," then click OK. When the project opens, you see View2 with two themes: Business and Streets. The Streets theme is active, and Ann's Mart Station #1963 is selected in the Business theme.

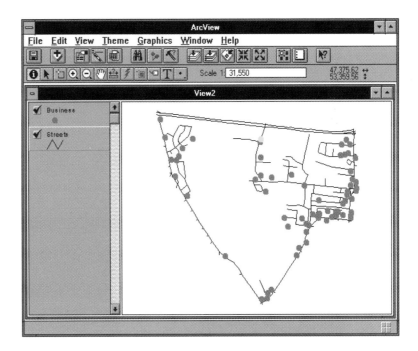

You'll use theme-on-theme selection to select businesses in the Business theme that are within a quarter mile (1,320 feet) of Ann's Mart Station #1963.

2. Make the Business theme active to make it the target theme and choose Select By Theme from the Theme menu. The Select By Theme dialog box displays. Select "Business" from the lower drop-down list to make it the selector theme. (In this case, one theme is used as both the selector theme and the target theme.) Then, from the upper drop-down list, select "Are Within Distance Of." Your

selections form this sentence: Select features of active themes that are within distance of the selected features of Business. Type **1320** feet as the Selection distance.

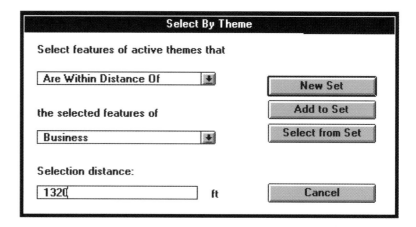

3. Click New Set. ArcView selects businesses within 1,320 feet of Ann's Mart Station, which is also selected.

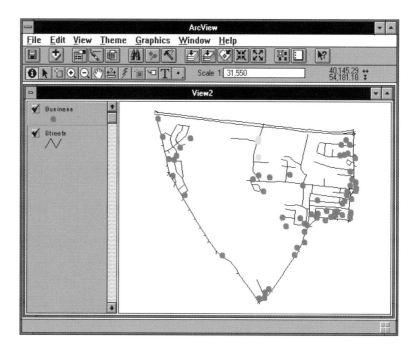

To see which businesses ArcView selected and examine their attributes, you'll open the theme table.

4. Click the Open Theme Table button to open the attribute table for the Business theme. The status portion of the Table tool bar shows that nine businesses are selected. Click the Promote button to move the selected records to the top of the table.

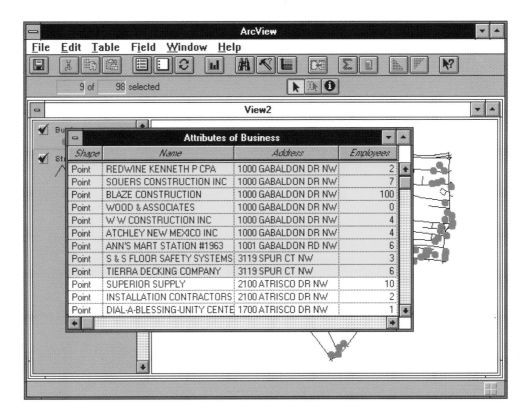

The other eight businesses have 126 employees. Many of the businesses have the same address, indicating that they are located in a shopping center.

5. Close the Attributes of Business table.

Next you'll examine the relationship of Larry's Exxon to surrounding businesses.

6. Close View2, then open View3 from the Project window. You see two themes: Business and Streets. Streets is active and Larry's Exxon is selected in the Business theme.

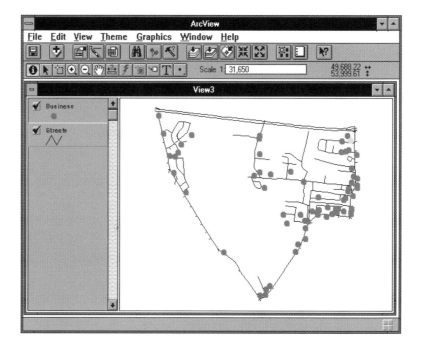

7. Make the Business theme active and choose Select By Theme from the Theme menu. The Select By Theme dialog box displays. Select "Business" from the lower drop-down list. Then, from the upper drop-down list, select "Are Within Distance Of." Your selections form this sentence: Select features of active themes that are within distance of the selected features of Business. Type **1320** feet as the Selection distance.

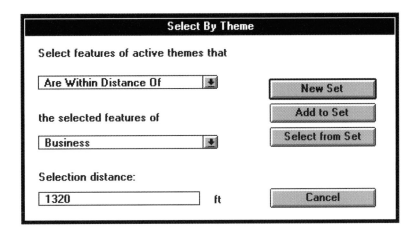

8. Click New Set. ArcView selects businesses within a quarter mile of Larry's Exxon.

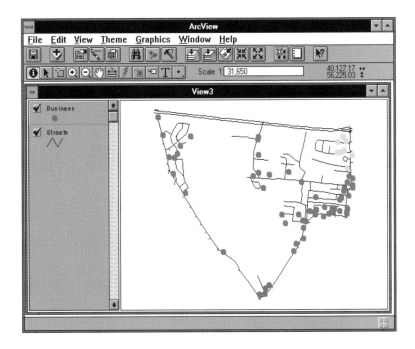

Now you can examine the attributes of these selected businesses.

9. Click the Open Theme Table button to open the attribute table for the Business theme. Click the Promote button to move the selected records to the top.

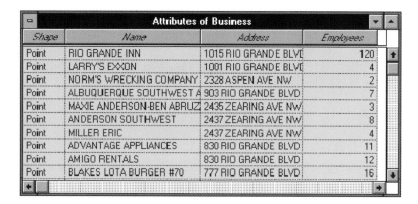

Shape	Name	Address	Employees
Point	RIO GRANDE INN	1015 RIO GRANDE BLVI	120
Point	LARRY'S EXXON	1001 RIO GRANDE BLVI	4
Point	NORM'S WRECKING COMPANY	2328 ASPEN AVE NW	2
Point	ALBUQUERQUE SOUTHWEST A	903 RIO GRANDE BLVD	7
Point	MAXIE ANDERSON-BEN ABRUZ	2435 ZEARING AVE NW	3
Point	ANDERSON SOUTHWEST	2437 ZEARING AVE NW	8
Point	MILLER ERIC	2437 ZEARING AVE NW	4
Point	ADVANTAGE APPLIANCES	830 RIO GRANDE BLVD	11
Point	AMIGO RENTALS	830 RIO GRANDE BLVD	12
Point	BLAKES LOTA BURGER #70	777 RIO GRANDE BLVD	16

Excluding Larry's Exxon, there are nine selected businesses, with 183 employees.

Larry's Exxon is not only closer to more businesses with more employees, but one of them is the Rio Grande Inn, a good business to have near a gas station. Now that you know something about its market potential, you can make a tempting offer.

Finding adjacent features

ArcView can also find features adjacent to a specific feature or features you select. To see how this works, consider a situation involving parcels of land. Suppose the City of Old Town wants to inform owners of land adjacent to a drainage system about a new program to improve it. The city needs answers to these questions: Which parcels are adjacent to the drainage ditches? How many of these parcels are in the city's jurisdiction and how many in the county's? What's the total acreage by jurisdiction?

Exercise 16c

1. From the File menu, choose Open Exercise. In the Exercises scrolling list, select "ex16c," then click OK. When the project opens, you see a view with one theme, Zoning. The Zoning theme is active and the parcels zoned for drainage ditches are selected.

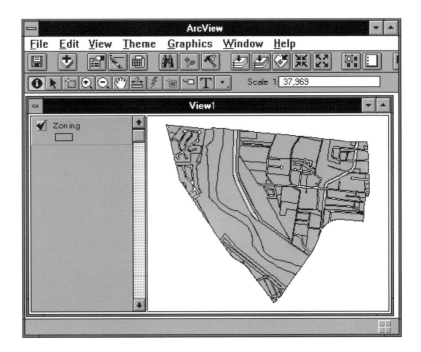

First you'll find out which parcels are adjacent to drainage ditches.

2. From the Theme menu, choose Select By Theme to display the Select By Theme dialog box. Select "Zoning" from the lower drop-down

list, unless it's already selected. Then, select "Are Within Distance Of" from the upper drop-down list. Your selections form this sentence: Select features of active themes that are within distance of the selected features of Zoning. Type **0** feet as the Selection distance.

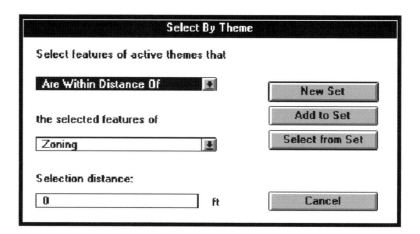

3. Click New Set. ArcView selects parcels adjacent to the drainage system.

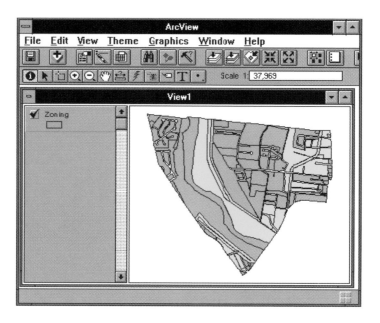

ENVIRONMENTAL SYSTEMS RESEARCH INSTITUTE, INC.

To find out how many parcels are selected, you'll open the theme table.

4. Click the Open Theme Table button, then the Promote button, to move the selected records to the top.

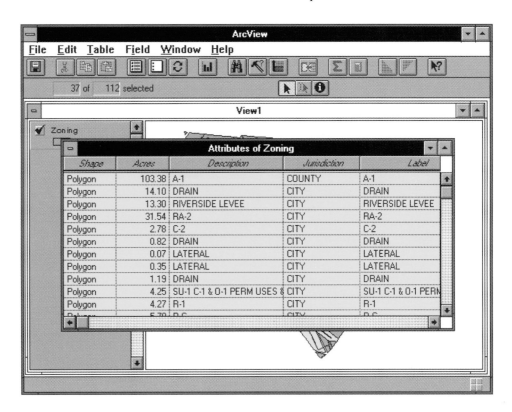

The new drainage improvement program will affect 37 parcels.

Next you'll determine the total acreage of these parcels by jurisdiction, using Summarize.

5. In the Attributes of Zoning table, click on the Jurisdiction field to make it active.

6. Click the Summarize button to display the Summary Table Definition dialog box. From the upper drop-down list (Field), select "Acres." From the lower drop-down list (Summarize by), select "Sum." Click Add to add your selections to the Summary statistics box. Click the Save As button to navigate to the *drive:\directory* where you want to save the new table ArcView creates and name it **acre_sum.dbf.**

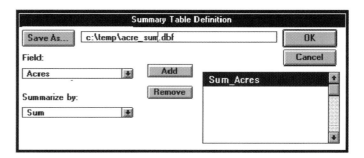

7. Click OK. ArcView sums the acres of selected parcels by jurisdiction and places the results in a new table.

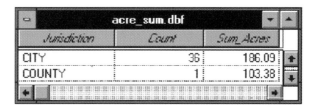

The total number of city parcels adjacent to the drainage system is 36, with a total acreage of 186.09. Only one county parcel, with an acreage of 103.38, is adjacent to the drainage system.

Now the City of Old Town knows how much city and county land the new drainage improvement program will affect, and it can notify the property owners about the program.

If you want to go on to the next chapter, leave ArcView running. Otherwise, choose Exit from the File menu.

SECTION 5:
Analyzing spatial relationships

Finding the features within

Finding points within polygons

Finding polygons within polygons

Finding the features within

With ArcView's theme-on-theme selection, you can find the points, lines, and polygons in one theme that fall completely within a polygon or polygons in another theme. Conversely, you can find polygons in one theme that contain particular points, lines, or polygons in another theme. This type of spatial relationship—features inside other features—is known as *containment*. Finding out whether a feature is inside or outside a boundary can be crucial to making decisions.

Finding points within polygons

Your company is transferring you to the Atlanta region, and you'd like to purchase a home after you get there. Before you call a real estate agent long distance (you're on the West Coast now), you'd like to become familiar with the region yourself, and possibly even identify some areas you might like to live in. You're primarily interested in areas where population is low compared to the rest of the region, and more importantly, areas where your 13-year-old daughter can attend middle school close to home.

Your company uses ArcView and you have access to a copy, along with the sample data that comes with it. The data includes demographic information you can use to study the population characteristics of the region, but no information about schools. Conveniently, one of your old college chums works for a regional planning agency in Georgia, and he's willing to send you some data containing the locations and names of public school facilities in the Atlanta region. You'll use these data sets and ArcView to find suitable areas to live.

Exercise 17a

1. If necessary, start ArcView. From the File menu, choose Open Exercise. In the Exercises scrolling list, select "ex17a," then click OK. When the project opens, you see a view with three themes: Middle Schools, Census Tracts, and Counties.

The Middle Schools theme contains the locations of all the middle schools in the region. The Census Tracts theme contains the census tracts in the region along with demographic information (i.e., per capita income, total population, population growth, age characteristics, and more). The Counties theme contains the boundaries of four counties in the region. You don't see it because ArcView draws the other two themes on top of it.

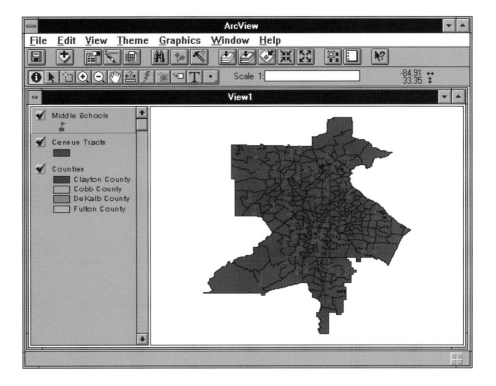

You'll use the Census Tracts theme to find areas with low population.

2. Make the Census Tracts theme active, then click the Open Theme Table button to open the Attributes of Census Tracts table.

When the table opens, you see fields containing demographic information for each census tract. The Pop_90 field contains the 1990 population value for each tract.

3. Click on the Pop_90 field to make it active.

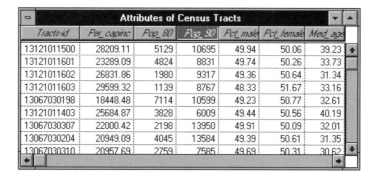

4. From the Field menu, choose Statistics. ArcView displays statistics for the Pop_90 field.

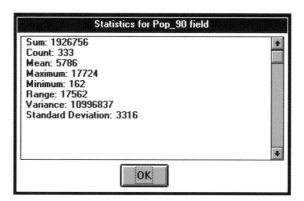

In the dialog box that displays, you see that the mean population for all the census tracts is 5,786. Because you want to live in an area with low population compared to the rest of the region, you'll start by finding census tracts that have a population that's less than the mean. You'll use the Query Builder to find these areas.

5. Click OK to close the Statistics dialog box, then close the Attributes of Census Tracts table.

6. Click the Query Builder button. The Query Builder dialog box displays.

7. In the Fields list, double-click on "[Pop_90]," click the "<" button, then type **5786** in the query text box. (By default, ArcView encloses the query in parentheses.)

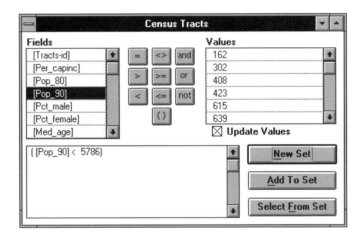

8. Click the New Set button. ArcView selects and highlights the census tracts that have a population less than 5,786. Close the Query Builder.

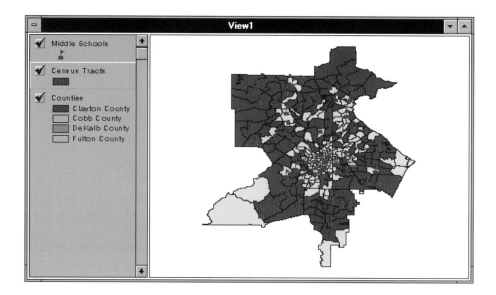

By looking at the view, you can see that some of the highlighted census tracts have middle schools. You want to find census tracts that have low population and also contain middle schools. Since the census tracts and middle schools are in separate themes, you'll use theme-on-theme selection to find census tracts that meet both of your criteria.

The Middle Schools theme is the selector theme. That is, features in this theme will be used to select features in the Census Tracts theme.

9. With the Census Tracts theme active, choose Select By Theme from the Theme menu. The Select By Theme dialog box displays.

The Census Tracts theme is the target (active) theme. Features in this theme will be selected by features in the Middle Schools theme.

10. From the lower drop-down list, choose "Middle Schools." From the upper drop-down list, choose "Completely Contain." Your selections form this sentence: Select features of active themes that completely contain the selected features of Middle Schools.

Because no features are selected in the Middle Schools theme, ArcView uses all the theme's features to find and select features in the Census Tracts theme.

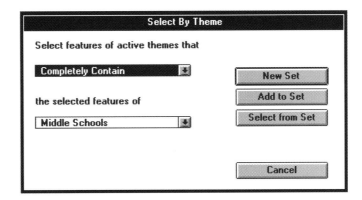

Because you've already selected a set of census tracts that meet your first criterion (low population), you want ArcView to select census tracts from this set.

11. Click the Select from Set button. ArcView selects census tracts from the currently selected set that also contain middle schools.

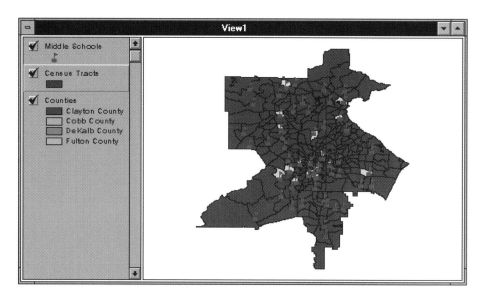

ArcView highlights those census tracts with a population less than 5,786 and at least one middle school. These areas meet both of your criteria for areas you'd like to live in.

If you want to go on to the next exercise, leave the project open.

ENVIRONMENTAL SYSTEMS RESEARCH INSTITUTE, INC.

Finding polygons within polygons

Suppose you've just learned from a future coworker in the Atlanta region that property taxes are lower in Cobb County than in other counties in the region. You want to use ArcView to find out which of the census tracts you selected are in Cobb County. This may help you narrow your search for a place to live. Once you narrow your choice of areas, you'll want to get information about the middle schools located there.

Exercise 17b

1. If *ex17a.apr* is open, continue. Otherwise, choose Open Exercise from the File menu. In the Exercises scrolling list, select "ex17b," then click OK. When the project opens, you see three themes: Middle Schools, Census Tracts, and Counties. (You don't see the Counties theme because ArcView draws the other two themes on top of it.) The census tracts you selected in the last exercise are highlighted in the Census Tracts theme.

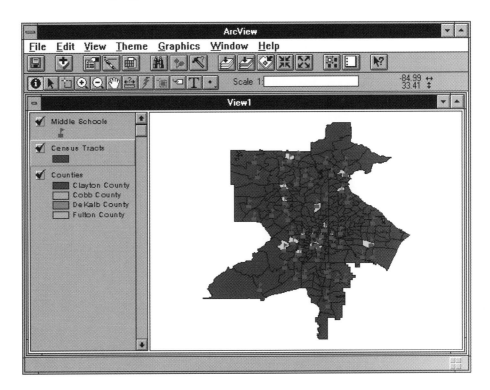

To find out which of the highlighted census tracts are in Cobb County, you first need to select Cobb County in the Counties theme. To make the Counties theme visible, you'll turn off the other themes.

2. Click on the check boxes for the Middle Schools and Census Tracts themes to turn them off. The Counties theme is now visible.

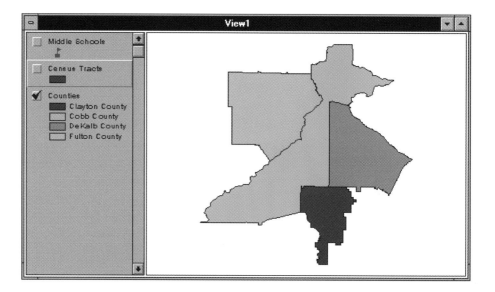

You can see from the legend that the counties are classified according to their names. You'll use the Select Feature tool to select the feature (polygon) that represents Cobb County.

3. Make the Counties theme active, click on the Select Feature tool, then click on Cobb County. ArcView selects and highlights this county.

ENVIRONMENTAL SYSTEMS RESEARCH INSTITUTE, INC.

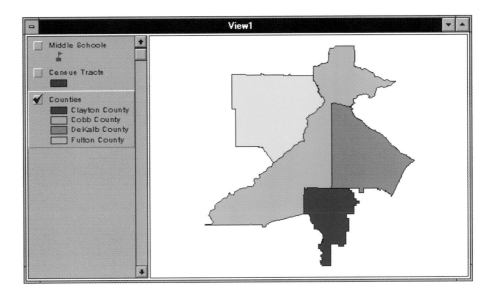

Now you want to see the Census Tracts and Middle Schools themes, so you'll turn them back on.

4. Click on the check boxes for the Census Tracts and Middle Schools themes to turn them on. These themes draw on top of the Counties theme.

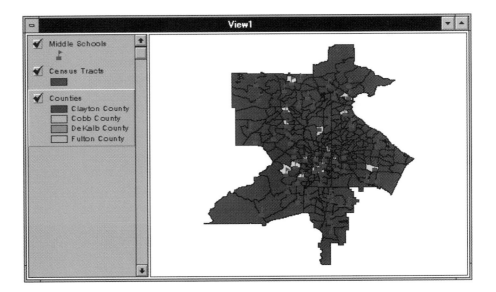

To find out which selected census tracts are inside Cobb County, you'll use theme-on-theme selection.

5.   Make the Census Tracts theme active to make it the target theme.

6.   From the Theme menu, choose Select By Theme to display the Select By Theme dialog box. From the lower drop-down list, select "Counties" to make it the selector theme. From the upper drop-down list, select "Are Completely Within." Your selections form this sentence: Select features of active themes that are completely within the selected features of Counties.

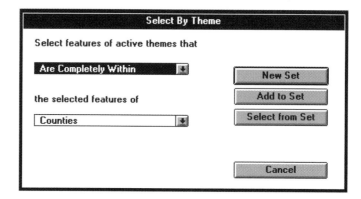

Because you've already selected a set of census tracts that meet two of your criteria (low population and at least one middle school), you want ArcView to select census tracts from this set.

ENVIRONMENTAL SYSTEMS RESEARCH INSTITUTE, INC.

7.   Click the Select from Set button. ArcView selects census tracts from the currently selected set that are completely inside Cobb County.

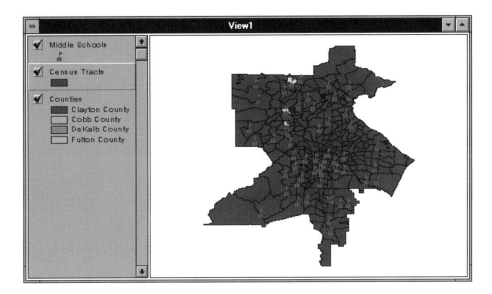

These census tracts meet all of your criteria. They have a population that's less than the average for the region, they have middle schools, and they're in Cobb County, where property taxes are lower.

Now that you've narrowed down the number of possible areas to move to, your final task is to get information about their middle schools. You'll select these schools using theme-on-theme selection, then examine their attributes to get their names.

8.   Make the Middle Schools theme active to make it the target theme.

9. From the Theme menu, choose Select By Theme to display the Select By Theme dialog box. From the lower drop-down list, select "Census Tracts" to make it the selector theme. From the upper drop-down list, choose "Are Completely Within." Your selections form this sentence: Select features of active themes that are completely within the selected features of Census Tracts.

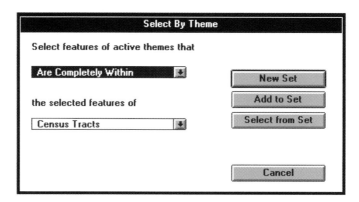

10. Click the New Set button. ArcView selects the middle schools that are inside the selected census tracts. (Selected census tracts and selected middle schools are highlighted in the view.)

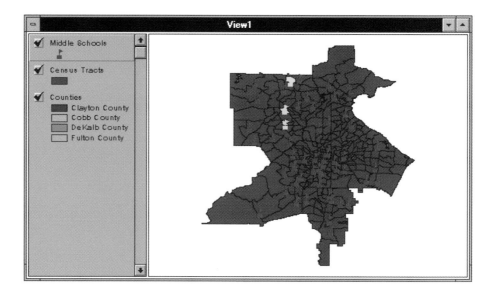

11. Click the Open Theme Table button to open the Attributes of Middle Schools table, then click the Promote button to move the selected schools to the top of the table.

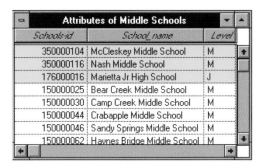

You now have the names of the schools in the areas that meet your criteria. You can contact the schools to ask when the next session begins, whether they operate year-round, what the average class size is, and so on. Answers to these questions may help you choose a place to live. Then you can call an agent and start looking for a home.

If you want to go on to the next chapter, leave ArcView running. Otherwise, choose Exit from the File menu.

SECTION 5:
Analyzing spatial relationships

Finding features that intersect other features

Finding lines that intersect other lines

Finding polygons that intersect other polygons

Finding features that intersect other features

When features share the same geographic space, they overlap, or *intersect*. ArcView can find features that intersect, whether they're in the same theme or in different themes. Using theme-on-theme selection, you can find and select lines that intersect other lines or polygons, and polygons that intersect other polygons.

Once you find and select intersecting features, you can perform other ArcView operations on them and on their attributes.

Finding lines that intersect other lines

Suppose that as part of an emergency planning strategy for a large city, the city's emergency preparedness committee is studying major earthquake faults in its suburban areas. One objective of the study is to develop a plan to deal with potential flooding and health risks associated with the rupture of water and sewer lines in the event of a major earthquake. As the first step in the study, the committee uses ArcView to find and select those water and sewer pipelines that intersect faults.

Exercise 18a

1. If necessary, start ArcView. From the File menu, choose Open Exercise. In the Exercises scrolling list, select "ex18a," then click OK. When the project opens, you see a view with two themes, Pipelines and Faults.

ENVIRONMENTAL SYSTEMS RESEARCH INSTITUTE, INC.

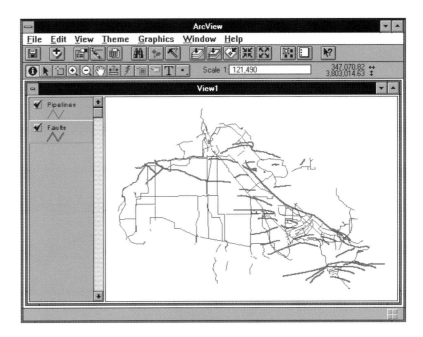

To find out which pipelines intersect faults, you'll use theme-on-theme selection.

The Pipelines theme is the *target* theme. Features in this theme will be selected by features in the Faults theme. (The target theme must be active to perform a theme-on-theme selection.)

The Faults theme is the *selector* theme. That is, features in this theme will be used to select features in the Pipelines theme.

2.   Make the Pipelines theme active and choose Select By Theme from the Theme menu. The Select By Theme dialog box displays.

3. Select "Faults" from the lower drop-down list. Then, choose "Intersect" from the upper drop-down list. Your selections form this sentence: Select features of active themes that intersect the selected features of Faults.

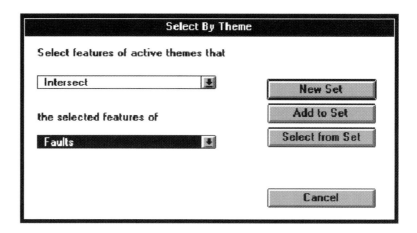

4. Click New Set. ArcView selects pipelines that intersect faults.

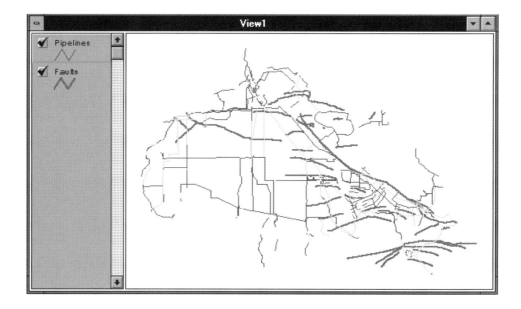

Now that the vulnerable pipelines are selected, the committee wants to determine their total number and length so they can estimate potential repair and replacement costs. Because the pipelines belong to more than one agency, they'll break down the totals by agency.

5. With the Pipelines theme active, click the Open Theme Table button. The Attributes of Pipelines table opens.

To see the selected records better, you promote them.

6. Click the Promote button. Records for the selected pipelines now appear at the top of the table.

Shape	Length	Code	Owner
PolyLine	744.482	4	LADWP
PolyLine	667.337	4	LADWP
PolyLine	4378.543	4	LADWP
PolyLine	2896.206	3	LADWP
PolyLine	4520.465	6	MWD
PolyLine	7036.618	4	LADWP
PolyLine	253.947	1	LADWP
PolyLine	2831.991	1	LADWP
PolyLine	2089.867	1	CITY OF SAN FERNANDO
PolyLine	1304.884	1	CITY OF SAN FERNANDO
PolyLine	791.750	3	LADWP
PolyLine	3365.647	1	LADWP

Attributes of Pipelines

Now you'll use the Summarize function to calculate the total number and length of these pipelines according to owner.

7. In the Attributes of Pipelines table, click on the Owner field to make it active. ArcView will use the unique values in this field to summarize the selected records in a new table.

8. Click the Summarize button. The Summary Table Definition dialog box displays.

9. From the upper drop-down list (Field), select "Length." From the lower drop-down list (Summarize by), select "Sum." Then click the Add button. This adds your selection to the Summary statistics box on the right. Click the Save As button to navigate to the *drive:\directory* where you want to save the new table ArcView creates and call it **owlength.dbf.**

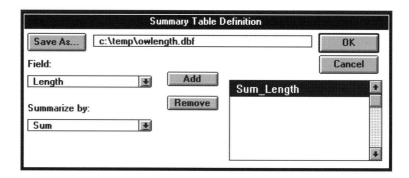

10. Click OK to create the summary table.

Owner	Count	Sum_Length
BURBANK PSD	9	14966.90
CITY OF GLENDALE	8	14564.49
CITY OF SAN FERNANDO	2	3394.75
LADWP	35	107416.77
MWD	7	45770.09

owlength.dbf

ArcView creates one record for each unique owner it finds. The new table shows there are five owners of the selected pipelines. The Count field reports the total number of pipelines for each owner, and the Sum_Length field lists their total length.

Now the committee can use this information as the starting point for working with the responsible agencies to develop a plan to deal with potential flooding and health risks.

Finding polygons that intersect lines. You can also use theme-on-theme selection to find and select polygons that intersect lines in another theme. For example, suppose you have one theme containing polygons that represent businesses and another containing lines that represent earthquake faults. You want to find out which businesses are vulnerable to earthquakes, so you perform a theme-on-theme selection. The theme containing businesses is the target theme; the theme containing earthquake faults is the selector theme. ArcView uses the earthquake fault lines to select businesses (polygons) they intersect. For more information, search for these Help Topics: *Select by Theme, Spatial relation types, Theme on theme selection.*

Finding polygons that intersect other polygons

Like earthquakes, floods require emergency planning and special programs for protection. Legislation requires communities in flood-prone areas to participate in flood insurance programs. These programs, aimed at protecting property owners, require owners to purchase flood insurance at government-subsidized rates.

As a participant in a flood insurance program, one city located on a major floodplain developed a database containing the boundaries of 100-year and 500-year flood zones. (These zones are expected to flood at least once during the designated time span.) The city wants to notify all property owners within the 100-year zone about special low-cost loans for elevating structures above the base flood level, thereby cutting insurance costs.

Using ArcView's theme-on-theme selection, the city can determine which land parcels are located within the 100-year flood zone and then notify the owners about the loan program.

Exercise 18b

1. From the File menu, choose Open Exercise. In the Exercises scrolling list, select "ex18b," then click OK. When the project opens, you see a view with two themes: Floodzones and Parcels. The 100-year flood zone is selected in the Floodzones theme.

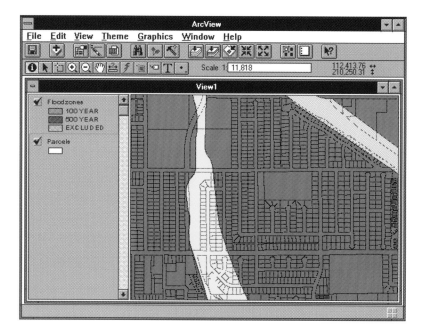

To see all the features in both themes, you'll zoom out.

2. Click the Zoom to Full Extent button.

Next you'll find out which parcels intersect the 100-year flood zone.

3. Make the Parcels theme active to make it the target theme and choose Select By Theme from the Theme menu. The Select By Theme dialog box displays. Select "Floodzones" from the lower drop-down list to make it the selector theme. Then, from the upper drop-down list, select "Intersect." Your selections form this sentence: Select features of active themes that intersect the selected features of Floodzones.

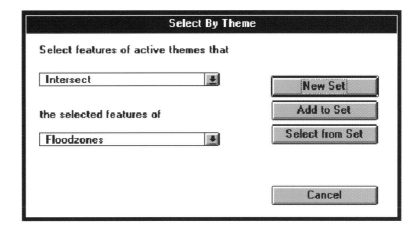

4. Click New Set. ArcView selects parcels that intersect the 100-year flood zone.

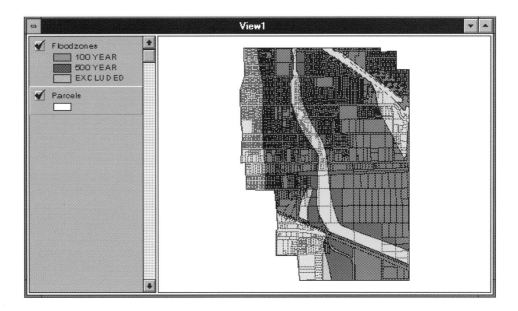

To see the selected parcels better, you'll turn off the Floodzones theme.

5. In the Table of Contents, click on the check box next to the Floodzones theme to turn it off. ArcView redraws the Parcels theme.

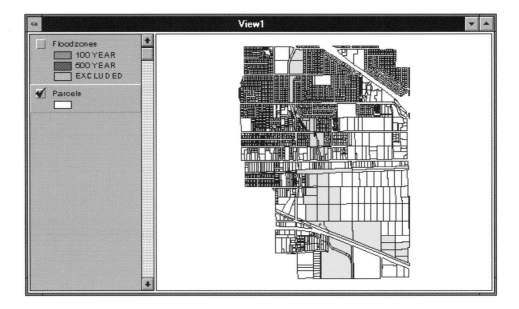

Next, open the theme table and examine the selected records.

6. With the Parcels theme active, click the Open Theme Table button, then click the Promote button. The selected records display at the top of the table. Scroll to the right to examine the attributes.

Zone	Gp92	Acreage	Year	Own	Own_name	
OS	EROS	7.402	0	ON	CITY OF ONTARIO	ADDR
OS	EROS	7.402	0	ON	CITY OF ONTARIO	ADDR
OS	EROS	9.661	0	ON	CITY OF ONTARIO	ADDR
OS	EROS	4.647	0	ON	CITY OF ONTARIO	ADDR
R1	LDR	0.165	1953	NO	HOGUE, ALBERT J AND MAR	1206
OS	EROS	1.008	0	ON	CITY OF ONTARIO	ADDR
R1	LDR	0.197	1953	NO	RICHARDSON, VERNON M	845 A
R1	LDR	0.165	1953	NO	CENICEROS, JESUS O	851 N
R1	LDR	0.191	1953	NO	FLORES, JOHN A	839 N
R1	LDR	0.165	1953	NO	SCOTT, FRANCIS A	857 N
R1	LDR	0.157	1953	NO	TOLENTINO, CIRILO	833 N
R1	LDR	0.136	1953	NO	RODRIGUEZ, JESUS P	827 A

Title bar: **Attributes of Parcels**

The parcel attributes include assessor's parcel number, zoning codes, General Plan codes, acreage, owner name, owner address, and more. The city now has a list of all parcels that would be affected by a 100-year flood as well as the information it needs to contact the owners about the special loan program.

If you want to go on to the next chapter, leave ArcView running. Otherwise, choose Exit from the File menu.

Finding features that don't intersect. Sometimes you need to find features that *don't* intersect other features. For example, suppose you want to find the parcels that are outside of the 100-year flood zone. You use ArcView's theme-on-theme selection to find and select the parcels that intersect the flood zone, then use ArcView's Switch Selection function to toggle the selected set from the parcels that do intersect (unselects these) to the parcels that *don't* intersect (selects these instead). For more information, search for this Help Topic: *Switch Selection.*

ENVIRONMENTAL SYSTEMS RESEARCH INSTITUTE, INC.

SECTION 5:
Analyzing spatial relationships

Finding features and joining their attributes

Joining attributes based on containment

Joining attributes based on proximity

CHAPTER 19

Finding features and joining their attributes

When you use theme-on-theme selection, ArcView uses the features in one theme to find and select features (and their attributes) in another theme. The selected features and attributes remain in separate themes.

In another type of spatial analysis, called *spatial join*, ArcView appends the fields of one theme table to those of another theme table, based on the locations of features in the two themes. In this way, you can join all of the attributes from a number of themes in one table.

ArcView uses two kinds of spatial relationships to compare the locations of features in two separate themes: *nearest* and *inside*. Whenever ArcView finds features that satisfy one of these spatial relationships, the attributes of features in one theme are appended to those in the other theme.

The relationship (*nearest* or *inside*) that ArcView uses to compare feature locations depends on the types of features in the two themes. For example, if you compare a theme of polygons with a theme of points, ArcView finds points *inside* polygons and appends the attributes of the polygons to the points they contain. However, if you compare two point themes, ArcView finds the *nearest* point in the second theme for each point in the first theme. Then ArcView appends the attributes of points in the second theme to the corresponding points in the first theme.

Joining attributes based on containment

Suppose you're a wildlife biologist studying water sources on protected lands, such as national parks, national forests, and wildlife reserves. When water sources become scarce during the dry season, wild animals in these areas often migrate to grazing lands that support cattle. You'd like to anticipate this situation and take measures to prevent it. To do so, you'll need to know how many water sources each area has. You'll perform a spatial join to append the attributes of these areas to the water sources found within them. Then you'll perform a query to find the water holes that are inside protected areas and summarize their attributes to determine the number of water holes in each protected area.

Exercise 19a

1. If necessary, start ArcView. From the File menu, choose Open Exercise. In the Exercises scrolling list, select "ex19a," then click OK. When the project opens, you see a view with two themes, Water Holes and Range. Features in the Range theme are divided into three classes: Unprotected Areas, Protected Areas, and Unknown.

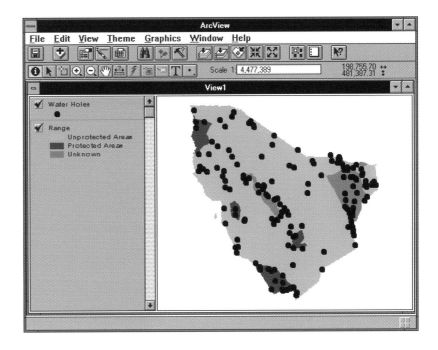

You want to know the characteristics of the area each water hole lies in, so you'll join the attributes of the Range theme to those of the Water Holes theme.

2.   With the Water Holes theme active, hold down the Shift key and click on the Range theme to make both themes active. Then click the Open Theme Table button to open the attribute tables for both themes.

> **Joining tables.** When you join two tables, one is the source table, the other the destination table. ArcView adds the fields of the source table to the fields of the destination table. In this case, Attributes of Range is the source table and Attributes of Water Holes is the destination table. The destination table is the one that's active when you perform the join. For more information, see chapter 15 or search for these Help Topics: *Joining tables, Join.*

3.   In the Attributes of Range table, click on the Shape field to make it active. Then do the same for the Attributes of Water Holes table. This field is common to both tables.

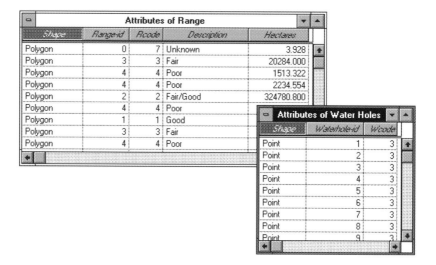

4. With the Attributes of Water Holes table active, click the Join button. ArcView joins the Attributes of Range theme table to the Attributes of Water Holes theme table based on the location of features in the two themes.

Shape	Waterhole-id	Wcode	Range-id	Rcode	Description	Hectares
Point	1	3	1	1	Good	3984488.000
Point	2	3	1	1	Good	3984488.000
Point	3	3	6	6	Siblioi National Park	147378.000
Point	4	3	6	6	Siblioi National Park	147378.000
Point	5	3	1	1	Good	3984488.000
Point	6	3	1	1	Good	3984488.000
Point	7	3	1	1	Good	3984488.000
Point	8	3	1	1	Good	3984488.000

Attributes of Water Holes

Understanding spatial join. In a spatial join, you join two theme tables by using the Shape field as the common field. For each feature in the first theme, a corresponding feature in the second theme is found that satisfies one of these spatial relationships: *nearest* or *inside*. In this case, ArcView uses the *inside* relationship to find the range area that each water hole lies in. The attributes of the range are then appended to the attributes of the water hole. If there is more than one water hole in a range area, the attributes of that area are appended to each. For more information, search for these Help Topics: *Joining tables, Spatial Join, Performing spatial analysis with ArcView.*

The Attributes of Water Holes table (destination table) now has fields appended from the Attributes of Range table (source table). For each water hole, there is now a range code (Rcode) and description. Water holes with a range code of 6 are located in national parks, forests, and reserves. You'll build a query to select them.

5. Make the view active. Both themes (Water Holes and Range) are active. Click on the Water Holes theme to make it the only active theme, then click the Query Builder button to display the Query Builder dialog box.

6. In the dialog box, double-click "[Rcode]" in the Fields list, then click the "=" button, then double-click "6" (national parks, forests, and reserves) in the Values list. Click New Set to select all the water holes in the national parks, forests, and reserves.

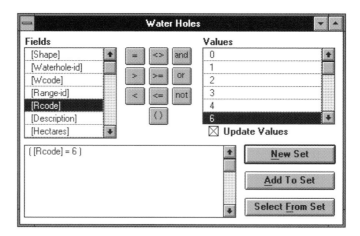

7. Close the Query Builder. You see the selected water holes highlighted in yellow in the view.

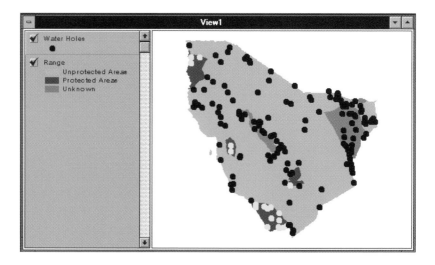

To see the attributes of the selected water holes, you'll open the theme table.

8. Click the Open Theme Table button, then click the Promote button to move the selected records to the top of the table. (You may need to widen the table or scroll to the right to see all the fields.)

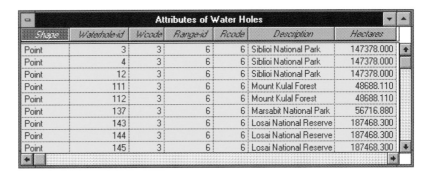

Shape	Waterhole-id	Wcode	Range-id	Rcode	Description	Hectares
Point	3	3	6	6	Siblioi National Park	147378.000
Point	4	3	6	6	Siblioi National Park	147378.000
Point	12	3	6	6	Siblioi National Park	147378.000
Point	111	3	6	6	Mount Kulal Forest	48688.110
Point	112	3	6	6	Mount Kulal Forest	48688.110
Point	137	3	6	6	Marsabit National Park	56716.880
Point	143	3	6	6	Losai National Reserve	187468.300
Point	144	3	6	6	Losai National Reserve	187468.300
Point	145	3	6	6	Losai National Reserve	187468.300

Next you'll summarize the selected water holes based on the values in the Description field to determine the number of water holes in each park, forest, and reserve.

9. In the Attributes of Water Holes table, make the Description field active. From the Field menu, choose Summarize. The Summary Table Definition dialog box displays.

10. Click the Save As button to navigate to the *drive:\directory* where you want to save the summary table ArcView creates and call it **watdes.dbf.** Click OK to create the summary table.

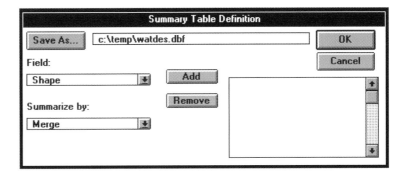

ArcView creates one record for each park, forest, and reserve that's named in the Description field. The Count field lists the number of water holes in each one.

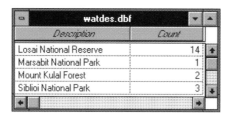

Description	Count
Losai National Reserve	14
Marsabit National Park	1
Mount Kulal Forest	2
Siblioi National Park	3

Now you know which protected areas have water sources and how many sources are in each area. You can study these sources to find out which can support local wildlife throughout the dry season, and which can't.

Joining attributes based on proximity

As a way of raising money to maintain protected areas, the government would like to sponsor camera safaris to water holes in those areas. Now your job is to evaluate access to water holes. You've discovered that only one of the four protected areas is accessible by land. The other three are too remote. As an alternative, the government would like to fly tourists into these areas. You'll need to know how far each water hole is from the nearest landing strip.

Because tourists will have to travel over bumpy, unimproved roads to get from landing strips to water holes, you want to find those water holes within 20 kilometers of a landing strip, to minimize driving time. To solve this problem, you'll perform a spatial join to append the attributes of landing strips to the water holes found nearest to them. ArcView calculates the distance from each water hole to the nearest landing strip and, in a field called *Distance*, appends this information to each water hole. You'll perform a query on this field to find out which water holes are located less than 20 kilometers from a landing strip.

Exercise 19b

1. If *ex19a.apr* is open, close View1 and the open tables, then open View2. Otherwise, choose Open Exercise from the File menu. In the Exercises scrolling list, select "ex19b," then click OK. When the project opens, you see a view with three themes: Airports, Water Holes, and Range.

In the Range theme, the three remote protected areas are labeled. The Water Holes theme shows only the water holes inside these protected areas. The Airports theme (active) shows all the landing strips for the entire region.

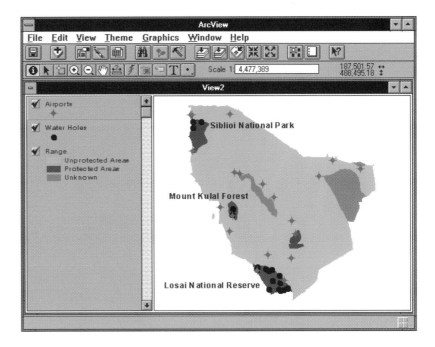

2. With the Airports theme active, hold down the Shift key and click on the Water Holes theme. Now both themes are active. Then click the Open Theme Table button to open the attribute tables for both themes.

3. In the Attributes of Airports table (source table), make the Shape field active. Do the same for the Attributes of Water Holes table (destination table).

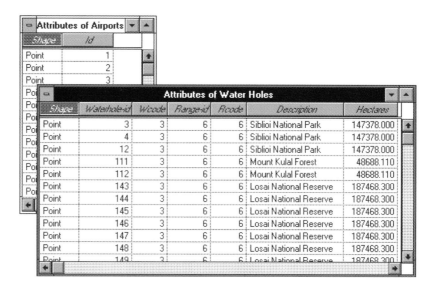

4. With the Attributes of Water Holes table active, click the Join button to join the Attributes of Airports table to the Attributes of Water Holes table.

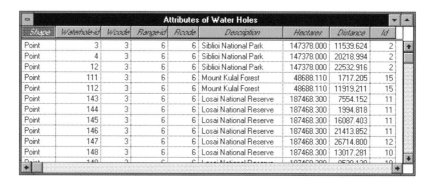

ArcView uses the *nearest* relationship to find the landing strip that each water hole lies closest to. The attributes of the landing strip (*Id*) are then appended to the attributes of the water hole. ArcView also calculates the distance between each water hole and the closest landing strip and places this value in a field called *Distance*. (For this view, the distance units are meters. For a review of distance units, see chapter 12.)

Whenever ArcView uses the *nearest* relationship in a spatial join, a distance field is added to the joined table.

Now you'll build a query to find the water holes that are less than 20 kilometers from a landing strip.

5. With the Attributes of Water Holes table active, click the Query Builder button to display the Query Builder dialog box. In the box, double-click "[Distance]" in the Fields list, then click the "<" button, then type **20000** (20,000 meters is equal to 20 kilometers) in the query text box.

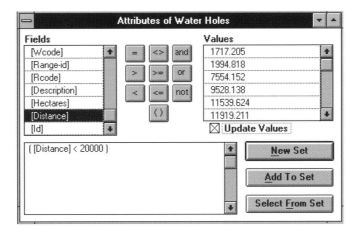

6. Click New Set to select all the water holes that are less than 20 kilometers from a landing strip. Close the Query Builder.

7. Click the Promote button to move the selected records to the top of the table.

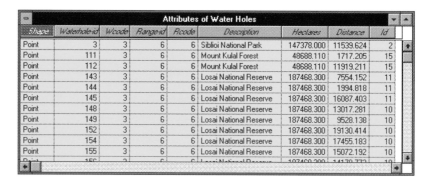

Shape	Waterhole-id	Wcode	Range-id	Rcode	Description	Hectares	Distance	Id
Point	3	3	6	6	Siblioi National Park	147378.000	11539.624	2
Point	111	3	6	6	Mount Kulal Forest	48688.110	1717.205	15
Point	112	3	6	6	Mount Kulal Forest	48688.110	11919.211	15
Point	143	3	6	6	Losai National Reserve	187468.300	7554.152	11
Point	144	3	6	6	Losai National Reserve	187468.300	1994.818	11
Point	145	3	6	6	Losai National Reserve	187468.300	16087.403	11
Point	148	3	6	6	Losai National Reserve	187468.300	13017.281	10
Point	149	3	6	6	Losai National Reserve	187468.300	9528.138	10
Point	152	3	6	6	Losai National Reserve	187468.300	19130.414	10
Point	154	3	6	6	Losai National Reserve	187468.300	17455.183	10
Point	155	3	6	6	Losai National Reserve	187468.300	15072.192	10

Now you know which water holes are closest to landing strips. These sites meet your criteria for good camera safari sites. However, you want to evaluate the remaining (unselected) sites for future development, so you'll change the selected set to water holes that are more than 20 kilometers away from landing strips.

8. Click the Switch Selection button to select the water holes that are more than 20 kilometers away from a landing strip, then Promote the selected records.

Switching selected records. When you use the Switch Selection button, ArcView changes the selected set of records to the previously unselected records. If the records belong to a theme table, the selected and unselected sets of features in the theme are also switched in the view. If no records are selected, using the Switch Selection button will select all the records. For more information, search for this Help Topic: *Switch Selection.*

ENVIRONMENTAL SYSTEMS RESEARCH INSTITUTE, INC.

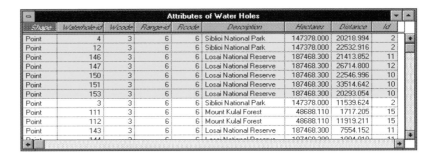

Shape	Waterhole-id	Wcode	Range-id	Rcode	Description	Hectares	Distance	Id
Point	4	3	6	6	Siblioi National Park	147378.000	20218.994	2
Point	12	3	6	6	Siblioi National Park	147378.000	22532.916	2
Point	146	3	6	6	Losai National Reserve	187468.300	21413.852	11
Point	147	3	6	6	Losai National Reserve	187468.300	26714.800	12
Point	150	3	6	6	Losai National Reserve	187468.300	22546.996	10
Point	151	3	6	6	Losai National Reserve	187468.300	33514.642	10
Point	153	3	6	6	Losai National Reserve	187468.300	20293.054	10
Point	3	3	6	6	Siblioi National Park	147378.000	11539.624	2
Point	111	3	6	6	Mount Kulal Forest	48688.110	1717.205	15
Point	112	3	6	6	Mount Kulal Forest	48688.110	11919.211	15
Point	143	3	6	6	Losai National Reserve	187468.300	7554.152	11

The highlighted records are water holes that are more than 20 kilometers from a landing strip. To examine the locations of these water holes, you'll make the view active.

9. Make the view active. Water holes more than 20 kilometers from landing strips are highlighted.

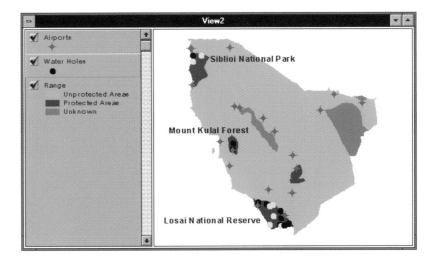

These water holes can be developed for future safaris by adding new landing strips or by improving the roads leading from them to the nearest existing landing strip.

ArcView helped you meet your initial objective of evaluating access to water holes for the purpose of offering camera safaris. You know how far each water hole is from the nearest landing strip, which ones are within

20 kilometers of existing landing strips, and which ones aren't. If the camera safari project is successful in raising revenues for protected areas, then both the local economy and the protected areas will benefit.

If you want to go on to the next chapter, leave ArcView running. Otherwise, choose Exit from the File menu.

SECTION 6

Presenting information

The next two chapters show you how to present information as charts and map layouts. In chapter 20, you'll chart an attribute in the theme table, then change the way the chart looks. You'll also query the chart and change the information it presents. In chapter 21, you'll create a map layout and add and manipulate all the elements you need to make it presentation-quality.

SECTION 6:
Presenting information

Creating
charts

Preparing your data for charting

Creating a chart and changing the way it looks

Querying and editing charts

Creating charts

Just as views are excellent for presenting spatial information, charts are ideal for displaying tabular information. A chart references tabular data in an existing ArcView table. Charts enhance your presentation by providing a graphic representation of the attributes associated with map features. With a chart, you can turn a list of complicated figures into brightly colored graphics that clarify complex relationships at a glance.

In ArcView, charts are simple to create and change. In this chapter, you'll create a chart, modify its characteristics, use it to access information, and edit its source table.

Preparing your data for charting

Suppose you're the marketing director for Miles From Nowhere, Inc., a company that offers recreational wilderness trips to remote parts of the world. Your company already offers treks across the Australian outback, cross-country skiing in Greenland, African safaris, and Amazon jungle bushwhacks. It's your job to come up with a new angle. Thumbing through an atlas one afternoon, you get inspired: what could be farther off the beaten path than an expedition to Siberia?

Your preliminary research reveals that population density throughout Siberia is less than three people per square mile, summer temperatures average between 50 and 70 degrees Fahrenheit, and rails run east and west, linking a number of cities (Krasnoyarsk, Bratsk, Irkutsk, Ust-Kut) that could serve as starting points for journeys into the interior. There are several major navigable waterways, suggesting that a river trip may be a good way to travel.

You'll use ArcView to develop your plan and present it at the quarterly business meeting. In your presentation, you'll include a view of Siberia and its major rivers as well as a chart comparing the attributes of the rivers.

Exercise 20a

1. If necessary, start ArcView. From the File menu, choose Open
    Exercise. In the Exercises scrolling list, select "ex20a," then click
    OK. When the project opens, you see a view with two themes:
    Siberian Rivers and Far East (a theme showing the region of Siberia
    and adjacent countries). The Siberian Rivers theme is active.

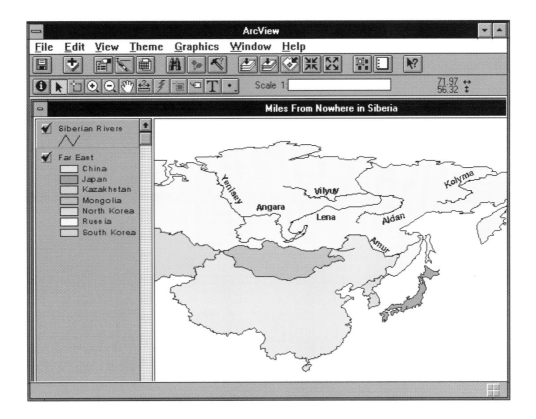

2. Click the Open Theme Table button to open the Attributes of Siberian Rivers table. The table contains the names of the major Siberian rivers, their lengths in miles, and other attributes.

Shape	River_	River_id	Name	Length	Direction	
PolyLine	1	1	Aldan	1500	N, NW	Lena
PolyLine	4	4	Amur	1780	E	Pacifi
PolyLine	5	5	Angara	1100	N, NW	Yenis
PolyLine	32	32	Kolyma	1110	NE	East S
PolyLine	34	34	Lena	3000	N, NE	Lapte
PolyLine	88	89	Vilyuy	1500	E	Lena
PolyLine	95	96	Yenisey	2300	N	Arctic

Attributes of Siberian Rivers

You want to create a chart comparing the attributes in this table. In the process, you may select certain records in the table to chart. But selecting these records also highlights the corresponding features in the view. If you don't want to highlight these features, you can make a separate copy of the theme table and use it to create your chart. The copy isn't linked to the view, so you can select its records without affecting the view.

To make a copy of the theme table, you'll export it to a dBASE file.

3. With the Attributes of Siberian Rivers table active, select Export from the File menu. The Export Table dialog box displays. dBASE is the selected (default) format, so click OK.

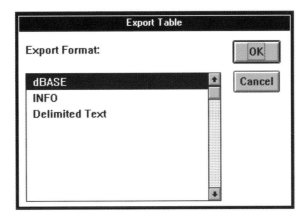

Another Export Table dialog box displays, where you specify the name and location of the file you want to export the table into.

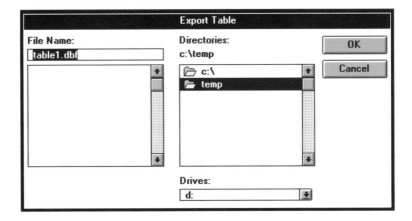

4. Specify the *drive:\directory* where you want to save the export table, then change the file name to **rivers.dbf.** Click OK. A new file is created containing all the records from the attribute table.

Next you'll add the new file to your project as a table, using the Project window.

5. From the Window menu, select "ex20.apr" to make the Project window active. In the Project window, click on the Tables icon. Click the Add button to display the Add Table dialog box.

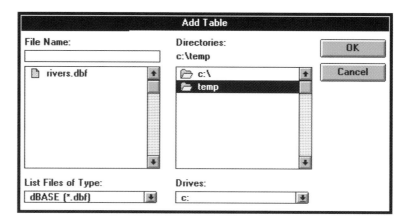

6. If necessary, navigate to the *drive:\directory* where you saved the export table, then select "rivers.dbf." Click OK. The rivers.dbf table displays, and its name is added to the list of tables in the project.

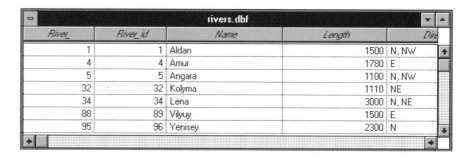

Next you'll hide some of the fields in rivers.dbf and rename it to make the name more descriptive.

7.   With rivers.dbf active, select Properties from the Table menu. The Table Properties dialog box displays.

The bottom of the dialog box contains a scrolling list of the table's fields with check marks indicating whether or not each field is visible.

8.   In the Title box, type **Major Siberian Rivers.** Then in the scrolling list, click on the check marks next to the River_ and River_id fields to make them invisible. Click OK. The River_ and River_id fields are now hidden.

9.   Close the Attributes of Siberian Rivers table (you won't need it) by making it active and then selecting Close from the File menu.

Now your data is ready for charting.

If you want to go on to the next exercise, leave the project open.

Creating a chart and changing the way it looks

You want to create a chart comparing the attributes of the rivers and present it, along with your view, at the quarterly business meeting. You'll use the Major Siberian Rivers table to generate the chart.

When you create a chart, ArcView displays it with the default format, axes, title, and legend, and assigns the default set of colors to the data markers (e.g., columns, bars, pie slices). You can change the way it looks by modifying any of these characteristics.

Exercise 20b

1. If *ex20a.apr* is open, continue. Otherwise, choose Open Exercise from the File menu. In the Exercises scrolling list, select "ex20b," then click OK. When the project opens, you see a view and an active table, Major Siberian Rivers.

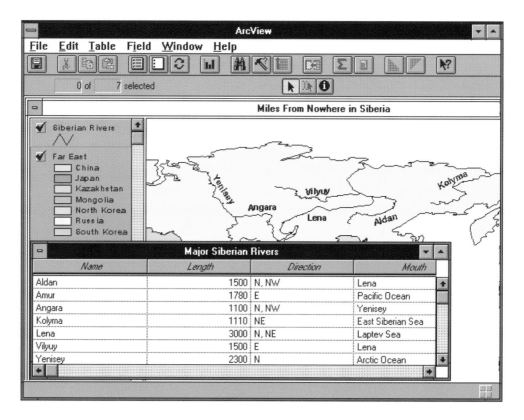

ENVIRONMENTAL SYSTEMS RESEARCH INSTITUTE, INC.

2. Click the Chart button to open the Chart Properties dialog box.

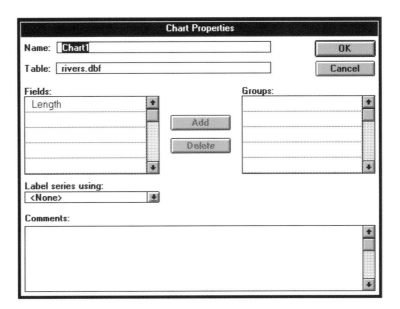

3. In the Name input box, change the name to **River Lengths.**

The Fields scrolling list displays the names of all chartable (numeric) fields in the active table, except hidden fields.

4. Click on "Length," then click the Add button. This puts the Length field in the list of groups to be charted.

Below the Fields list, a drop-down list (Label series using) displays the fields you can use to label each item in your chart.

5. In the lower drop-down list (Label series using), click on the downward-pointing arrow and choose "Name," then click OK.

ArcView plots the river lengths in the default chart format.

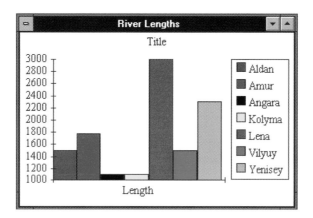

A colored bar, or *data marker,* indicates the length of each river. The name of each river appears in the chart's legend.

> **Choosing a chart format.** ArcView offers six types of charts: area, bar, column (the default), line, pie, and x,y scatter. The type you choose depends on the nature of your data and the message you want to convey. Line charts, for instance, are good for showing changes in values over time. Pie charts, on the other hand, show relationships between parts and the whole. For more information, search for this Help Topic: *Chart - choosing a chart format.*

The River Lengths chart compares the values of a single variable (length). For this type of comparison, a column or bar chart is best.

Next you'll refine the chart. (You may want to enlarge the chart window so the elements are easier to see.)

Notice the labels on the y-axis. The lowest is 1000, the highest 3000, and the increment is 200. You'll modify these settings using Chart Axis Properties so the data markers for shorter rivers are more prominent.

6. With the chart active, click on the Chart Element Properties tool, then click anywhere on the y-axis of the chart. The Chart Axis Properties dialog box displays.

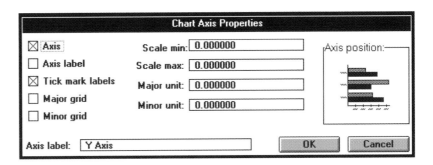

7. In the Scale max text box, highlight the default value and type **3500.** This sets the upper limit on the y-axis. (The lower limit is already set to 0.) In the Major unit text box, replace the default value with **500** to adjust the increment. Finally, in the Axis label text box at the bottom of the dialog box, highlight "Y Axis" and replace it with the word **Miles.** Click on the Axis label check box (near the top left of the dialog box) to turn it on. Click OK. The chart redraws with the changes you made.

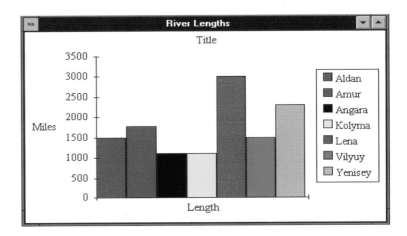

The chart looks better, but it's still difficult to follow the y-axis labels across to the columns.

8. Click again on the chart's y-axis to reopen the Chart Axis Properties dialog box. Click on the Major grid check box, then click OK. The chart redraws with gridlines that make it easier to read.

Notice that the attribute you're charting, "Length," is currently displayed along the bottom of the chart. This is the Group label. You'll also add an x-axis label to the bottom of the chart.

9. Click somewhere on the chart's x-axis to open its Chart Axis Properties dialog box.

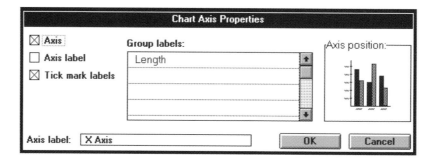

10. In the Axis label text box at the bottom of the dialog box, highlight "X Axis" and replace it with the words **Note: The Mississippi River is 2470 miles long.** Click on the Axis label check box above to turn it on, then click OK. At this point, your chart should look like this:

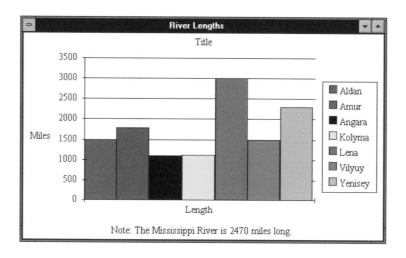

Changing the chart's legend. You can edit the labels that appear in the legend or change the position of the legend using Chart Legend Properties. Access the Chart Legend Properties dialog box by clicking on the chart's legend with the Chart Element Properties tool. For more information, search for these Help Topics: *Chart Legend Properties, Chart Element Properties tool.*

Now you'll give your chart a title.

11. Click on the word "Title" at the top of your chart to open the Chart Title Properties dialog box.

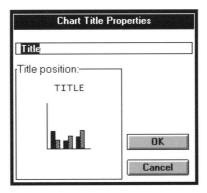

The title has five fixed positions you can click on: top, bottom, left, right, or middle. (If you choose the middle position, you can place the title anywhere you wish.) You'll leave the title at the top (the default position).

12. In the text box, type the words **Major Siberian Rivers,** then click OK. The chart redraws with the new title.

Your chart looks good, but you want to change the gray color representing the Yenisey to a more vivid color. For this you'll use the Chart Color tool.

13. Click on the Chart Color tool in the Chart tool bar. When the Symbol Palette displays, choose the Color Palette.

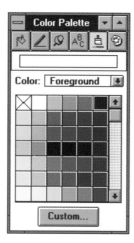

You can use the Chart Color tool to change the color of any chart element, such as data markers, title, and labels.

ENVIRONMENTAL SYSTEMS RESEARCH INSTITUTE, INC.

14. In the Color Palette, click on the "russet" square (the one diagonal to black). A black border appears around it to indicate that it's selected. Now bring the cursor over to the chart and click on the gray data marker for the Yenisey River. The color of the data marker changes to russet, and the legend symbol changes to match. Close the Color Palette.

Your chart should now look like this:

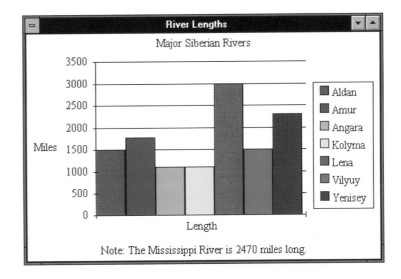

If you want to go on to the next exercise, leave the project open.

Querying and editing charts

Because ArcView charts are dynamically linked to the tables from which they're created, you can get information from the table by simply clicking on the chart. In addition, you can edit the source table for the chart and the chart immediately reflects the change.

Your chart is almost ready for presentation at the quarterly business meeting. You realize that attendees will have questions about the information behind the chart, and you must be prepared. You also want to remove any information from the chart that's not useful to your presentation.

Exercise 20c

1. If either *ex20a.apr* or *ex20b.apr* is open, continue. Otherwise, choose Open Exercise from the File menu. In the Exercises scrolling list, select "ex20c," then click OK. When the project opens, you see a view and an active chart, River Lengths.

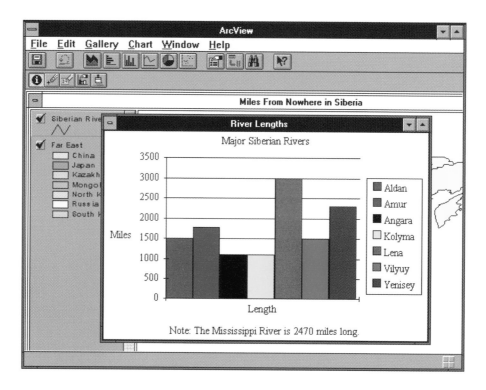

Each data marker in your chart corresponds to a record in the Major Siberian Rivers table. Using the Identify tool, you can click on any data marker to display the corresponding record in the table.

2. Choose the Identify tool from the Chart tool bar if it's not already selected. Click on the green data marker for the Amur River. The corresponding record displays in the Identify Results dialog box.

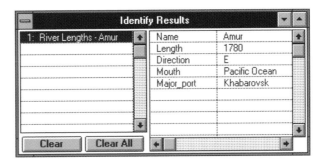

Clicking on additional data markers adds them to the Identify Results dialog box.

3. Close the dialog box when you're finished.

With the view active, you can see that the Kolyma River in northeastern Siberia is extremely remote and inaccessible, making it too expensive and difficult to launch an expedition there. You want to remove the Kolyma from your chart.

4. Select the chart and the table so that both are visible in front of the view. Resize them to fit in the bottom half of the ArcView window.

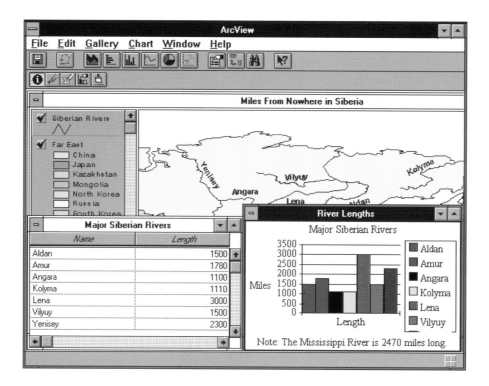

5. With the chart active, click on the Erase tool. Now bring the cursor over to the chart and click on the yellow data marker for the Kolyma River.

Notice that the Kolyma data marker disappears from the chart and its corresponding record is no longer selected in the table. Notice also that the colors of the data markers have shifted one position to the right, eliminating the russet color.

Adding and deleting data markers. Because a chart is dynamically linked to a table, selecting or unselecting records in the table affects the data markers in the chart. You can add data markers to a chart by selecting more records in the table, or delete data markers by unselecting records or by using the Erase tool. For more information, search for these Help Topics: *Adding and erasing data markers on a chart, Erase tool.*

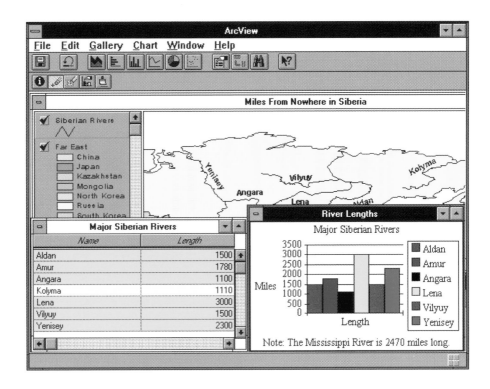

You're ready to present your preliminary ideas at the quarterly business meeting. The chart, together with the view, communicates something of the vastness of Siberia, focusing attention on its rivers as perhaps the best means of exploring the interior. You realize that further research will be needed to refine your plan. You'll need information on river navigability, the business climate in Russia, a cost analysis, and sample itineraries. If this research proves favorable, there is every chance that senior management will support your idea.

If you want to go on to the next chapter, leave ArcView running. Otherwise, choose Exit from the File menu.

SECTION 6:
Presenting information

Creating
map layouts

Making a basic map layout

Adding charts and tables

Adding the finishing touches and printing

Creating map layouts

You've seen how ArcView creates views, tables, and charts. Each of these documents presents information in a different format. But what if you want to display all of these formats at the same time on your screen, or print them on a single piece of paper? And what if you want to add a scale bar, north arrow, border, and title to create a presentation-quality map?

You can do all these things with ArcView. It allows you to dynamically place views, tables, charts, images, and any graphic elements you want in one document, called a *layout*. You can think of a layout as representing the final piece of paper your map will be printed on. If you change your mind later, you can add, remove, resize, and move each element in a layout as required. Instead of a static map, you have a dynamic document that can adapt to your needs.

Making a basic map layout

Suppose you're publishing a book on the social and economic growth of Canada. You want to include a population density map to show where most Canadians live and work. You'll create a layout that includes a view of population density by province, a table of population statistics, and a chart comparing the population of major Canadian cities.

ENVIRONMENTAL SYSTEMS RESEARCH INSTITUTE, INC.

Exercise 21a

1. If necessary, start ArcView. From the File menu, choose Open Exercise. In the Exercises scrolling list, select "ex21a," then click OK. When the project opens, you see a view, a table, and a chart.

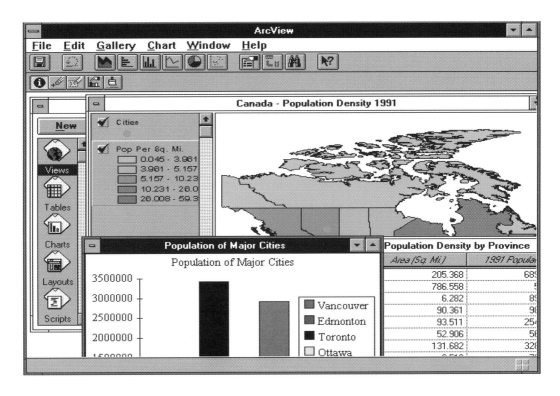

You'll create a layout containing these documents.

2. Click on the Layouts icon in the Project window, then click New. A blank layout page appears.

If the orientation of your layout page is landscape (horizontal), choose Page Setup from the Layout menu and change the orientation to portrait (vertical).

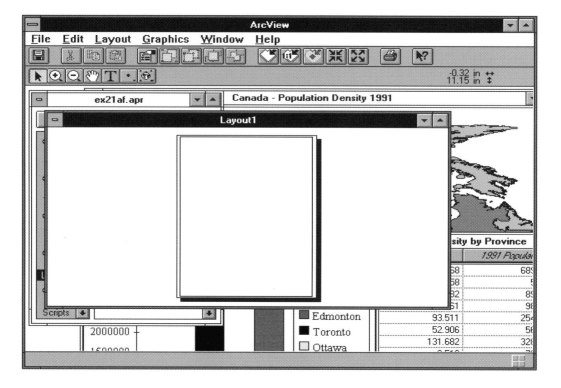

The layout page is too small to work with effectively, so you'll enlarge it.

3. Click on the up arrow in the layout window banner to make the lay-out window full size.

4. Click the Zoom to Page button to fit the layout page to the enlarged layout window.

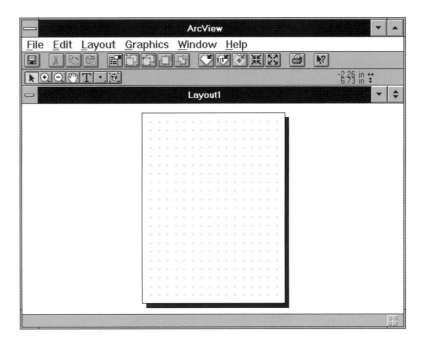

Now that the layout page is larger, you see grid dots. These dots are used to snap elements to precise locations in the layout.

Grid dots appear only on the screen, not on the printout. If you don't want to show the grid as part of an on-screen presentation, you can hide it by clicking Hide Grid in the Layout menu.

Before you add elements to your layout, you'll set up the layout page.

5. Click on the Layout menu and choose Properties. The Layout Properties dialog box displays.

6. Click in the Name field and change the name to **Population Density 1991.** Click in the Horizontal and Vertical Grid Spacing text boxes and change each to **0.5.** This sets the grid points 0.5 inches apart. Click OK.

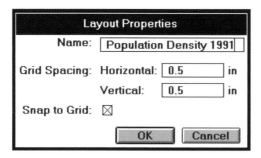

7. Click on the Layout menu again and choose Page Setup. The Page Setup dialog box displays. Click the Page Size drop-down arrow and choose "Letter 8.5 x 11.0 in." Click OK. This sizes the layout to fit on an $8^1/_2$-by-11-inch piece of paper.

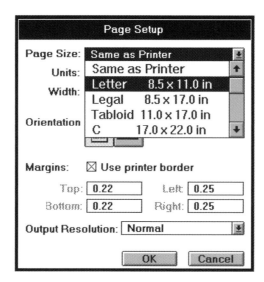

Now that you've finished the basic page setup for the layout, you can begin to add views, tables, charts, and other elements to the layout using the Frame tool.

Adding documents to a layout. Each document you add to a layout has its own box, or *frame.* There's a different tool for creating each document frame, and each has its own properties. For example, you can use the Chart Frame tool to draw a frame for your population chart of Canadian cities. After you draw the frame, the Chart Frame Properties dialog box displays, which enables you to choose the chart you want from all of the available charts. After specifying the properties you want, the chart draws inside the frame. For more information, search for these Help Topics: *Adding frames, Frame tool, Types of frames.*

The Frame tool is a set of drop-down tools on the Layout tool bar. It includes an icon for each of the following types of frames: view, legend, scale bar, north arrow, chart, table, and picture. You'll use the View frame tool first.

8.   Click on the Frame tool and hold down the mouse button to display the drop-down tools. Drag the cursor down to the View frame tool and release. The View frame tool is now selected.

9. Move the cursor inside the layout. Place the cursor (now crosshairs) on the upper left grid point, then click and hold down the mouse button as you drag the cursor to draw a view frame in the upper portion of the layout. When you release the button, the View Frame Properties dialog box displays.

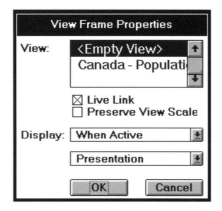

10. Click on "Canada - Population Density 1991" in the View scrolling list. Live Link should already be checked, specifying that the view frame will be linked to the view. This means that changes to the view are automatically reflected in the view frame. Preserve View Scale is not checked, so the view will be resized to fit inside the view frame. (When you check Preserve View Scale, the scale of the view is preserved in the view frame, and you may not see the entire view.)

11. Click on the upper Display drop-down list and choose "Always" to display the view in the view frame, even when the layout document is not active. "Presentation," the default choice in the lower Display drop-down list, indicates that the view rather than a shaded box will display in the frame.

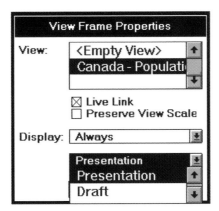

12. Click OK. The Canada - Population Density 1991 view draws in the view frame. The four black handles indicate that this is the currently selected frame.

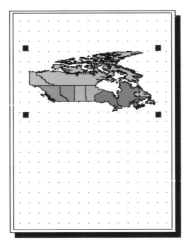

You're ready to add a legend to your layout. The legend is a representation of the view's Table of Contents and stays inside a legend frame (in the layout).

13. Click on the Frame tool and hold down the mouse button to display the drop-down tools. Drag the cursor down to the Legend frame tool and release. The Legend frame tool is now selected.

14. Move the cursor inside the layout. Below the view frame, click and hold down the mouse button as you drag the cursor to draw a box for the legend frame about one-third the size of the view frame. Release the button and the Legend Frame Properties dialog box displays.

The View Frame scrolling list shows the view frames that have already been placed in the layout.

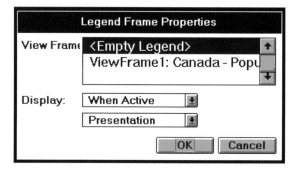

15. Click on "View Frame 1: Canada - Population Density 1991." Then click OK. The legend associated with this view frame draws on the layout.

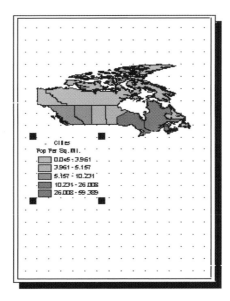

Don't like the size of the legend? You can change it with the Pointer tool.

 16. Click on the Pointer tool and move the cursor over one of the four handles around the legend frame until it changes to a double-headed arrow. Hold the mouse button down and drag the handle to change the size. The legend frame snaps to the nearest grid point and the legend redraws.

To move a layout element without resizing it, select it with the Pointer tool, move the cursor over the element (not on a handle), and drag it to a new location as you hold the mouse button down.

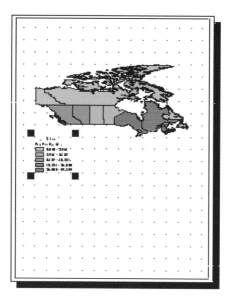

Next you'll add a scale bar to the layout. The scale bar has its own frame in the layout and is associated with a view frame.

17. Choose the Scale bar frame tool from the drop-down tools. Drag a scale bar frame box in the layout just as you did the view and legend frames. The Scale Bar Properties dialog box displays.

Scale Bar Properties

View Frame:	\<Empty Scalebar\>
	ViewFrame1: Canada - Population
Style:	
Units:	miles
Interval:	1
Intervals:	2
Left Divisions:	2

OK   Cancel

18. Select "View Frame 1: Canada - Population Density 1991." Then click on the drop-down arrow for the Style field and choose a scale bar style. Click OK. The scale bar draws inside the scale bar frame in the layout.

Understanding scale bars. The scale bar draws to the size that accurately represents the scale of the view frame. When the view frame is live-linked to the view, the scale bar updates to reflect any change to the scale of the view. For more information, search for these Help Topics: *Adding a scale bar to a layout, Scale bar frame tool.*

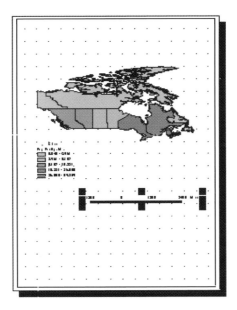

Finally, you'll add a north arrow to the layout.

19. Select the North arrow frame tool from the drop-down tools and drag a north arrow frame box in the layout. The North Arrow Manager dialog box displays.

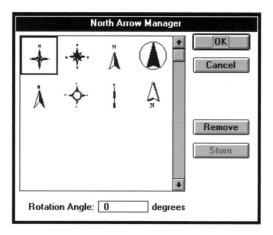

20. Select a north arrow and click OK. The north arrow draws inside its frame.

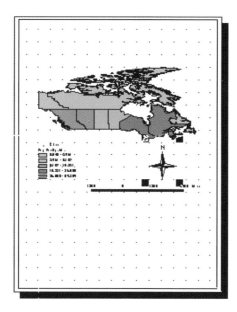

If you want to go on to the next exercise, leave the project open.

Adding charts and tables

The map layout for your book on social and economic growth of Canada is almost finished. It includes a view showing population density by province with a legend, scale bar, and north arrow. To enhance your presentation, you'll add a chart comparing the population of major cities in Canada and a table of population statistics.

Exercise 21b

1. If *ex21a.apr* is open, continue. Otherwise, choose Open Exercise from the File menu. In the Exercises scrolling list, select "ex21b," then click OK.

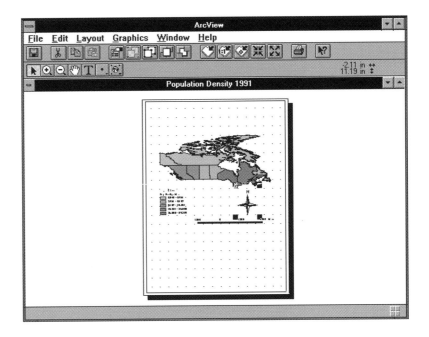

2. Select the Chart frame tool from the drop-down tools and drag a chart frame in your layout. The Chart Frame Properties dialog box displays.

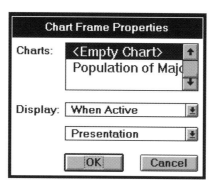

3. Select "Population of Major Cities" and click OK. The chart draws inside the chart frame.

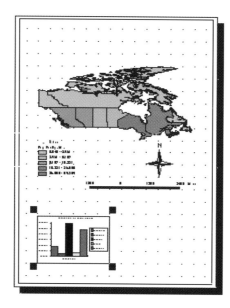

4. Next, select the Table frame tool from the drop-down tools and drag a table frame in your layout. The Table Frame Properties dialog box displays.

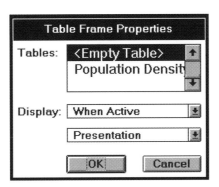

5. Choose the "Population Density by Province" table and click OK. The table draws in your layout.

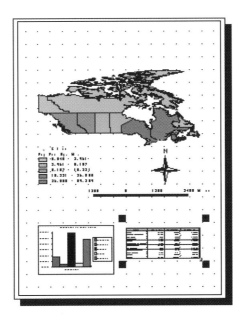

Importing scanned images. Want to really add impact to your layout? The Picture frame tool lets you add images to your layout. You can import scanned images in several different file formats into a picture frame. Just choose the Picture frame tool and create a picture frame. Then in the Picture Frame Properties dialog box, specify the file to import into the picture frame. For more information, search for these Help Topics: *Picture frame tool, Adding imported graphics to a layout.*

If you want to go on to the next exercise, leave the project open.

Adding the finishing touches and printing

Congratulations! You've added all the frames you need for your final layout presentation called "Population Density 1991." Now it's time to add some finishing touches (a title and a neatline) to make your layout look professional.

Exercise 21c

1. If *ex21b.apr* is open, continue. Otherwise, choose Open Exercise from the File menu. In the Exercises scrolling list, select "ex21c," then click OK.

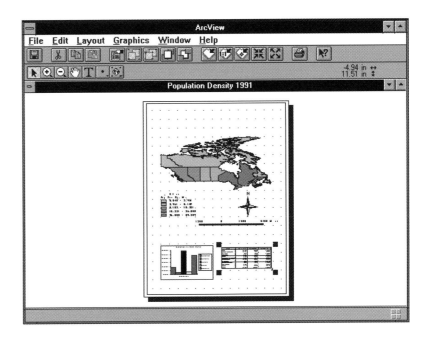

To give your layout a title, you'll use the Text tool.

 2.   Click on the Text tool in the Layout tool bar, then click inside the layout, near the top, where you want your title to start. The Text Properties dialog box displays.

3.   Type in **Population Density 1991,** then click OK.

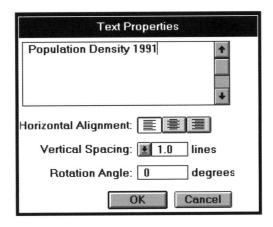

The title draws in the layout.

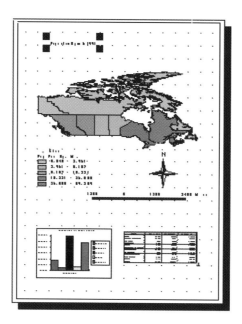

The title is too small. You can make it bigger by using the Symbol Palette to change the font size.

4. Click on the Window menu and select Show Symbol Palette. The Symbol Palette displays.

5. Select the Font Palette if it's not already selected.

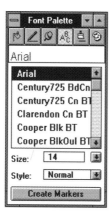

6. Click on the Size drop-down arrow and select "36." The title changes to 36-point text. Close the Font Palette.

If your title isn't centered, use the Pointer tool to drag the text to the desired position.

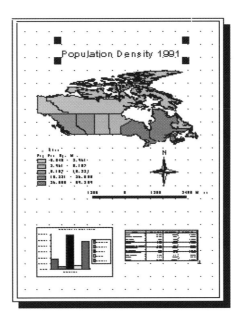

Aligning frames and graphics. You can align the frames and graphics in your layout with one another. To do this, first select the elements to align with the Pointer tool, then choose Align in the Graphics menu. In the Align dialog box, use the buttons to align selected elements along the top, bottom, right, left, or center of your layout. For more information, search for these Help Topics: *Align, Aligning graphics*.

Next you'll add a neatline.

7. Click on the Draw tool and hold down the mouse button to display the drop-down tools. Drag the cursor down to the Rectangle tool, then release. The Rectangle tool is now selected. Drag a rectangle around your layout so it encompasses all of the frames and graphics.

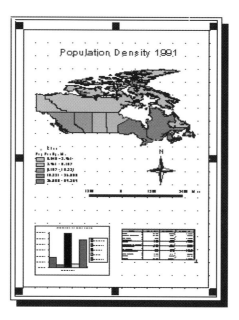

If all the elements in your layout don't fit inside the neatline, you may need to rearrange them. With the rectangle selected, choose Send to Back from the Graphics menu to place the rectangle behind the other elements in your layout. Then use the Pointer tool to select and move any elements.

Now that you've completed the layout page for your book, you're ready to print it.

8. From the File pulldown menu, select Print. The Print dialog box displays. If you have a printer connected to your computer and it's turned on, click OK to print the layout. Otherwise, click Cancel.

```
┌─────────────────────────────────────────────────┐
│                     Print                         │
├─────────────────────────────────────────────────┤
│  Print:  │ Population Density 1991           │▼│  │
│  Printer: HP Color LaserJet on LPT2:    │ Setup... │
│  To file: │                          │  │ Browse... │
│                              │ OK │  │ Cancel │    │
└─────────────────────────────────────────────────┘
```

Storing a layout as a template. You've done a lot of work to create this layout and position all of the frames exactly where you want them. Suppose you have many layouts to create and you want each of them to have the same look. Because the current layout can be stored as a template for future layouts, you won't have to do all the work over again. For more information, search for these Help Topics: *Store as template, Using a layout as a cartographic template.*

You've seen how to display a view, table, chart, and other graphic elements in a layout. Because your layout is a dynamic document, you can easily change it anytime you need to.

If you want to go on to the next chapter, leave ArcView running. Otherwise, choose Exit from the File menu.

SECTION 7

Creating your own data

In the next three chapters, you'll learn several ways to create your own data. In chapter 22, you'll convert features from existing themes to create new ones. You'll also create a new theme by drawing shapes, editing them, and adding attributes. In chapter 23, you'll create a point theme from a file of x,y coordinates. In chapter 24, you'll create a point theme from a list of addresses by matching the list against a theme containing address information.

Creating themes from shapefiles

Working with shapefiles

Editing shapes

Creating theme attributes

Creating themes from shapefiles

In chapter 8, you learned that ArcView shapefiles are ArcView's own format for storing feature locations and attributes. You can create your own shapefile by converting all or part of an existing theme to a shapefile, then adding it to a view as a theme. You can also create a new theme by drawing shapes and saving them as a shapefile, then creating a new theme based on the shapefile. Once you create a theme based on a shapefile, you can add attributes for each shape.

Working with shapefiles

Imagine that you are a biologist working for an agency that protects ecological biodiversity in the Bahia region of Brazil. Because your agency's resources are limited, your job is to target areas for protection to benefit the largest number of species. You decide to use ArcView to display themes showing the habitats of various threatened species. By displaying these themes together in a view, you'll be able to identify which areas have the most species in need of protection. Your agency can then concentrate its conservation efforts on these ecological "hotspots."

Your first task is to create a detailed map of frog habitats in a small subsection of the Bahia region. To do this, you'll select the features you want to show from several themes that cover the entire region. Then you'll convert these selected features to a shapefile and create a new theme.

ENVIRONMENTAL SYSTEMS RESEARCH INSTITUTE, INC.

Exercise 22a

1. If necessary, start ArcView. From the File menu, choose Open
    Exercise. In the Exercises scrolling list, select "ex22a," then click
    OK. When the project opens, you see View1 of Bahia with point
    themes that show the habitats of various species.

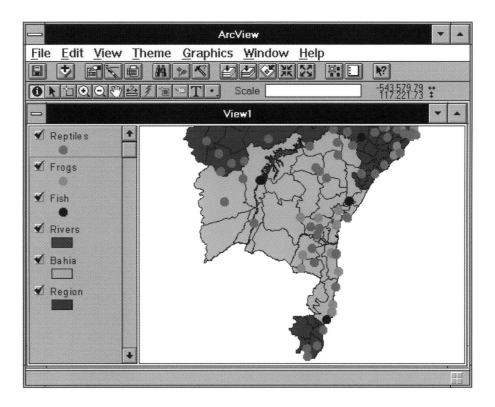

First you'll select the features for the new theme you want to create.

2. Click on the Frogs theme to make it active. Then hold down the Shift key and click on the Bahia theme to make it active as well.

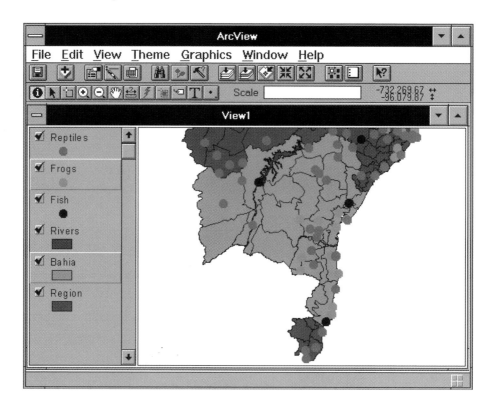

3. Click on the Draw tool to display the drop-down list of tools and select the Rectangle tool.

4. Draw a rectangle on the view where you see a concentration of frogs.

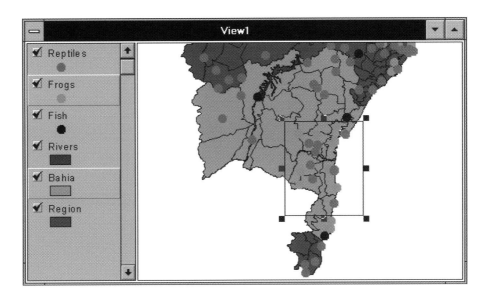

You'll use this rectangle to select features for a new shapefile theme.

 5.   Click the Select Features Using Shape button. The features in both the Frogs and Bahia themes that lie within or partially within the rectangle are selected and highlighted in yellow.

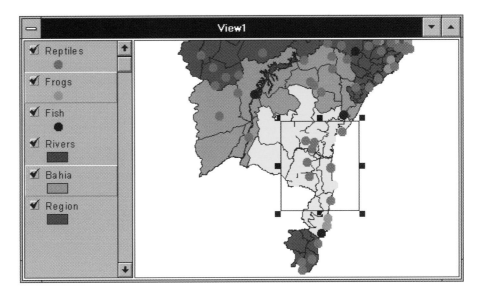

6. From the Theme menu, select Convert to Shapefile. The Convert to Shapefile dialog box displays.

7. Select a *drive:\directory* where you want to save the shapefile. In the File Name text box, change the name to **frogs2.shp,** then click OK.

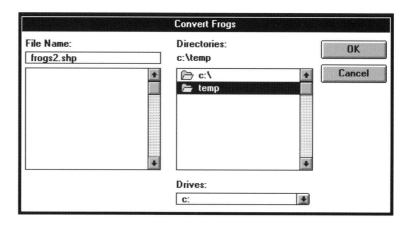

Another Convert to Shapefile dialog box displays. You're asked if you want to "Add shapefile as theme to a view?" If you answer No, the selected features are saved in a shapefile, but not displayed. If you answer Yes, you'll be prompted to select a view for displaying the new theme.

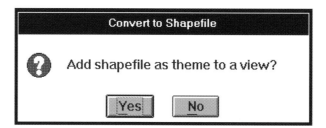

8. Click Yes. Another dialog box displays with a list of available views.

The project already contains two views. You'll create a new view to display the new themes.

ENVIRONMENTAL SYSTEMS RESEARCH INSTITUTE, INC.

9.   Choose "<New View>" and click OK.

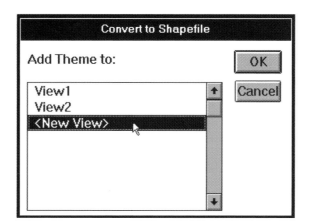

ArcView creates a new view, called View3, with a new theme based on the frogs2.shp file, but the view doesn't display yet. The Convert Bahia dialog box displays next.

10.   As in step 7, select a *drive:\directory* location for the shapefile. In the File Name text box, change the name to **bahia2.shp** and click OK.

11.   When the Convert to Shapefile dialog box displays, click Yes. The next dialog box displays a list of available views.

12.   Choose "View3" and click OK. This adds the Bahia2.shp theme to View3, which already contains the Frogs2.shp theme.

View3 appears with two themes, Frogs2.shp and Bahia2.shp, listed in its Table of Contents. The theme added last (Bahia2.shp) appears at the top of the list. Both themes are turned off.

You'll change the draw order so the Frogs2.shp theme draws on top of the Bahia2.shp theme, then turn both themes on to see them.

13. With the cursor over the Bahia2.shp theme in the Table of Contents, hold down the mouse button and drag the theme down until it's below the Frogs2.shp theme. Turn both themes on by clicking on their check boxes. ArcView draws the Frogs2.shp theme on top of the Bahia2.shp theme.

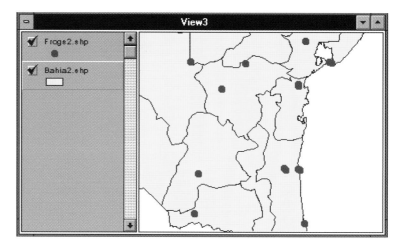

You've completed your first task by creating a detailed map of frog habitats in a small section of Bahia. You now have a new view with two new themes created from features in two existing themes. Next you'll create a new theme by drawing features.

If you want to go on to the next exercise, leave the project open.

Editing shapes

Your next task is to create a new theme showing the areas where the highest concentrations of endangered species live. To do this you'll display themes showing the habitats of endangered species. Then you'll create a new theme by drawing polygons around areas that have the most species. Then you'll edit one of the polygons to make it more accurate.

Exercise 22b

1. If *ex22a.apr* is open, close View1 and View3, then open View2 from the Project window. Otherwise, choose Open Exercise from the File menu. In the Exercises scrolling list, select "ex22b," then click OK. When the project opens, you see View2 displaying the Bahia region with several species themes.

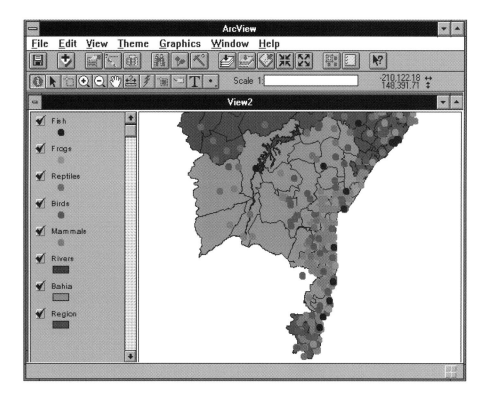

You'll create a new theme, then add shapes to it.

2. From the View menu, choose New Theme. The New Theme dialog box displays.

3.   Click on the drop-down arrow for Feature type, select "Polygon," then click OK.

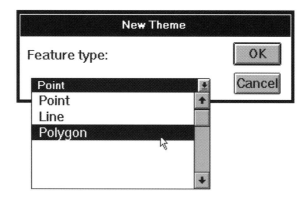

Another dialog box displays, asking you for a theme name.

4.   Specify the *drive:\directory* where you want to save the new theme, then change the file name to **hotspots.shp.** Click OK.

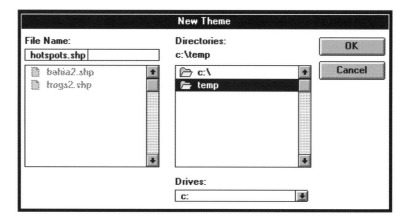

A new theme called Hotspots.shp is added to your view, but it's empty.

By default, the new theme is editable. If you don't want to edit the theme or don't want to save the edits you've made, choose Stop Editing from the Theme menu.

Next you'll add shapes to the new theme.

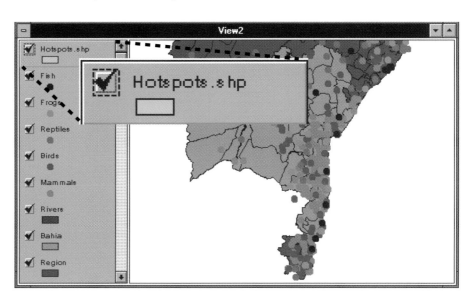

Notice that the check box for the Hotspots.shp theme has a dashed line around it, indicating that editing is allowed. Before you add features (shapes) to this theme, you'll specify a new draw symbol.

5.   Double-click on the Hotspots.shp theme to open the Legend Editor. In the Legend Editor, double-click on the symbol to open the Fill Palette. Choose the pattern shown in the graphic below, then click Apply in the Legend Editor. When you're finished, close the Fill Palette and the Legend Editor.

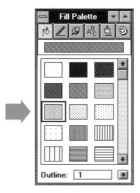

With the new symbol, you'll be able to see theme features underneath the shapes you draw.

6.   From the Draw tool's drop-down list, choose the Polygon tool.

7.   Draw three polygons in the areas with the highest concentration of different species in Bahia. (The shapes you draw don't need to look exactly like the ones you see below.) Each time you click on the view, a vertex is added to the polygon. Double-click to close each polygon.

The Hotspots.shp theme now contains three shapes.

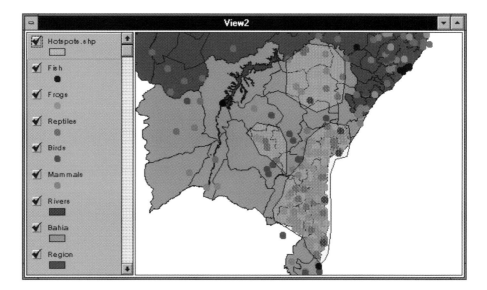

Modifying shapes. You can change the position or size of a shape, or delete it altogether. First click on the Pointer tool, then click on the shape to select it. You can use the Pointer tool to drag it, resize it, or delete it. If you want to change the color of a shape or use a non-solid fill pattern so that the themes below it show through, select the shape with the Pointer tool and change the color or fill pattern with the Symbol Palette. For more information, search for this Help Topic: *Editing a theme*.

You've decided that one of the shapes needs to be edited because it doesn't include all of the species habitats you wanted.

You'll need to use the Pointer tool to move the shape's vertices. There's a vertex at the beginning and end of each line segment of the shape, but they're hidden until you display them with the Pointer tool.

8. Click on the Pointer tool, then click on a shape to select it. Selection handles appear around it.

9. Use the Zoom to Selected button to enlarge the selected shape.

10. Click once again on the selected shape with the Pointer tool to display the vertices.

The selection handles disappear and a vertex handle appears at each of the shape's vertices. Any vertex can be moved to change the shape of the polygon.

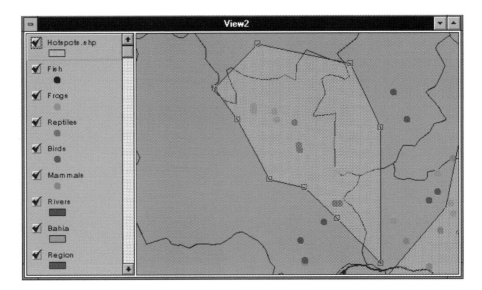

11. Move the Pointer tool over one of the vertices until the cursor changes to crosshairs. Drag the vertex to a new position. You just edited the outline of the shape.

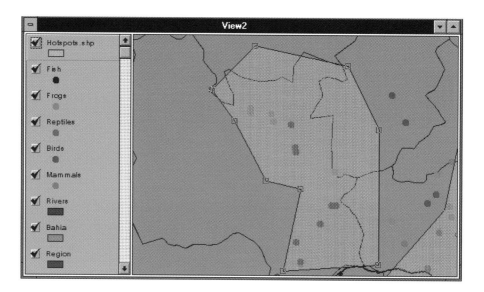

12. Click the Zoom to Active Themes button to display the entire shape-file theme again.

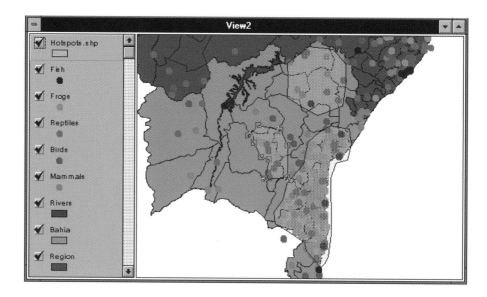

The vertices are still visible, but if you click anywhere on the view with the Pointer tool, they'll disappear.

13. From the Theme menu, select Stop Editing. The changes you just made to the shape are saved in the shapefile.

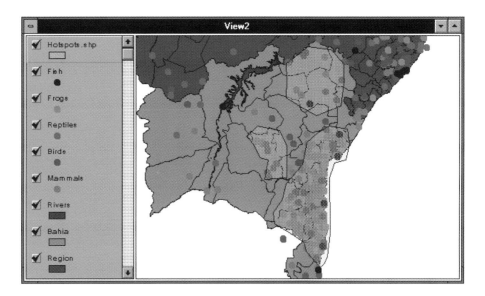

Notice that the dashed line around the Hotspots.shp check box in the Table of Contents is gone. This indicates that the theme is no longer editable. The polygon you just edited is now the selected feature (highlighted in yellow).

14. Click the Clear Selected Features button to unselect the selected polygon.

You've created a new theme containing three polygons that denote ecological hotspots, areas where the highest concentrations of endangered species live. Now you want to add attributes to the theme.

Creating theme attributes

For each feature you create in a new theme, ArcView adds a record to the theme's attribute table. But the attribute table has only one default field, called *Shape*. In the next exercise, you'll add a new field called *Name* to the Hotspots.shp attribute table, then add values to it. To do this, you'll make the theme table editable.

Exercise 22c

1. If either *ex22a.apr* or *ex22b.apr* is open, continue. Otherwise, choose Open Exercise from the File menu. In the Exercises scrolling list, select "ex22c," then click OK. When the project opens, you see a view in which the Hotspots.shp theme is active.

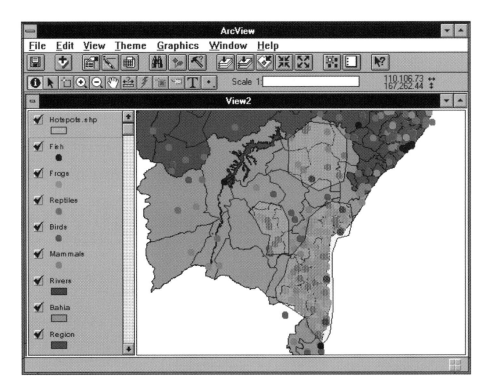

2. From the Theme menu, select Table. The Attributes of Hotspots.shp table displays.

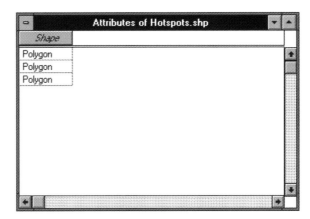

The table currently shows one field, *Shape.* Notice that the Shape field name appears in *italics*. This indicates that editing is not allowed. You'll make the table editable.

3. From the Table menu, choose Start Editing. The Shape field name now appears in plain text, indicating that editing is allowed.

4. From the Edit menu, choose Add Field. The Field Definition dialog box displays.

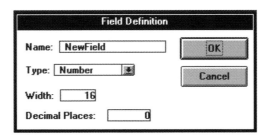

5. In the Name text box, type **Hotspot Name.** Click on the Type drop-down arrow and choose "String." Click OK.

A new field named Hotspot Name is added to the attribute table. Next you'll add values to this field.

6. Click on the first record with the Select tool. ArcView highlights the record in the table and the shape it's linked to in the view.

You'll use the Edit tool to assign a value to the record.

7. Click on the Edit tool, then click in the first cell in the Hotspot Name field. Type a name that describes the shape linked to this record, such as Coastal Plain, Interior (the polygon you just edited), or River Basin, then press the Enter key. (The order of the records corresponds to the order in which you added the shapes.)

Editing the values in a table. To use the Edit tool, place the cursor in the field of the record you want to edit, then type the new value into the field. Use the following keyboard accelerators to control the movements of the cursor: Tab, to move it one cell to the right; Shift–Tab, to move it one cell to the left; Enter, to move it down a cell; and Shift–Enter, to move it up a cell. When you finish editing the table, choose Stop Editing from the Table menu. Your edits are saved as soon as you move the cursor to a new cell, change tools, or use a control from the button or menu bar. For more information, search for these Help Topics: *Edit tool, Editing the values in a table, Start/Stop Editing.*

ENVIRONMENTAL SYSTEMS RESEARCH INSTITUTE, INC.

Repeat steps 6 and 7 to add values to the remaining two records. Use the Select tool to highlight each record and its corresponding shape. Then use the Edit tool to assign a value to the record. When you finish, the table will look similar to this one:

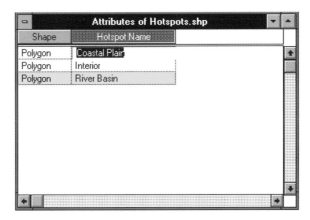

8. From the Table menu, choose Stop Editing. The field names appear in *italics* to indicate that the table is no longer editable. ArcView saves your changes in the source data file hotspots.dbf.

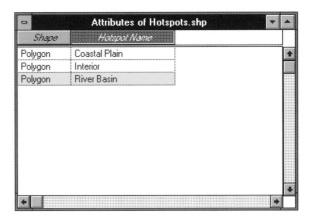

Now you can build a query using the new attribute field or use it to label the shapes in the view.

The detailed map of frog habitats and the map of hotspots can help you target those areas most in need of protection. Because both themes are based on shapefiles, you can edit their features and attributes any time.

If you want to go on to the next chapter, leave ArcView running. Otherwise, choose Exit from the File menu.

SECTION 7:
Creating your own data

Creating themes
from coordinate files

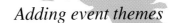

Adding event themes

CHAPTER 23

Creating themes from coordinate files

ArcView lets you create themes from location information in a table, information in the form of geographic coordinates, street addresses, or mileposts along a route. Chapter 24 focuses on creating themes from addresses. This chapter focuses on creating themes from geographic coordinates.

Geographic coordinates can be expressed either as degrees of latitude and longitude, or as pairs of x,y coordinates (see chapter 5). ArcView reads the geographic coordinates from fields you specify in a table and creates a point feature for each location.

Geographic coordinates can be obtained from paper maps, locations in a view, field surveys, Global Positioning System (GPS) receivers, geocoded tables of addresses, and so on. (When ArcView geocodes a table of addresses, it calculates an x,y coordinate pair for each address. See chapter 24.) The geographic coordinates can be in any tabular data format that ArcView supports.

ENVIRONMENTAL SYSTEMS RESEARCH INSTITUTE, INC.

Adding event themes

In ArcView, locations stored in a tabular format are referred to as *event locations* or simply *events,* and the table containing them is referred to as an *event table.* Events let you map data that contains geographic locations but isn't in a spatial format (e.g., a file of addresses, a table of information referenced to milepost locations along a route, or latitude–longitude locations stored as records in a table).

Suppose you're involved in a unique conservation program designed to help endangered African wildlife and develop local economies. As a part of this program, permits are sold to foreign hunters allowing them to hunt certain species of African wildlife, in limited numbers. The money collected from the sale of permits goes to local villages for building schools and hospitals. In return, villagers agree to monitor protected areas and prevent poaching inside these areas.

During the last month, more than 20 antelope have fallen prey to poachers inside protected areas. You want to know exactly where these incidents took place and which protected areas they occurred in.

You've sent inspectors out, armed with portable GPS equipment, to capture precise x,y locations. The x,y locations are measured in decimal degrees (degrees of latitude and longitude expressed as a decimal), where x is the longitude and y is the latitude. You've received the data in a dBASE-formatted file.

Exercise 23a

1. If necessary, start ArcView. From the File menu, choose Open Exercise. In the Exercises scrolling list, select "ex23a," then click OK. When the project opens, you see a view with two themes, Villages and Protected Areas. Each village is a point; each protected area is a polygon defining a conservation unit. There is one conservation unit for each village. Beyond the Village Protection areas is a large Federal Protection area.

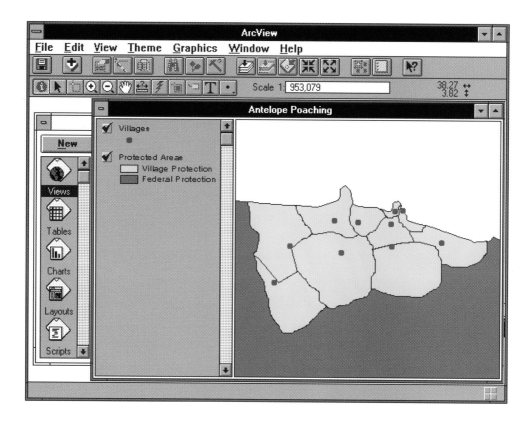

You'll bring the dBASE file containing x,y locations into the current project as an ArcView table.

2.   Make the Project window active, then click on the Tables icon.

3.   Click the Add button to open the Add Table dialog box. From the lower left drop-down list (List Files of Type), choose "dBASE [*.dbf]." This indicates you want to create a table from a dBASE file. From the Drives list, select your CD–ROM drive (or the drive where you installed the data for this book), then navigate to \gtkav\data\ch23 in the Directories list. From the File Name list, choose "antelope.dbf."

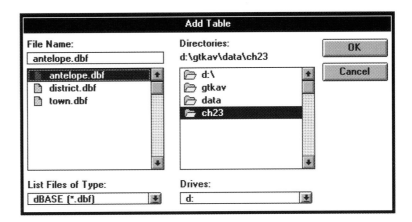

4.   Click OK to add the antelope.dbf table to your project.

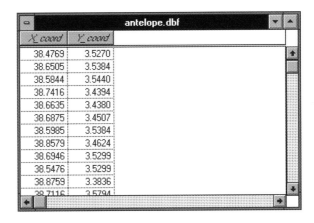

When the table opens, you see two fields, *X_coord* and *Y_coord*. You'll use the location coordinates in these fields to create a new theme of point features based on ArcView's shapefile format. Since the table doesn't need to remain open, you'll close it first.

5. Close the antelope.dbf table. Make the view active, then choose Add
    Event Theme from the View menu. The Add Event Theme dialog
    box displays.

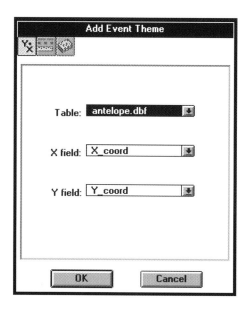

At the top of the Add Event Theme dialog box, you see three buttons.
Each button represents a category of events: XY (selected), Route, and
Address. (Clicking a button displays the fields appropriate for the cate-
gory you choose.)

Antelope.dbf is already selected in the Table list. ArcView reads the field
names in this table to find fields likely to contain x,y coordinates. The
names of these fields, *X_coord* and *Y_coord,* appear in the X field and
Y field lists.

6.   Click OK to create a new theme from the x,y coordinates in the antelope.dbf table.

The new theme, Antelope.dbf, appears in the view's Table of Contents.

7.   Click on the check box in front of the theme name to turn it on. ArcView draws the view with the new theme.

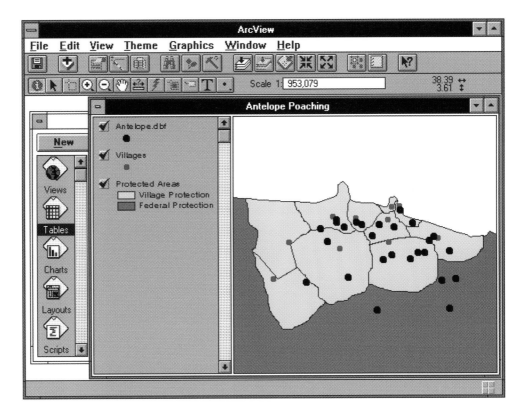

Now you can see exactly where the antelope poachings took place.

For each poaching site, you want to know the name of the protected area it's in. So you'll perform a spatial join.

8. Make the Antelope.dbf and Protected Areas themes active by holding down the Shift key and clicking on each theme, then click the Open Theme Table button to open the attribute tables for both themes.

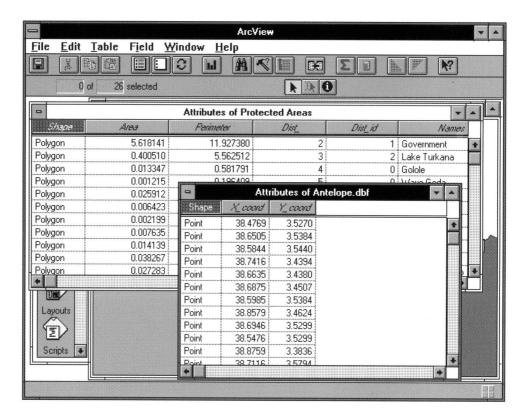

9. Make the Attributes of Protected Areas table active, then click on its Shape field to make it active. (This is the source table.) Do the same to the Attributes of Antelope.dbf table. (This is the destination table.)

10. With the Attributes of Antelope.dbf table active, select Join from the Table menu. ArcView appends the attributes of each protected area to the poaching sites it contains. (See chapter 19 for more information on the spatial join operation in ArcView.)

The Attributes of Antelope.dbf table displays with additional fields appended from the Attributes of Protected Areas table. For each antelope poaching site, there's now a name, the name of the protected area it's found in.

Y coord	Area	Perimeter	Dist	Dist_id	Names
3.5270	0.013347	0.581791	4	0	Golole
3.5384	0.007635	0.386484	9	0	Sololo
3.5440	0.006423	0.326627	7	0	Anona
3.4394	0.027283	0.643229	12	0	Sololo Makutano
3.4380	0.027283	0.643229	12	0	Sololo Makutano
3.4507	0.027283	0.643229	12	0	Sololo Makutano
3.5384	0.006423	0.326627	7	0	Anona
3.4624	0.014139	0.599093	10	0	Dabela
3.5299	0.007635	0.386484	9	0	Sololo
3.5299	0.013347	0.581791	4	0	Golole
3.3836	5.618141	11.927380	2	1	Government
3.5794	0.002199	0.268220	8	0	Mado Adi

Now that you know the names of the protected areas where poaching incidents occurred, you could use Summarize (chapters 11 and 14) to find out how many antelope were slain in each protected area and which villages need to be more vigilant.

If you want to go on to the next chapter, leave ArcView running. Otherwise, choose Exit from the File menu.

ENVIRONMENTAL SYSTEMS RESEARCH INSTITUTE, INC.

SECTION 7:
Creating your own data

Address geocoding

Creating point themes from addresses

Matching a list of addresses

Handling unmatched addresses

Address geocoding

Address geocoding is the process of matching addresses in a table to locations on a map. To geocode addresses, ArcView needs a table of addresses and a theme of streets, both containing address information formatted in a particular style. ArcView looks for matches between addresses in the table and address attributes linked to features in the street theme. For each match, ArcView creates a point feature in a new theme, deriving geographic coordinates from the matched street feature and assigning them to the point.

In this chapter, you'll learn how to prepare a theme for address matching, how to locate a single address on a map, and how to match an entire list of addresses to locations on a street map.

Creating point themes from addresses

Suppose that you work for Zuckerberg's Office Supply Company. Twice a year, it's your job to assign sales territories based upon the distribution of thousands of Zuckerberg customers across the state of Georgia. Traditionally, you print out a customer list from a database, open a box of pushpins, walk up to the wall map, look at the first address, try to find the street in the correct city or town, then attempt to guess where 555 is located. You continue this process for several days. Over time you've gotten a little tired of this approach. You've heard that Zuckerberg's distribution staff is using ArcView to locate where its products should be delivered. It makes sense that you could use ArcView to find the locations of all of Zuckerberg's customers.

Instead of trying to geocode Zuckerberg's thousands of customers, you decide to make a test run with a small portion of the customer database, just to see how it works. To begin, you'll make the street data "matchable" so ArcView can use it for geocoding.

Exercise 24a

1. If necessary, start ArcView. From the File menu, choose Open Exercise. In the Exercises scrolling list, select "ex24a," then click OK. When the project opens, you see a view with a street theme for a portion of the Atlanta area. You also see the theme table.

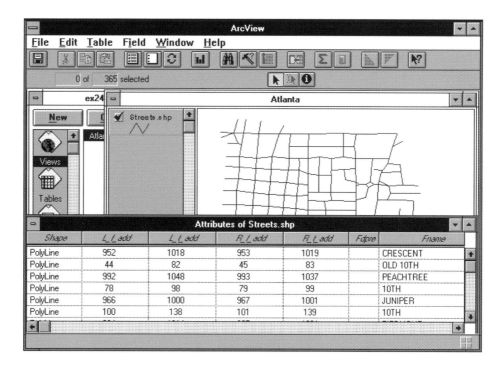

The theme table contains addresses divided into a number of components, each occupying a field in the table. For each street feature, you see four street address numbers ranging from low to high for each side of the street (e.g., L_f_add contains low address numbers for the left side of the street; R_t_add contains high address numbers for the right side of the street). The range indicates the possible numbers that could fall within a particular block, and the numbers are divided into even numbers on one side of the street and odd numbers on the other. In addition to these four address fields, there's one field containing street names and one containing street types (e.g., ST or AVE).

You'll make the street theme matchable by specifying the fields ArcView will use for geocoding.

Making a theme matchable. To prepare a theme for address matching, you must specify an address style for it. The style you choose defines which address components (fields) in the theme's attribute table will be used to match addresses. Once you specify an address style (there are eight styles to choose from), ArcView builds a geocoding index file to speed access to these fields. Specifying an address style and building a geocoding index are referred to as making a theme "matchable." For more information, search for these Help Topics: *The geocoding process, Address components, Geocoding Theme Property, Setting a theme's geocoding properties, Geocoding Index.*

To specify an address style and indicate which fields in the street theme's attribute table ArcView will use for address matching, you'll use Geocoding Theme Properties.

2. Make the view active and choose Properties from the Theme menu. The Theme Properties dialog box displays.

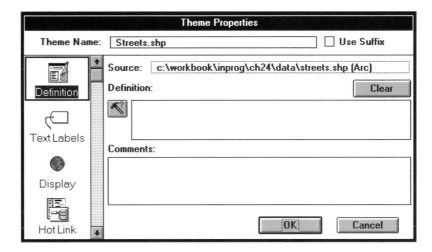

3. Scroll down the list of icons along the left side of the dialog box until you see the "Geocoding" icon, then click on it. The geocoding theme properties display.

4. Use the drop-down list to change the Address Style to "US Streets." ArcView lists the address components of this style on the left (required components have a check mark in front of them), and the corresponding fields in the street theme's attribute table on the right. The field names for the required address components are set correctly.

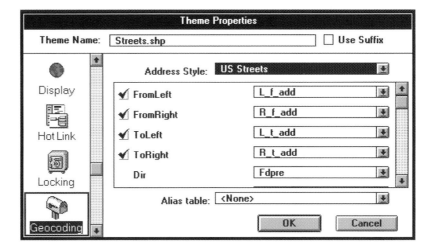

5. Click OK to set the geocoding theme properties, then click Yes to build a geocoding index file using the selected address style.

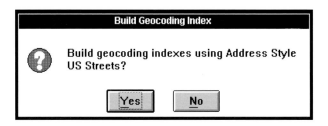

The Streets.shp theme is now matchable. This means you can use it to find an address interactively or to match a list of addresses.

Finding an address interactively

The street theme is now ready to geocode your test list of customer addresses. You're about to proceed when you receive a call from a prospective customer. You want to know exactly where the caller is located so you can determine which sales representative should handle the call. Instead of running over to the wall map, you decide to use ArcView's Locate function to find the address in the view.

6. Click the Locate button to display the Locate dialog box. (This button is available only when the active theme is matchable.)

7. In the Locate dialog box, type **400 4TH ST NE.** Click OK.

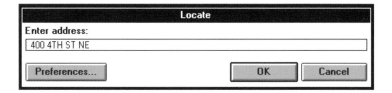

ArcView searches the street theme, finds the address, and places a point at the location. (If the location is outside the current display area, ArcView pans the view.)

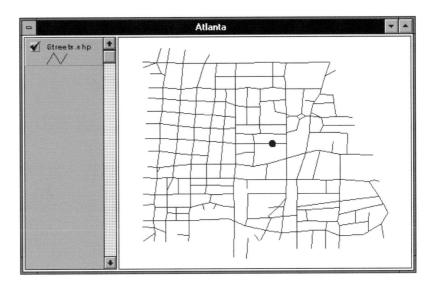

Now you can determine which sales rep should handle the call.

The point ArcView draws when you use Locate is only a graphic in the view, not a point feature.

Locating a street intersection. You can use ArcView's Locate function to find a street intersection. Just enter the names of two intersecting streets in the Enter Address text box, placing an "&" between the street names (e.g., GLENDALE AVE NE & 7TH ST NE). ArcView searches for the intersection in the matchable theme and places a point at the intersection in the view. For more information, search for these Help Topics: *Geocoding street intersections, Locate, Locating an address on a view.*

Matching a list of addresses

You just used Locate to find a single address in a view. But what you really want to do is locate your test list of customer addresses. With ArcView's address-matching capabilities, you can match a list of addresses to the matchable theme and display each address as a point feature. In this way, you can map the distribution of the addresses. Then you can assign each one to a sales territory.

Exercise 24b

1. From the File menu, choose Open Exercise. In the Exercises scrolling list, select "ex24b," then click OK. When the project opens, you see a view with one theme, Streets.shp, and a table called "customer.dbf." This table contains addresses and other information about customers, gathered by one of Zuckerberg's sales representatives. You'll use this table to perform address matching.

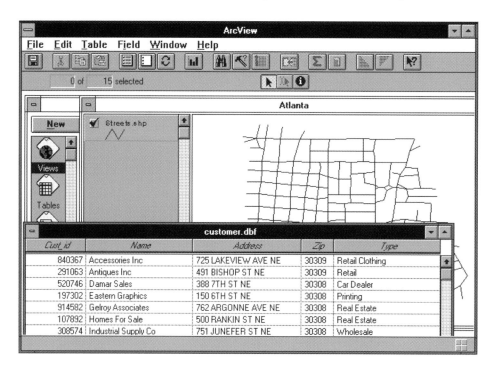

ENVIRONMENTAL SYSTEMS RESEARCH INSTITUTE, INC.

The customer.dbf table contains the addresses you want to match to the Streets theme. To add this table as a theme in the view and begin the address-matching process, you'll use the Add Event Theme dialog box.

2. With the view and the Streets.shp theme active, choose Add Event Theme from the View menu. The Add Event Theme dialog box displays.

In chapter 23, you used the Add Event Theme dialog box to create a theme from x,y coordinates. In this exercise, you'll use it to create a theme from a table of addresses. The theme you create is called an *event theme,* and the table of addresses is called an *event table.*

3. Click the Address button at the top of the dialog box to display the options for adding address events.

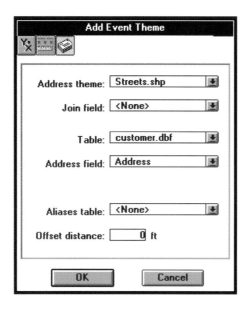

The Address theme drop-down list shows the matchable theme, "Streets.shp." The Table list shows the table containing addresses, "customer.dbf." ArcView reads the field names in this table and selects the field that's likely to contain addresses. In the customer.dbf table, the name of this field is "Address."

4. Type **50** feet in the Offset distance text box. ArcView uses this distance to offset address locations (points) from street segments (lines).

___

Normally when you geocode, the point features are placed directly on the corresponding street segments. Using an offset distance will shift the points the specified distance, on the correct side of the street.

___

ENVIRONMENTAL SYSTEMS RESEARCH INSTITUTE, INC.

5. Click OK. The Geocoded Theme Name dialog box displays. Specify the *drive:\directory* where you want to save the geocoded theme ArcView will create and call it **cust-loc.shp.**

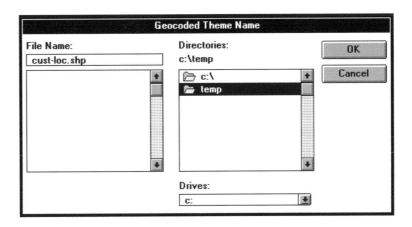

A *geocoded* theme is a shapefile containing point features. Each point represents an address in the event table (customer.dbf) that has been successfully matched to the matchable theme (Streets.shp).

6. Click OK. The Geocoding Editor dialog box displays.

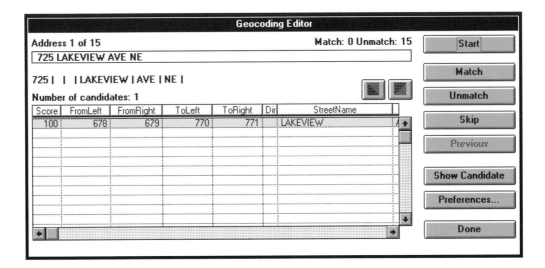

Understanding the Geocoding Editor. The Geocoding Editor dialog box shows the current address, the total number of addresses in the event table, the number of addresses that are matched and unmatched, and the number of candidates (possible matches) from the matchable theme. The match score and address components of each candidate are listed in a scrolling table. (The match score is a value from 0–100 that ArcView assigns to each candidate; a value of 100 is a perfect match.) ArcView highlights the candidate with the highest score. The Geocoding Editor also allows you to access the Geocoding Preferences dialog box (for setting conditions and preferences for matching), manually match an address to a selected candidate, and edit the current address if there are errors. For more information, search for these Help Topics: *Geocoding Editor, Geocoding Preferences.*

The Geocoding Editor shows the address of the first customer in the event table. You'll start the geocoding process with the default settings.

7.   Click the Start button to start geocoding.

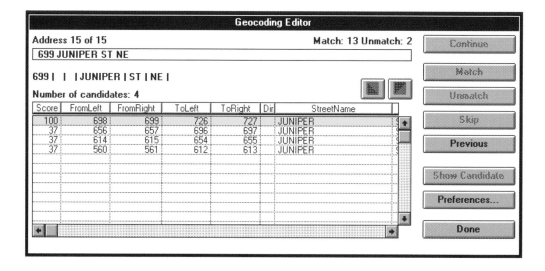

ENVIRONMENTAL SYSTEMS RESEARCH INSTITUTE, INC.

ArcView tries to match each of the 15 addresses. When there are no more addresses to match, the Geocoding Editor displays the last address in the customer.dbf table, along with its candidates. As you can see, ArcView found matches for 13 of the 15 addresses in the table, using the default settings. Two addresses are unmatched. (In the next exercise, you'll attempt to match the unmatched addresses.)

Making a match. Address matching compares two addresses to determine whether they are the same. To match addresses, ArcView looks at the address components (e.g., street numbers, street name, street type) in both the address (event) table and the matchable street theme. If a match is found, ArcView locates the address along the correct side of the street by looking at whether the house number is even or odd. A point is placed at the appropriate spot along the street by interpolating where the number falls along the range. Thus, 230 SUNSET ST matches to a segment with the address range 201 299 200 298 SUNSET ST and falls about one-third of the way along the right side of the segment. The coordinates of the point are based on the location of the matching street segment. For more information, search for these Help Topics: *Address matching, Geocoding Editor, Overview of address geocoding.*

8. Click the Done button. ArcView dismisses the Geocoding Editor and adds the new geocoded theme to the view's Table of Contents.

9. Make the new theme active, then click on its check box to see the geocoded locations.

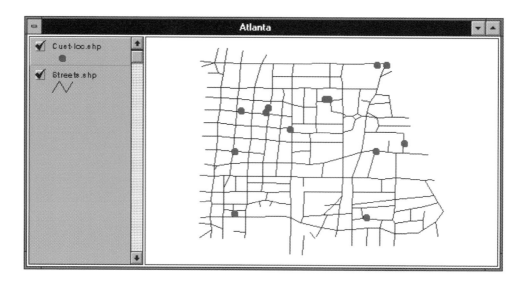

Handling unmatched addresses

You just performed your test run of matching addresses with ArcView. It was pretty fast and easy. There were two addresses that ArcView couldn't match, so you'll need to change the geocoding preferences to increase the likelihood of finding a match.

Exercise 24c

1. If *ex24b.apr* is open, continue. Otherwise, choose Open Exercise from the File menu. In the Exercises scrolling list, select "ex24c," then click OK. You see a view with the Streets.shp theme and the theme you just created, Cust-loc.shp.

ENVIRONMENTAL SYSTEMS RESEARCH INSTITUTE, INC.

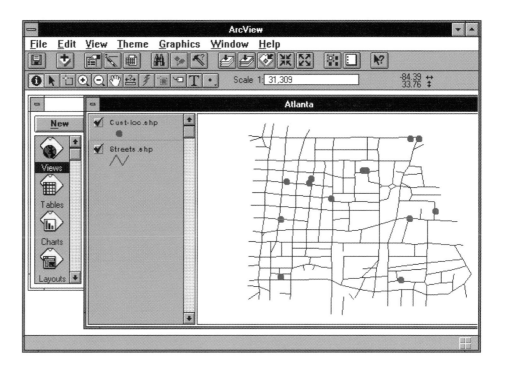

 2. With the Cust-loc.shp theme active, click the Open Theme Table button to open the theme attribute table. By scrolling to the right in the table, you see that ArcView copied all the fields from the original "customer.dbf" table into this table. ArcView also appended some new fields created by the address-matching process. Unmatched records, indicated by "U" in the Av_status field, have no points in the view.

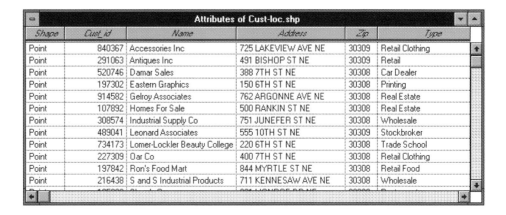

Shape	Cust_id	Name	Address	Zip	Type
Point	840367	Accessories Inc	725 LAKEVIEW AVE NE	30309	Retail Clothing
Point	291063	Antiques Inc	491 BISHOP ST NE	30309	Retail
Point	520746	Damar Sales	388 7TH ST NE	30308	Car Dealer
Point	197302	Eastern Graphics	150 6TH ST NE	30308	Printing
Point	914582	Gelroy Associates	762 ARGONNE AVE NE	30308	Real Estate
Point	107892	Homes For Sale	500 RANKIN ST NE	30308	Real Estate
Point	308574	Industrial Supply Co	751 JUNEFER ST NE	30308	Wholesale
Point	489041	Leonard Associates	555 10TH ST NE	30309	Stockbroker
Point	734173	Lomer-Lockler Beauty College	220 6TH ST NE	30308	Trade School
Point	227309	Oar Co	400 7TH ST NE	30308	Retail Clothing
Point	197842	Ron's Food Mart	844 MYRTLE ST NE	30308	Retail Food
Point	216438	S and S Industrial Products	711 KENNESAW AVE NE	30308	Wholesale

Before you can rematch the unmatched addresses, you need to select them with the Query Builder.

3. With the attribute table active, click the Query Builder button. In the dialog box that displays, double-click "[Av_status]" in the Fields list, click the "=" button, then double-click "U" (unmatched) in the Values list.

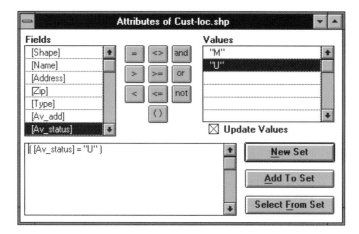

4. Click New Set to select all the unmatched records, then close the Query Builder.

ArcView selects the two unmatched records. (You may have to scroll down to see the second one.) Now you can attempt to rematch these records.

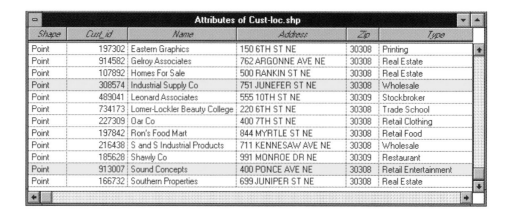

Shape	Cust_id	Name	Address	Zip	Type
Point	197302	Eastern Graphics	150 6TH ST NE	30308	Printing
Point	914582	Gelroy Associates	762 ARGONNE AVE NE	30308	Real Estate
Point	107892	Homes For Sale	500 RANKIN ST NE	30308	Real Estate
Point	308574	Industrial Supply Co	751 JUNEFER ST NE	30308	Wholesale
Point	489041	Leonard Associates	555 10TH ST NE	30309	Stockbroker
Point	734173	Lomer-Lockler Beauty College	220 6TH ST NE	30308	Trade School
Point	227309	Oar Co	400 7TH ST NE	30308	Retail Clothing
Point	197842	Ron's Food Mart	844 MYRTLE ST NE	30308	Retail Food
Point	216438	S and S Industrial Products	711 KENNESAW AVE NE	30308	Wholesale
Point	185628	Shawly Co	991 MONROE DR NE	30309	Restaurant
Point	913007	Sound Concepts	400 PONCE AVE NE	30308	Retail Entertainment
Point	166732	Southern Properties	699 JUNIPER ST NE	30308	Real Estate

          ENVIRONMENTAL SYSTEMS RESEARCH INSTITUTE, INC.

5. Make the view active and select Re-match from the Theme menu. The Geocoding Editor displays.

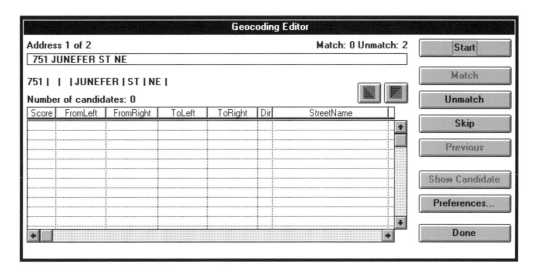

You see the first unmatched address at the top of the Geocoding Editor. Notice that there aren't any candidate street segments for this address. To increase the likelihood of finding a match, you'll relax some of the matching preferences.

6. Click the Preferences button in the Geocoding Editor. The Geocoding Preferences dialog box displays.

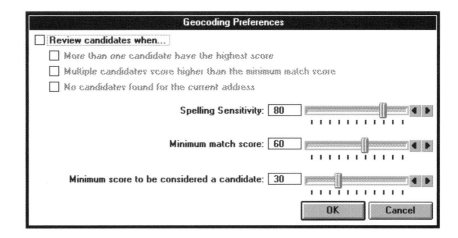

Your guess as to why the addresses didn't match the first time is that there is a misspelling. You've seen this type of error when you were matching addresses manually. You decide to adjust the spelling sensitivity.

7. Adjust the slider for Spelling Sensitivity from **80** (the default) to **70.**

Lowering the value for Spelling Sensitivity allows ArcView to find additional potential candidates for matching the unmatched addresses.

8. Click OK to apply your preferences and display the Geocoding Editor again. ArcView uses the new matching preferences to find candidates for the current address.

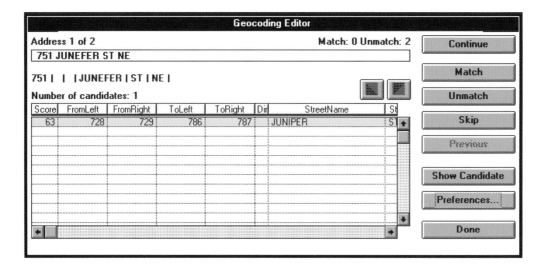

Notice that the first address, 751 JUNEFER ST NE, now has one candidate. You decide that JUNEFER is probably an incorrect spelling of JUNIPER, so you'll manually match the address to the highlighted candidate.

9. Click the Match button to match the first address to the highlighted candidate.

The second address, 400 PONCE AVE NE, displays with two candidates. There are no candidate streets named PONCE AVE, but there is one named PONCE DE LEON. You decide that the first candidate is the closest match, so you'll select it, then make the match.

10. Click on the first candidate in the list to highlight it, then click Match. ArcView matches the second address to the highlighted candidate.

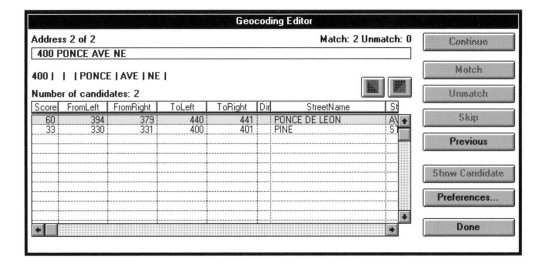

11. Click the Done button. ArcView dismisses the Geocoding Editor, adds two point features to the geocoded theme, and changes the values in the theme's attribute table to indicate that the addresses are matched. Because you selected the addresses when you began the address-matching process, they are highlighted in the view.

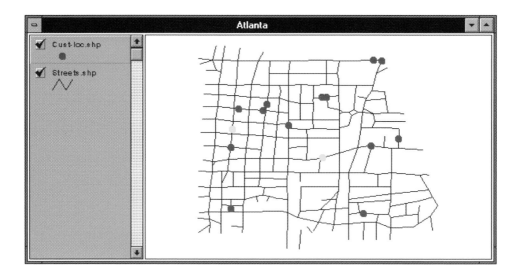

Setting geocoding preferences. In addition to spelling sensitivity, you can set other geocoding preferences with the Geocoding Preferences dialog box. For example, if you want ArcView to prompt you for decisions when certain conditions are met, or you want to increase the likelihood of a match or the number of candidates ArcView finds, you can set these conditions and tolerances in the Geocoding Preferences dialog box. For more information, search for this Help Topic: *Geocoding Preferences.*

You've matched all of the test customer addresses to the street network, and you can see the distribution of addresses in the view. Now you're ready to load the street network for Georgia, make it matchable, and geocode all of your customers. Then you can use ArcView to create a new theme of sales territories (see chapter 22) on top of the geocoded theme instead of just drawing shapes on a wall map.

If you want to go on to the next chapter, leave ArcView running. Otherwise, choose Exit from the File menu.

SECTION 8

Customizing ArcView

This section introduces you to ArcView's programming language, Avenue. You'll see how to use Avenue to create a custom application, including writing Avenue scripts and customizing ArcView's interface. Then you'll test the new interface.

Introducing
Avenue

How Avenue and ArcView work together

Creating the custom application

Writing Avenue scripts

Customizing ArcView's interface

Testing the new interface

Introducing Avenue

ArcView meets a wide variety of GIS needs. But you might still need to customize it. And you can, with ArcView's programming language called *Avenue*.

You can use Avenue™ software to customize the standard graphical user interface (GUI) that comes with ArcView. For example, you can reorganize the controls (menus, buttons, and tools), change text or icons, and add or remove choices. With Avenue you can also create new functions for a specific application. For example, you can combine a series of steps you frequently perform and execute them with a single click of a button. You can even use Avenue to develop a complete application that has its own GUI.

Avenue provides an easy-to-use framework for customizing controls and creating new functions. You use the Customize dialog box to modify controls (menus, buttons, tools) and the Script Editor to write Avenue programs, called *scripts*. Your scripts contain the code that executes a new function. By using controls and scripts together, you build a new ArcView GUI.

How Avenue and ArcView work together

Avenue is an object-oriented programming language. An *object* is an element, such as a view, theme, button, or symbol, that you work with in ArcView. Objects with common characteristics belong to the same *class*. Each object is associated with a set of actions or *requests*. For example, requests for a layout object include opening, closing, and printing. A marker symbol object has a different set of requests, such as setting

ENVIRONMENTAL SYSTEMS RESEARCH INSTITUTE, INC.

marker size and color. If you can identify objects and their associated requests, you can write Avenue scripts.

Avenue and ArcView use the same interface; in fact, all of the menus, buttons, and tools (collectively called "controls") in the ArcView interface run Avenue scripts. When you add a new view, you are actually running the Avenue script "View.Add." To change the way a control works, you modify the script it runs.

You create an Avenue script by opening a Script document window in ArcView, then using the Script Editor to write, compile, run, and debug it. In this chapter, you'll see how Avenue might be used to customize the ArcView interface for a specific application. You won't be able to perform the steps yourself, because the Script Editor is not available in the sample version of ArcView that accompanies this book; however, the finished project is provided so you can run the application.

A standard version of ArcView includes Avenue and all of the customization capabilities mentioned here.

Creating the custom application

Maria works as a public information consultant. She's been hired to design a public information system for the 1996 Olympics in Atlanta, Georgia. Her goal is to make it easy for visitors to find their way around the city. She plans to use ArcView to set up automated information kiosks at several sites for the public to view maps showing locations of points of interest, shopping centers, hotels, and banks. She needs a simple, easy-to-use interface that anyone can understand. She doesn't want visitors to delete or modify her project, so she plans to remove all existing controls, then add new controls that visitors can use to quickly switch between the various map displays. Visitors will be using a sophisticated GIS without even knowing it.

Maria creates an ArcView project containing a number of different views, one for hotels, one for shopping centers, and so forth. She uses the standard ArcView interface to create the project components, so she has full processing capabilities.

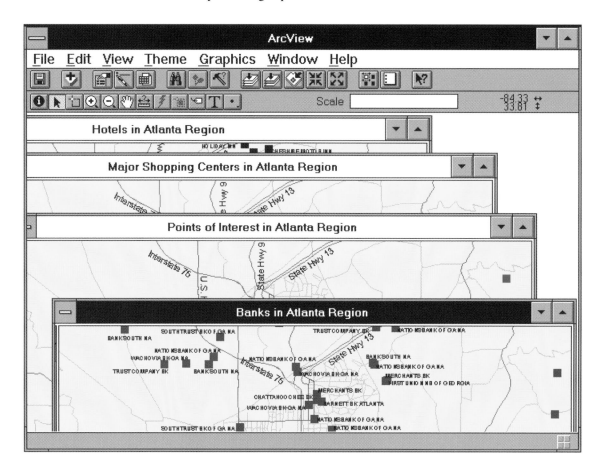

Maria decides to have only five buttons on her new View interface: one to display each view, and one Help button. To implement her design, she'll write five Avenue scripts, four to pop up the different views, and one to pop up a Help message. She'll also remove all other tools, buttons, and menus from the View interface. She'll use the menu bar to label the function of each button.

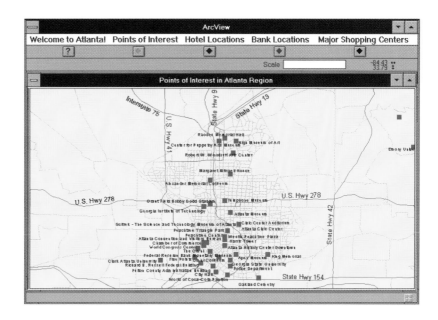

Writing Avenue scripts

Maria creates a simple Avenue script that finds a view, then makes it active, bringing it to the front of the screen. From the ArcView Project window, she opens a new Script window, then uses the Script Editor to type in the script.

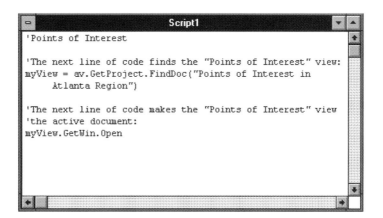

Understanding Avenue syntax. Scripts contain action lines (perform an action) and comment lines (explain what the script is doing). The format of an action line is: *Object.Request.* Comment lines begin with an apostrophe (').

Maria uses Script Properties from the Script menu to name the script and enter a comment describing what it does.

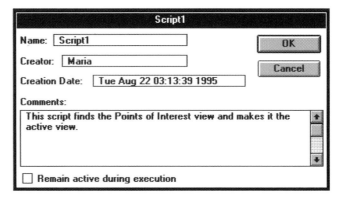

She creates three more scripts like this one. Each one finds a different view and is named accordingly.

She writes a fifth script, called "HelpBox." It opens a message box that provides instructions for the user.

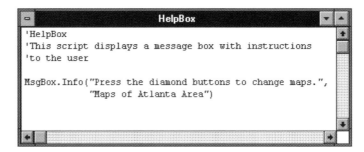

She compiles each script using the Compile button on the Script button bar. Then she runs each script using the Run button to make sure it works. She verifies that each view displays at the front of the screen. When she runs the "HelpBox" script, a help message box displays.

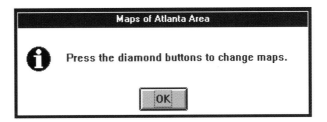

Customizing ArcView's interface

Maria's final task is to customize the ArcView interface. She'll remove all the existing controls, then add her own and link them to the five scripts she's written. She uses the Customize dialog box, which she accesses by double-clicking on any blank portion of the Script button or tool bar.

The Type field lists the parts of the ArcView interface you can customize (views, tables, charts, layouts, scripts). The Category field lists the kinds of controls you can customize (menus, buttons, tools). Maria wants to customize the View menu bar. By pressing the Delete button repeatedly, she removes all of the View menus.

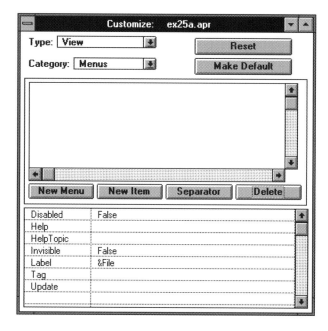

She changes the Category to Buttons and deletes all the buttons, then changes the Category to Tools and deletes all the tools. The View interface is now completely blank.

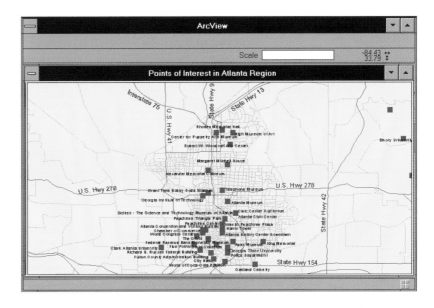

With the "Buttons" category selected, Maria presses New to add a new button to the Button bar. By default, no icon appears on the button.

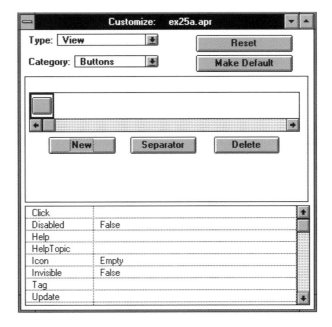

Next she sets the button's Click property. This property names the script to execute when the user clicks the button. Double-clicking on the "Click" property field displays the Script Manager, a dialog box that lists all the scripts available in the project. Maria selects the "Points of Interest" script.

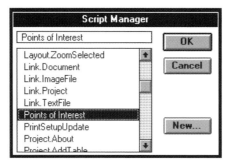

This script is now assigned to the new button.

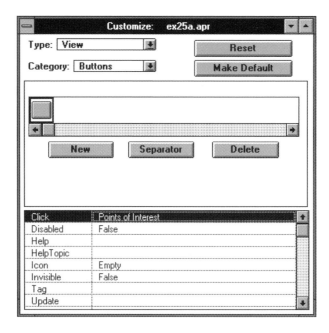

ENVIRONMENTAL SYSTEMS RESEARCH INSTITUTE, INC.

Next she double-clicks on the "Help" field to define the help message the user sees in the status bar when placing the cursor over the button.

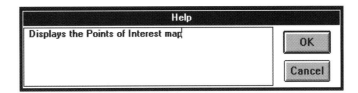

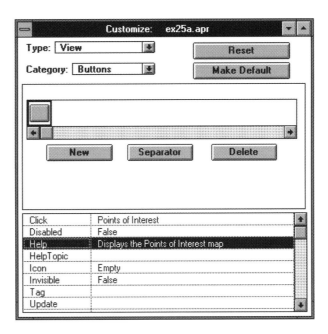

The button needs an icon, so Maria double-clicks on the "Icon" field to display the Icon Manager. She chooses the red diamond icon for this button.

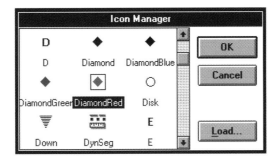

The icon displays in the dialog box.

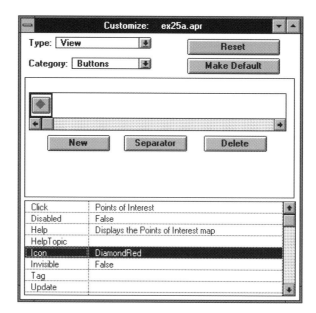

The first button is now defined. Maria creates the other buttons, assigning a script, help string, and icon to each.

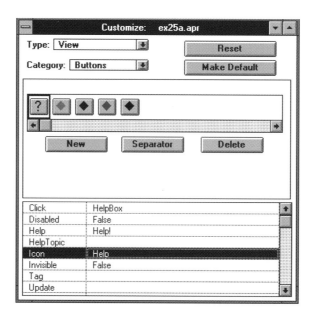

She uses the Separator button to put some space between the buttons.

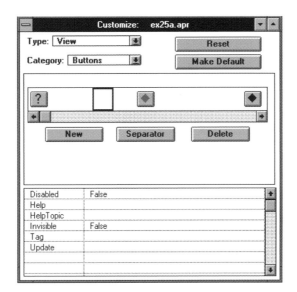

For menus, Maria creates text labels to describe each button. With "Menus" selected in the Category list, she chooses New Menu, then double-clicks on the "Label Property" field. Here she specifies the menu text that will appear in the Menu bar above each button.

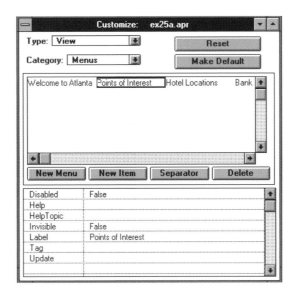

The View interface is now complete, but there's one more thing to do. With the Project window active, Maria chooses Properties from the Project menu. She specifies "Points of Interest" as the Startup script (the script that executes when you start up the project), then clicks OK. When the project opens, it will automatically display the Points of Interest view.

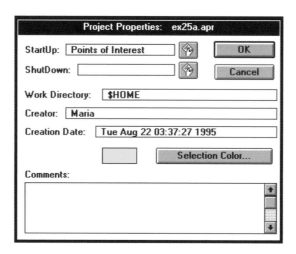

Testing the new interface

You can open Maria's project and test each button to see that everything works. With just a few simple scripts and some customizing, ArcView is transformed into a point-and-click map display interface that doesn't require any GIS knowledge.

The application you're about to see uses these display options: 1024x768 screen resolution, 256 colors, large font. For the best viewing results, use Windows Setup to duplicate these settings before you open the exercise.

Exercise 25a

1. If necessary, start ArcView. From the File menu, choose Open Exercise. In the Exercises scrolling list, select "ex25a," then click OK. When the project opens, you see the modified View interface and the Points of Interest view.

ENVIRONMENTAL SYSTEMS RESEARCH INSTITUTE, INC.

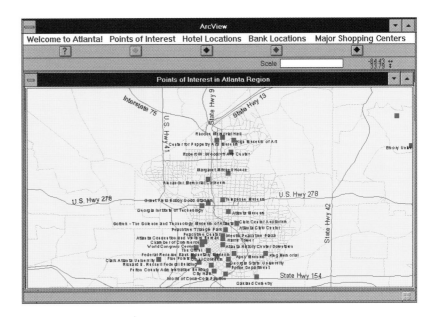

2. Click the Help button, labeled "Welcome to Atlanta." A message box with instructions displays. Click OK to dismiss it.

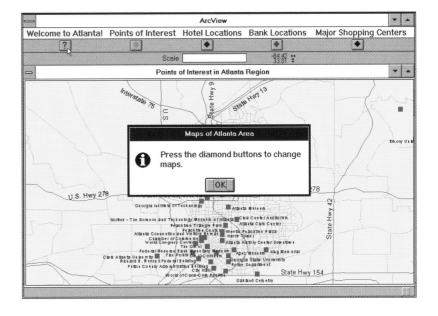

3. Click each of the other buttons to change the map display.

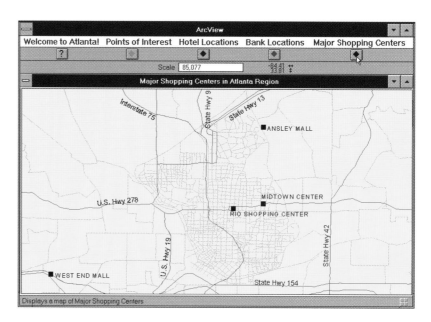

4. When you finish, close all of the views. You see the Project window. Choose Exit from the File menu to exit ArcView.

Studying existing Avenue scripts is one way to learn Avenue. In the standard ArcView release, Avenue Help comes with a Script Library—a collection of scripts useful for many applications. You can copy any of these scripts into the Script window and modify them to suit your needs. All of the system scripts that come with ArcView are also available to you.

You've seen how flexible the ArcView interface is and how, with a little Avenue programming and customization, you can extend it far beyond its original design. This is only the beginning. The possibilities are endless.

What's next?

Environmental Systems Research Institute, Inc. (ESRI), builds quality GIS software products to meet a wide variety of application needs. Our product family covers the full range of GIS solutions, from general-use desktop GIS software to high-end systems used primarily for engineering and scientific applications.

ArcView® software, the newest member of the ESRI® family, is the easy-to-learn, easy-to-use desktop GIS for everyone. ArcView's affordable price and its compatibility with other ESRI products make it ideal for those who want to get started with GIS. And ArcView runs on most computers, including PC, Macintosh®, and UNIX® and OpenVMS™ workstation platforms.

For more information, give us a call at 1-800-GIS-XPRT (1-800-447-9778) (outside the United States, call 909-793-2853, extension 1235) or send E-mail to *info@esri.com*. Or, learn more about ArcView and other ESRI products and services (including ArcView classes) by connecting to our World Wide Web home page on the Internet: *http://www.esri.com*.

We look forward to hearing from you!

Corporate headquarters

ESRI
380 New York Street
Redlands, CA 92373-8100 USA
Telephone: 909-793-2853
Fax: 909-793-5953

Regional offices

Anchorage
Telephone: 907-344-6613
Fax: 907-344-6813

Boston
Telephone: 508-777-4543
Fax: 508-777-8476

California
Telephone: 909-793-2853, extension 1906
Fax: 909-307-3025

Charlotte
Telephone: 704-541-9810
Fax: 704-541-7620

Denver
Telephone: 303-449-7779
Fax: 303-449-8830

Minneapolis
Telephone: 612-454-0600
Fax: 612-454-0705

Olympia
Telephone: 360-754-4727
Fax: 360-943-6910

Philadelphia
Telephone: 610-725-0901
Fax: 610-725-0903

St. Louis
Telephone: 314-949-6620
Fax: 314-949-6735

San Antonio
Telephone: 210-340-5762
Fax: 210-340-1330

Washington, D.C.
Telephone: 703-506-9515
Fax: 703-506-9514

International offices

ESRI–Australia
Telephone: 61-9-242-1005
Fax: 61-9-242-4412

ESRI–Canada
Telephone: 416-441-6035
Fax: 416-441-6838

ESRI–Europe
Telephone: 31-10-217-0690
Fax: 31-10-217-0691

ESRI–France
Telephone: 33-1-46-23-6060
Fax: 33-1-450-70560

ESRI–Germany
Telephone: 49-8166-380
Fax: 49-8166-3838

ESRI–Italy
Telephone: 39-6-406-96-1
Fax: 39-6-4069-6800

ESRI–Poland
Telephone: 48-22-256-482
Fax: 48-22-255-705

ESRI–South Asia
Telephone: 65-735-8755
Fax: 65-735-5629

ESRI–Spain
Telephone: 34-1-559-4375
Fax: 34-1-559-7071

ESRI–Sweden
Telephone: 46-23-84094
Fax: 46-23-84485

ESRI–Thailand
Telephone: 66-2-678-0707
Fax: 66-2-678-0321-3

ESRI–United Kingdom
Telephone: 44-1-923-210-450
Fax: 44-1-923-210-739

ESRI also has more than 60 distributors in other countries around the world. For more information, contact ESRI at 909-793-2853, extension 1235.

Data providers

Finding GIS data isn't hard; you just need to know where to look. You can get lists of GIS data vendors from a variety of sources. Here is a list of lists, as well as some providers of free or low-cost data.

ArcData Catalog

This catalog is a collection of digital information products developed cooperatively by ESRI and more than 30 data providers. Included are data sets for such applications as business siting, market analysis, health care service, urban and transportation planning, education, and agriculture.

These data sets come from both public and private sources and include spatial, attribute, and image data. ArcData℠ Publishing Program data sets are compatible with ArcView® desktop GIS software.

To receive your own copy of the *ArcData Catalog,* call 1-800-GIS-XPRT (1-800-447-9778) or direct E-mail to *info@esri.com.*

You can get more information about ArcData data sets by connecting to our World Wide Web home page on the Internet: *http://www.esri.com.*

Internet users can also download a regularly updated list of ArcData data sets and data publishers through ESRI's ftp site as follows:

1. Ftp to redlands.esri.com or 198.102.62.1
2. Log in as *anonymous*
3. Type your E-mail address as the password
4. Within ftp, type the following:

   ftp> **cd/pub/arcdata**
   ftp> **mget *.text**

Other data resources

The Global Directory of Financial Information Vendors

James Essinger and Joseph Rosen. Business One Irwin (Publishers), 1994. ISBN 1-55623-788-X. A guide to more than 200 vendors of databases for the financial market.

World Mapping Today

R. B. Perry and C. R. Perkins. Butterworth & Co. (Publishers) Ltd., 1987. ISBN 0-408-02850-5.

A guide to maps available from around the world. It provides an overview of world mapping in the late 1980s and lists worldwide mapping agencies, graphic indexes, and catalogs of map publishers by country.

Manual of Federal Geographic Data Products

Published by the United States Federal Geographic Data Committee (FGDC).

Describes over 150 federal geographic products distributed by 21 U.S. federal agencies. Topographic data includes maps, imagery, and digital geographic locational data. It also includes data description, data coverage, delivery format, and ordering information.

Contact: Federal Geographic Data Committee Secretariat, United States Geological Survey, 590 National Center, Reston, Virginia 22092. Telephone: (703) 648-4533. Internet address: gdc@usgs.gov.

Statistical Abstract of the United States 1994

Published by the United States Department of Commerce, Economics and Statistical Administration, Bureau of the Census.

The standard summary of statistics on the social, political, and economic organizations of the United States. It includes comparative international statistics, foreign commerce and aid, and a guide to 29 foreign statistical abstracts.

Contact: Customer Service, Bureau of the Census, Washington, D.C. 20233-8300. Telephone: 301-763-4100. Fax: 301-763-4794.

United States Census Bureau

The United States Census Bureau offers a variety of geographic tools, maps, reports, and tapes containing information about the population of the United States.

The Bureau reports on population and housing, economics, agriculture, and government censuses. A geographic database is also available: TIGER/Line Files (Topographically Integrated Geographic Encoding and Referencing).

Contact: Customer Service, Bureau of the Census, Washington, D.C. 20233-8300. Telephone: 301-763-4100. Fax: 301-763-4794.

GIS periodicals

Business Geographics

Contact: Business Geographics c/o GIS World, Inc., 155 East Boardwalk Drive, Suite 250, Fort Collins, Colorado 80525. Telephone: 970-223-4848. Fax: 970-223-5700. E-mail: BG@gisworld.com.

Geo Info Systems

Contact: Geo Info Systems, P. O. Box 6139, Duluth, Minnesota 55806-6139. Telephone: 800-346-0085, extension 226. Outside the United States: 218-723-9477.

GIS Europe

Contact: GeoInformation International, 307 Cambridge Science Park, Milton Road, Cambridge, CB4 4ZD, United Kingdom. Telephone: 44 181 402 8181. Fax: 44 181 402 8383.

GIS World

Contact: GIS World, Inc., 155 East Boardwalk Drive, Suite 250, Fort Collins, Colorado 80525. Telephone: 970-223-4848. Fax: 970-223-5700. E-mail: info@gisworld.com.

License Agreement

Important: Read carefully before opening the sealed media package

ENVIRONMENTAL SYSTEMS RESEARCH INSTITUTE, INC. (ESRI), IS WILLING TO LICENSE THE ENCLOSED SOFTWARE, DATA, AND RELATED MATERIALS TO YOU ONLY UPON THE CONDITION THAT YOU ACCEPT ALL OF THE TERMS AND CONDITIONS CONTAINED IN THIS LICENSE AGREEMENT. PLEASE READ THE TERMS AND CONDITIONS CAREFULLY BEFORE OPENING THE SEALED MEDIA PACKAGE. BY OPENING THE SEALED MEDIA PACKAGE, YOU ARE INDICATING YOUR ACCEPTANCE OF THE ESRI® LICENSE AGREEMENT. IF YOU DO NOT AGREE TO THE TERMS AND CONDITIONS AS STATED, THEN ESRI IS UNWILLING TO LICENSE THE SOFTWARE, DATA, AND RELATED MATERIALS TO YOU. IN SUCH EVENT, YOU SHOULD RETURN THE MEDIA PACKAGE WITH THE SEAL UNBROKEN AND ALL OTHER COMPONENTS TO ESRI.

ESRI License Agreement

This is a license agreement, and not an agreement for sale, between you (Licensee) and Environmental Systems Research Institute, Inc. (ESRI). This ESRI License Agreement (Agreement) gives Licensee certain limited rights to use the software and related materials (Software, Data, and Related Materials). All rights not specifically granted in this Agreement are reserved to ESRI and its Licensors.

Reservation of Ownership and Grant of License:

ESRI and its Licensors retain exclusive rights, title, and ownership to the copy of the Software, Data, and Related Materials licensed under this Agreement and, hereby, grant to Licensee a personal, nonexclusive, non-transferable, royalty-free, worldwide license to use the Software, Data, and Related Materials based on the terms and conditions of this Agreement. Licensee agrees to use reasonable effort to protect the Software, Data, and Related Materials from unauthorized use, reproduction, distribution, or publication.

Proprietary Rights and Copyright:

Licensee acknowledges that the Software, Data, and Related Materials are proprietary and confidential property of ESRI and its Licensors and are protected by United States copyright laws and applicable international copyright treaties and/or conventions.

Permitted Uses:

Licensee may install the Software, Data, and Related Materials onto permanent storage device(s) for Licensee's own internal use.

Licensee may make only one (1) copy of the original Software, Data, and Related Materials for archival purposes during the term of this Agreement unless the right to make additional copies is granted to Licensee in writing by ESRI.

Licensee may internally use the Software, Data, and Related Materials provided by ESRI for the stated purpose of GIS education.

Uses Not Permitted:

Licensee shall not sell, rent, lease, sublicense, lend, assign, time-share, or transfer, in whole or in part, or provide unlicensed Third Parties access to the Software, Data, and Related Materials or portions of the Software, Data, and Related Materials, any updates, or Licensee's rights under this Agreement.

Licensee shall not remove or obscure any copyright or trademark notices of ESRI or its Licensors.

Term:

The Agreement shall automatically terminate without notice if Licensee fails to comply with any provision of this Agreement. Licensee shall then return to ESRI the Software, Data, and Related Materials. The parties hereby agree that all provisions that operate to protect the rights of ESRI and its Licensors shall remain in force should breach occur.

Limited Warranty:

THE SOFTWARE, DATA, AND RELATED MATERIALS CONTAINED HEREIN ARE PROVIDED "AS-IS," WITHOUT WARRANTY OF ANY KIND, EITHER EXPRESS OR IMPLIED, INCLUDING, BUT NOT LIMITED TO, THE IMPLIED WARRANTIES OF MERCHANTABILITY AND FITNESS FOR A PARTICULAR PURPOSE.

ESRI does not warrant that the Software, Data, and Related Materials will meet Licensee's needs or expectations, that the use of the Software, Data, and Related Materials will be uninterrupted, or that all nonconformities, defects, or errors can or will be corrected. ESRI is not inviting reliance on the Software, Data, and/or Related Materials for planning or analysis purposes, and Licensee should always check actual data.

Limitation of Liability:

ESRI shall not be liable for direct, indirect, special, incidental, or consequential damages related to Licensee's use of the Software, Data, and Related Materials, even if ESRI is advised of the possibility of such damage.

No Implied Waivers:

No failure or delay by ESRI or its Licensors in enforcing any right or remedy under this Agreement shall be construed as a waiver of any future or other exercise of such right or remedy by ESRI or its Licensors.

Order for Precedence:

Any conflict between the terms of this Agreement and any FAR, DFAR, purchase order, or other terms shall be resolved in favor of the terms expressed in this Agreement, subject to the government's minimum rights unless agreed otherwise.

Export Regulation:

Licensee acknowledges that this Agreement and the performance thereof are subject to compliance with any and all applicable United States laws, regulations, or orders relating to the export of data thereto. Licensee agrees to comply with all laws, regulations, and orders of the United States in regard to any export of such technical data.

Severability:

If any provision(s) of this Agreement shall be held to be invalid, illegal, or unenforceable by a court or other tribunal of competent jurisdiction, the validity, legality, and enforceability of the remaining provisions shall not in any way be affected or impaired thereby.

ENVIRONMENTAL SYSTEMS RESEARCH INSTITUTE, INC.

Governing Law:

This Agreement, entered into in the County of San Bernardino, shall be construed and enforced in accordance with and be governed by the laws of the United States of America and the State of California without reference to conflict of laws principles. The parties hereby consent to the personal jurisdiction of the courts of this county and waive their rights to change venue.

Entire Agreement:

The parties agree that this Agreement constitutes the sole and entire agreement of the parties as to the matter set forth herein and supersedes any previous agreements, understandings, and arrangements between the parties relating hereto.

ENVIRONMENTAL SYSTEMS RESEARCH INSTITUTE, INC.

D

How to use the CD–ROM

The Getting to Know ArcView CD–ROM contains a multimedia application divided into two parts, the Desktop GIS Primer and the ArcView Showcase. It also contains a copy of ArcView® software that can be used to perform the exercises in chapters 7–25 of the book.

Desktop GIS Primer

Select this choice from the main screen of the application to see illustrations of the concepts presented in chapters 1–5 of the book.

ArcView Showcase

Select this choice from the main screen of the application to see how ArcView software implements the concepts presented in chapters 1–6 of the book.

ArcView Tutorial

Select this choice from the main screen of the application to start ArcView and begin doing the exercises in chapters 7–25 of the book. You can also use the ArcView tutorial without the book. It contains a help system with all of the exercises from the book and "helper" videos that show you how to perform the tasks.

Installing the application

To install the application,

- Start Windows, place the Getting to Know ArcView disc in the plastic disc holder (if required), and insert it into the CD–ROM drive. Open the Program Manager window and choose **Run** from the File menu. (If running Windows 95, choose **Run** from the Start menu.)

- In the Command Line box, type the letter of your CD–ROM drive, a colon, a backslash, and the word SETUP (for example: **e:\setup**).

- Follow the instructions that appear on the screen.

The setup program will automatically install the required pieces of the Getting to Know ArcView application. In part of the install you'll be asked to install optional components. These include the data used in the tutorial, the multimedia presentations, and the AVI "helper" videos. We strongly recommend that you install the data. The other components can be left on the CD. Just be sure that the CD is in your CD–ROM drive when you run the application. When finished, installation will create a Program Group and Windows® icons for the application.

ENVIRONMENTAL SYSTEMS RESEARCH INSTITUTE, INC.

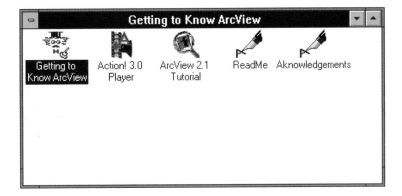

With the disc still in the CD–ROM drive, start the application by double-clicking on the "Getting to Know ArcView" icon.

Using the application

After you've started Getting to Know ArcView, you can select which of the three parts you'd like to see, the Desktop GIS Primer, the ArcView Showcase, or the ArcView Tutorial.

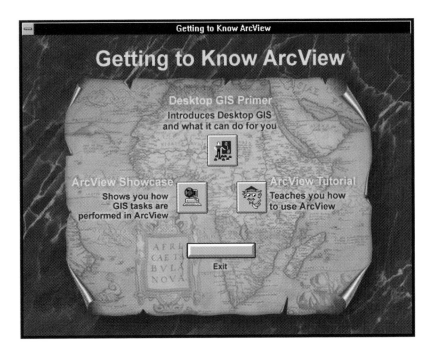

Using the Desktop GIS Primer and the ArcView Showcase

After you've selected the Desktop GIS Primer or ArcView Showcase to run, you can select one of six presentations to view. Once the presentation starts, you can control it with the buttons shown on the scene below.

Beginning takes you to the beginning of the chosen section.

Scene Start takes you to the beginning of the current scene.

Prev. Scene takes you to the beginning of the previous scene.

Next Scene takes you to the beginning of the next scene.

Pause pauses the presentation.

Continue restarts the presentation after it's been paused.

Return to Menu stops the presentation and returns you to the Desktop GIS Primer or ArcView Showcase menu.

Using the ArcView Tutorial

After you've selected the ArcView Tutorial button, the tutorial version of ArcView will start. To use the tutorial, you have to load the data for each exercise. If you're using the book, step 1 of any exercise shows you how to load the data for it. Alternately, you can choose Tutorial Contents from the Help menu or click the button shown at the left to start the Getting to Know ArcView help. You can then navigate to any chapter and exercise and work completely online.

In each exercise in the online help you'll see **Show Me** and **Load Data** buttons. Clicking **Show Me** starts a Windows video showing each step of the exercise in ArcView. Clicking **Load Data** loads the data for the current exercise into ArcView.

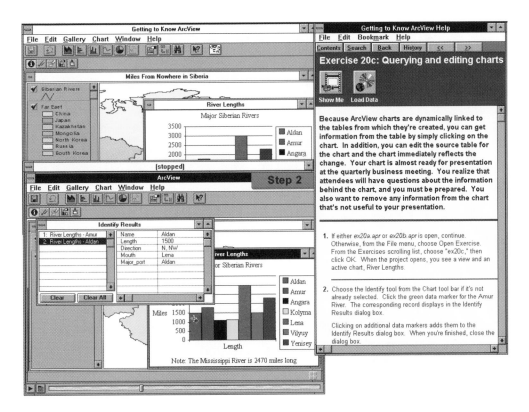

Improving the performance

This application has been designed to run well from any CD–ROM, but will run better from a triple- or quad-speed drive.

System requirements

- A multimedia PC, 486/33MHz

- 12MB of RAM (16MB recommended)

- 10MB of hard disk space

- CD–ROM drive

- 256-color display adapter

- Microsoft® Windows version 3.1, Windows NT, or Windows 95

Technical support

While there is no direct technical support available for the software on the CD, feel free to use either of our two self-help channels to get help with ArcView 2.1: Fax On Demand and the World Wide Web. These services are free (other than provider charges and phone time), require no waiting, and are available 24 hours a day, seven days a week.

Fax On Demand

By simply dialing (909) 301-3111, users of ESRI desktop products can request that FAQ (Frequently Asked Questions) documents be faxed to a number anywhere in the United States and Canada. Full instructions are given for retrieving documents. Users can request an index of available documents or get up to three documents per phone call.

FAQs on the World Wide Web

Users with access to the Internet and the Web can now access FAQ documents on ArcView software. These are available in the Technical Support section of ESRI's World Wide Web home page and are updated at least once a week. Point your Web browser to *http://www.esri.com.*

Known problems

The CD–ROM has been thoroughly tested on many platforms and we have encountered one problem in the Desktop GIS Primer and the ArcView Showcase. The combination of the following hardware, screen resolution, and number of colors causes the images in the presentation to appear as static:

Dell Dimension 466 DM (16MB RAM)
Diamond Viper Pro (2MB)
Dell S3 monitor
Windows 3.1
800 x 600 x 16.7M colors @ 75Hz

To correct this, reduce the number of colors to 256.

There may be problems with other hardware configurations. If you encounter any problems with the presentations themselves, we recommend that you change your screen resolution to 640 x 480 and the number of colors to 256. This is the target use configuration and should solve any problems. For the latest list of known problems, please read the **Read Me** file installed with the application.

ENVIRONMENTAL SYSTEMS RESEARCH INSTITUTE, INC.

Glossary

active theme
In ArcView, a theme that appears raised in a view's Table of Contents; many operations performed in a view work only on active themes.

address geocoding
The process of assigning x,y coordinates to addresses so they can be displayed as points on a map.

address matching
A process that compares a table of addresses to the address attributes of a theme to determine whether they are the same.

alias
In ArcView, an additional name for a field in a table. ArcView displays the alias instead of the original name.

application
A specific use of GIS; a GIS project.

area
A closed shape (polygon) defined by the line or lines that comprise its boundary; also, an attribute of a polygon.

area feature
A shape on a map representing a geographic object too large to be depicted as a point or line. Examples of area features include counties, census tracts, and lakes.

attribute
A characteristic of a map feature. Attributes of a river might include its name, length, average depth, and so on. A desktop GIS stores attributes in tables and links them to the map features they describe.

attribute table
Information about the features on a map, stored in rows and columns. Each row relates to a single feature; each column contains the values for a single characteristic.

Avenue
The programming language that comes with ArcView. Avenue provides tools for customizing ArcView and developing applications.

chart | A graphic representation of tabular data. A component of an ArcView project used for representing tabular data graphically.

class | A group or category of attribute values.

classifying | The process of sorting or arranging attribute values into groups or categories; all members of a group are represented on a map by the same symbol.

color ramp | A range of colors used in a map to show ranking or order among classes.

data | A collection of related facts usually arranged in a particular format and gathered for a particular purpose.

database | A collection of related files organized for efficient retrieval of information.

data dictionary | A catalog containing information about the data stored in a GIS database. A data dictionary includes such information as the full names of attributes, meanings of codes, scale of the source data, accuracy of locations, and the map projection used.

data marker | A column, bar, area, pie slice, or point symbol in a chart representing tabular data.

decimal degrees | Degrees of latitude and longitude expressed as a decimal rather than in degrees, minutes, and seconds. Decimal degrees are computed using this formula: Decimal Degrees = Degrees + Minutes/60 + Seconds/3,600. (73° 59' 15" longitude is equal to 73.9875 decimal degrees.)

desktop GIS | A form of desktop mapping that has the ability to display, query, update, and analyze geographic locations and the information linked to those locations, and that runs on personal computers.

desktop mapping | A system used for mapping information on personal computers. Desktop mapping systems range from display-only systems to full-featured geographic information systems.

digital map data | The locations and shapes of map features stored in a computer-readable format.

distance units | The units (e.g., feet, miles, meters, or kilometers) ArcView uses to report measurements, dimensions of shapes, and distance tolerances and offsets.

document	A component of an ArcView project. Each document type (view, table, chart, layout, script) has its own window and interface.
electronic atlas	A display-only mapping system that provides pictures (maps) of geographic areas.
event location	In ArcView, a location stored in a tabular data format rather than a spatial one; also known as an *event*. Examples of event locations are addresses, mileposts along a route, and latitude–longitude coordinates.
event table	In ArcView, a tabular data source containing location information (event locations) and used for creating a spatial data theme.
event theme	A spatial data theme created from a table of event locations.
feature	A shape and its associated location, used to represent a real-world object on a map.
field	A column in an ArcView table. Each field contains the values for a single attribute.
filtering	A desktop GIS operation used to hide (but not delete) features in a map theme.
geocoding	The process of assigning x,y coordinates to data that is not in a spatial data format. See *address geocoding*.
geographic coordinates	A measurement of a location on the earth's surface expressed in degrees of latitude and longitude. See *planar coordinate system*.
geographic data	Information about objects found on the earth's surface, including their locations, shapes, and descriptions. Geographic data comes in three basic forms: spatial, tabular, and image.
geographic information system	An organized collection of computer hardware, software, and geographic data designed for capturing, storing, updating, manipulating, analyzing, and displaying all forms of geographically referenced information.
GIS	See *geographic information system*.
GIS database	A collection of map themes (including features and related descriptive information) organized for efficient storage and retrieval by many users.
hot link	In ArcView, a way to display data (e.g., a file, image, ArcView document, or project) directly from a view, by clicking on a feature.

image data   Graphic representations of objects. Examples include satellite pictures, aerial photographs, and scanned documents. One of the three basic kinds of geographic data (spatial and tabular data are the others).

join   In ArcView, an operation used to attach tabular data to a theme. The fields of one table are appended to another table (usually the theme table) using a common field. Join establishes a one-to-one or many-to-one relationship between records in the two tables.

layout   The design or arrangement of elements in a digital map display or printed map. A component of an ArcView project used for creating presentation-quality maps.

legend   A list of the symbols appearing on a map; includes a sample of each symbol and text describing what each symbol means.

line   A shape defined by at least two pairs of x,y coordinates.

line feature   A shape on a map representing a real-world object too narrow to be depicted as an area. Examples of line features include roads, rivers, and elevation contours.

link   In ArcView, an operation used to define a relationship between two tables, without appending any fields, and using a common field. Link establishes a one-to-many relationship between records in the two tables.

map   A graphic representation of an area, using shapes to represent objects and symbols to describe their nature, organized according to location.

map display   A graphic representation on a computer screen of a geographic area and the features in it.

map feature   Same as *feature*.

map projection   A mathematical formula that converts latitude–longitude locations on the earth's spherical surface to x,y locations on a map's flat surface. Map projections cause distortion in one or more of these spatial properties: distance, area, shape, and direction.

map scale   Same as *scale*.

map symbol   Same as *symbol*.

map units   The units (e.g., feet, miles, meters, or kilometers) in which the coordinates of spatial data are stored. ArcView uses the current map units to calculate a view's scale.

neatline　　A border commonly drawn around geographic features, often to separate them from other map graphics.

north arrow　　A map component that shows how a map is oriented.

planar coordinate system　　A two-dimensional measurement system that locates features on a map based on their distance from an origin (0,0) along two axes, a horizontal *x* axis representing east–west and a vertical *y* axis representing north–south. See also *geographic coordinates*.

point　　A shape defined by a single x,y coordinate.

point feature　　A shape on a map representing a geographic object too small to show as a line or area. Examples of point features include wells, hydrants, and bench marks.

polygon　　Same as *area feature*.

project　　In ArcView, a file for organizing your work. Projects use five types of documents to organize information: views, tables, charts, layouts, and scripts.

query　　A question or request used for selecting features or records. A query often appears in the form of a statement or logical expression. In ArcView, a query contains a field, an operator, and a value.

record　　A row in an ArcView table. If the table is a theme table, each record corresponds to a single map feature.

scale　　The relationship between the dimensions of features on a map and the geographic objects they represent on the earth, commonly expressed as a fraction or a ratio. A map scale of 1/100,000 or 1:100,000 (for example) means that one unit of measure on the map equals 100,000 of the same unit on the earth; that is, features on the map are 100,000 times smaller than what they represent in the real world.

scale bar　　A map component that graphically shows a map's scale.

scanned data　　Information, such as a photograph or document, that has been converted from printed to digital format.

script　　A component of an ArcView project used for writing, loading, and modifying programs that contain Avenue code. ArcView scripts are used for automating tasks, adding new capabilities to ArcView, and building complete applications.

select To choose from a number or group of features or records; to create a separate set, or subset.

selected set A subset of the features or records in a theme. ArcView provides several ways to select features and records graphically or according to their attribute values.

shape The characteristic appearance or visible form of a geographic object. Most geographic objects can be represented on a map using three basic shapes: points, lines, and areas. In ArcView, a map feature stored in a shapefile format.

shapefile ArcView's format for storing the location, shape, and attribute information of geographic features.

spatial analysis The study of the locations and shapes of geographic features and the relationships between them.

spatial data The locations and shapes of geographic features. One of the three basic kinds of geographic data (image and tabular data are the others).

spatial join A type of spatial analysis in which the attributes of features in two different themes are joined together based on the relative locations of the features.

spatial overlay The process of superimposing layers (themes) of geographic data that occupy the same space in order to study the relationships between them.

spatial relationship A relationship between geographic features based on their locations. Spatial relationships are shown on maps.

street-based mapping A form of desktop mapping that links information to geographic locations and displays address locations as point features on a map.

street network A system of interconnecting lines that represent thoroughfares.

symbol A graphic element used in a map to help identify and provide information about a feature.

table Information formatted in rows and columns. A component of an ArcView project used for displaying tabular data. See *attribute table*.

tabular data Descriptive information, including locations, that is stored in rows and columns and can be linked to map features. One of the three basic kinds of geographic data (image and spatial data are the others).

text label Text added to a map to help identify a feature.

thematic mapping	A form of desktop mapping that uses information stored in a spreadsheet or database to create map displays for graphic presentations.
theme	A set of related geographic features, such as streets, parcels, or rivers, and the attributes (characteristics) of those features.
theme-on-theme selection	In ArcView, an operation that selects features in one theme using the features of another theme. Answers questions about spatial relationships between features, such as whether one feature lies within another, whether it completely contains another, whether it is within a specified distance of another, and so on.
theme table	In ArcView, a table of attributes linked to features in a theme. See *attribute table*.
topographic maps	Graphic representations of natural and man-made features showing their relative positions and elevations.
view	A component of an ArcView project used for displaying, querying, and analyzing geographic themes.
x axis	In a planar coordinate system, the horizontal axis representing east–west.
x,y coordinates	On a flat map, a location (its distance, horizontally and vertically, from an origin) that corresponds to the same location on the earth's spherical surface.
y axis	In a planar coordinate system, the vertical axis representing north–south.

ENVIRONMENTAL SYSTEMS RESEARCH INSTITUTE, INC.

Index to part 2

ENVIRONMENTAL SYSTEMS RESEARCH INSTITUTE, INC.

ENVIRONMENTAL SYSTEMS RESEARCH INSTITUTE, INC.